A2
— LEVEL —

BIOLOGY
FOR CCEA A2 LEVEL

**COLOURPOINT
EDUCATIONAL**

Rewarding Learning

Dr James Napier

ISBN: 978-1-78073-010-3

First Edition
Second Impression

Layout and design: April Sky Design
Printed by: W&G Baird Ltd, Antrim

COLOURPOINT EDUCATIONAL

Colourpoint Educational
An imprint of Colourpoint Creative Ltd
Colourpoint House
Jubilee Business Park
21 Jubilee Road
Newtownards
County Down
Northern Ireland
BT23 4YH

Tel: 028 9182 6339
Fax: 028 9182 1900
E-mail: info@colourpoint.co.uk
Web site: www.colourpoint.co.uk

The Author

James Napier is a former Vice-Principal in a large Northern Ireland Grammar School and is now a full time author. Dr Napier has written, and co-written, a number of Biology and Science textbooks supporting the work of teachers and students in Northern Ireland. He has also published a range of popular science books throughout the areas of genetics and evolution. In addition, James Napier has written *Living on the Ledge*, a book raising awareness about attention deficit disorder (ADHD).

The author would like to thank all at Colourpoint for their expertise and support during the development of this book. Thanks also to Dr Terence Henry for his extensive and invaluable feedback and advice throughout the process.

Rewarding Learning

CONTENTS

A2 1 Physiology and Ecosystems

A2 2 Biochemistry, Genetics and Evolutionary Trends

Unit A2 1: Physiology and Ecosystems

Chapter 1 – Homeostasis and the Kidney

Homeostasis

Mammalian tissue is essentially made up of a collection of cells bathed in a fluid medium or 'extracellular' fluid (tissue fluid). The composition of this fluid (and consequentially the **blood** due to the permeable nature of the capillary walls) must be kept **constant** in terms of factors such as water and ion content, temperature, pH and oxygen levels, **irrespective of the external conditions** outside the body.

Homeostasis is the maintenance of constant or steady state conditions within the body. Most homeostatic responses have three basic features.

- A **control system** with **sensors (receptors)** which provides information allowing the **monitoring** of the factor being controlled. The receptors can be in the brain or localised throughout the body. However, the monitor (control centre) is usually in the brain.

- If the receptors show a departure from normal levels (the **set point**) for the factor being controlled, for example temperature, then a **corrective mechanism** brings about the changes required to return the factor to its normal level. For example, if mammals overheat, the corrective measures can include sweating and the vasodilation of blood vessels in the skin.

- The corrective mechanism involves a **negative feedback** system. *Negative* feedback occurs as the return of the factor being controlled to its normal level (set point) causes the corrective measures to be turned off. This prevents over-correction. In our example of temperature regulation, the stimulation of the sweat glands and the degree of vasodilation of blood capillaries is reduced as blood (body) temperature returns to normal.

Communication between the sensors/receptors and the monitor (and between the monitor and the effectors that bring about the corrective response) can be by **nervous** or **hormonal** control. The control of temperature, as described on page 5, is primarily under nervous control, whereas control of blood glucose levels is under hormonal control.

Homeostatic control of mammalian body systems is essential for many reasons including:

- providing the optimum conditions for enzyme reactions in terms of pH and temperature.
- avoiding osmotic problems in cells and in body fluids.

While mammals have complex and effective homeostatic controls, many other animals have simpler controls that are less able to keep the internal environment constant, for example, the body temperature of insects usually varies with the external environment. Consequently, many species of less complex animals avoid large swings in body conditions by living in an environment where the external environment is relatively constant, such as the sea.

Normal level
(set point)

Increase   Decrease

Corrective   Corrective
action   action

Negative feedback
reduces corrective action
as set point approaches

Normal level
(set point)

The general principles of homeostatic control

The kidney

A major homeostatic organ in mammals is the kidney. The kidney has two very important functions:

Excretion is the removal of the toxic waste from metabolism. The main toxic waste product excreted by the kidneys is **urea**, a nitrogenous waste produced during the breakdown of excess amino acids (and nucleic acids) in the liver. Other toxic products are also excreted by the kidneys, for example, creatinine, a waste product produced from the breakdown of creatine phosphate (a molecule important in ATP synthesis) in muscles.

Osmoregulation is the control of the water potential of body fluids. The kidney helps regulate the water potential of the blood through controlling both the volume and concentration of urine produced.

The structure of the urinary (excretory) system

Note: Traditionally the body system including the kidneys, ureters, bladder and urethra has been called the excretory system. However, this is perhaps not the best term as excretion is also carried out by other parts of the body (for example, CO_2 is excreted from the lungs); consequently, many textbooks now refer to it as the urinary system.

The following figure shows the urinary (excretory) system. Blood travelling through the aorta and renal artery reaches the kidneys at the high pressures required for filtration. In essence, the kidney operates as a complex filter, keeping useful products in the blood and eliminating excretory products and excess water.

Filtered blood leaves the kidney via the renal vein whereas the excretory products and excess water pass into the ureter as urine, which takes it to the bladder for storage. Sphincter muscles in the base of the bladder control the release of the urine, which exits the body through the urethra.

Kidney structure

A section through a kidney shows that it contains two main zones (regions) of tissue.

- The **cortex** is the outer dark region immediately under the thin covering layer (capsule).
- The **medulla** is the inner lighter region. The medulla is subdivided into a number of pyramids whose apices extend down into a large central cavity called the **pelvis**.

The functional unit of the kidney is the **nephron**. There are over one million nephrons in each kidney – each operating as an individual filter. As seen in the diagram below, the nephron originates and ends in the cortex, with a long central region (the loop of Henle) extending down into the medulla. Many nephrons join with a collecting duct, which also extends down through the medulla.

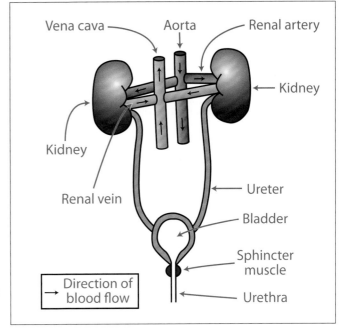

The urinary (excretory) system

The structure of the nephron

The nephron originates as a cup-shaped **Bowman's capsule** (also called the **renal capsule**). Each Bowman's capsule is supplied with blood from an **afferent arteriole** (a

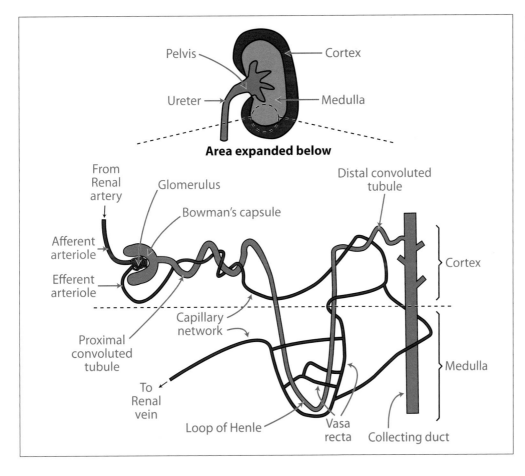

The location and structure of a nephron

branch of the renal artery) and the blood leaves through an **efferent arteriole**. Within the 'cup' of the capsule the arteriole branches to form a tightly coiled knot of capillaries called the **glomerulus** – capillaries which subsequently unite before forming the efferent arteriole.

After leaving the Bowman's capsule, the efferent capillary branches to form a capillary network (the **vasa recta**) that remains closely associated with the rest of the nephron.

In the nephron itself, the Bowman's capsule extends into a coiled tube called the **proximal convoluted tubule** (proximal = first; convoluted = coiled). The proximal convoluted tubule extends into the **loop of Henle** which dips down into the medulla of the kidney. The descending part of the loop is, not unsurprisingly, called the descending limb. The loop of Henle then bends sharply and returns back up through the medulla (the ascending limb) to reach the cortex again. At this stage it becomes the **distal convoluted tubule**. The distal convoluted tubule (and the distal convoluted tubules from many other nephrons) joins a **collecting duct**. The collecting ducts converge at the base of the pelvis and empty their contents (now called urine) into the ureter which takes the urine to the bladder.

Kidney function 1 (excretion –producing urine)

Kidney (and nephron) function involves two main processes, **ultrafiltration** and **reabsorption**.

- **Ultrafiltration** – the filtration of plasma and substances below a certain size into the Bowman's capsule (nephron).
- **Reabsorption** – as ultrafiltration is based purely on molecular size (and not whether products are useful or not), it is essential that filtered useful products are selectively reabsorbed back into the blood stream from the nephron.

Ultrafiltration

Blood entering the glomerulus has a **high hydrostatic pressure** for a number of reasons:

1. The short distance from the heart that the blood travels down the aorta and into the renal artery before branching into the kidney arterioles.
2. The fact that the afferent arteriole of each glomerulus is wider than its efferent arteriole.
3. The coiling of the capillaries in the glomerulus further restricts blood flow therefore increasing pressure.

The high hydrostatic pressure produced forces the smaller components in the blood (glucose, amino acids, salts, water and urea) out of the capillaries and into the Bowman's capsule. However, the larger components of the blood including blood cells and plasma proteins are too large to pass through into the nephron.

The process of ultrafiltration is aided by the structure of the capillary walls of the glomerulus and the lining of the Bowman's capsule itself.

As seen in the following diagram, the single layer of squamous (flattened) endothelial cells that form the walls of glomerular capillaries contain small **pores** and the Bowman's capsule is lined with specialised cells known as **podocytes**. Podocytes have extensions in two planes that allow the filtered material to pass through easily. It is the

basement membrane (separating the capillary and podocytes) that is the **effective filter** and determines which components of the blood enter the Bowman's capsule – it is the basement membrane that prevents the blood cells and plasma proteins from leaving the blood.

In effect, each of the **three layers** separating the blood in the capillary and the inside of the Bowman's capsule is specialised through either being porous (capillary epithelial cells and podocytes) or through acting as a filter (basement membrane).

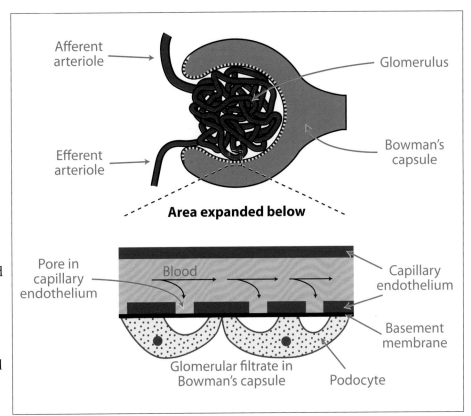

The site of ultrafiltration

The **glomerular filtrate** (the substances that pass through the basement membrane and enter the Bowman's capsule) is similar to blood (except for the plasma proteins and blood cells that are too large to penetrate the membrane).

Note: Apart from the podocytes lining the Bowman's capsule the remaining epithelial cells lining the nephron (and the collecting duct) are cuboidal (cube shaped) epithelial cells.

The filtration force – Ultrafiltration is a necessary process in kidney function. However, the hydrostatic pressure forcing through water and small molecules is not the only force involved. In terms of water potential, it is important to compare the forces on each side of the membrane. For filtration to occur, the water potential within the glomerular capillaries (blood plasma) must exceed the water potential within the Bowman's capsule (glomerular filtrate), ie the glomerular filtrate must have a more negative water potential. How is this difference in water potential produced?

Remember that water potential has two components – pressure potential and solute potential. The hydrostatic pressure **(pressure potential)** of the blood is much greater than the hydrostatic pressure (back pressure) created by the filtrate in the nephron for reasons listed above.

The **solute potential** is represented by the plasma proteins, as there are plasma proteins in the blood in the glomerular capillaries but not in the filtrate, the filtrate has a less negative solute potential than the blood in the glomerulus. Therefore, although the difference in solute potential **opposes** filtration, this effect is insignificant when compared to the differences in hydrostatic pressure across the basement membrane; a difference that very strongly promotes filtration. Consequently, the **net filtration pressure** causes fluid to move from the glomerular capillaries into the Bowman's capsule.

Worked example

In this example the water potential of the blood plasma in the glomerulus is higher, ie more positive or less negative (2.0 kPa) compared to the water potential of the glomerular filtrate in the Bowman's capsule (0.7 kPa) therefore producing the net filtration force or pressure (+ 1.3 kPa) that forces liquids and small molecules through the basement membrane.

Blood plasma (in glomerulus)	Glomerular filtrate (in Bowman's Capsule)
$\psi_s = -3.5$ (due to presence of plasma proteins) $\psi_p = 5.5$ (high hydrostatic pressure)	$\psi_s = -0.7$ (less negative due to absence of plasma proteins) $\psi_p = 1.4$ (low hydrostatic pressure)
$\psi_{plasma} = 2.0$	$\psi_{filtrate} = 0.7$
Net filtration force = +1.3	

Reabsorption

Useful blood products temporarily lost to the glomerular filtrate are reabsorbed back into the blood, mainly as the filtrate passes along the **proximal convoluted tubule**. **Glucose** and **amino acids** – small enough to pass through the basement membrane but too valuable to be lost in the urine – are **selectively reabsorbed** by **facilitated diffusion** and **active transport**.

> **Note:** The term selectively reabsorbed is used as toxic substances such as urea are not actively reabsorbed but (mainly) remain in the filtrate.

As glucose, amino acids and some salts are actively reabsorbed into the blood the osmotic effect created causes over **70%** of the **water** in the filtrate to re-enter the blood capillaries passively by **osmosis**. **Small plasma proteins** which may have passed through the basement membrane in the glomerular filtrate are reabsorbed by **pinocytosis**.

The table below shows relative values of some of the substances filtered into the nephron and subsequently reabsorbed in the proximal tubule.

Substance	Amount in blood plasma/%	Amount filtered into glomerular filtrate/%	Amount reabsorbed back into blood in proximal convoluted tubule/%
Large plasma proteins	100	0	N/A
Glucose	100	100	100
Amino acids	100	100	100
Urea	100	100	< 50 (by diffusion)

> **Note 1:** Although urea (being a toxic metabolic waste) is not selectively reabsorbed, some urea passes from the nephron back into the blood by diffusion. Theoretically up to 50% can diffuse back into the blood.

Note 2: The glucose and amino acids can be absorbed by **facilitated diffusion** as long as the concentration gradient permits. **Active transport** is necessary to ensure that all the glucose is reabsorbed from the nephron back into the capillary network.

The epithelial cells of the proximal tubule have high levels of metabolic activity and continually carry out energy-demanding processes such as active transport. Consequently, they are highly adapted for this role as seen in the diagram below.

By the time the filtrate reaches the end of the proximal tubule it will have no glucose or amino acids present as they will have all been reabsorbed. Although some urea diffuses back into the blood by diffusion along the length of the proximal convoluted tubule, as noted in the table, the **concentration of urea** in the filtrate increases along its length due to the reabsorption of water. At the end of the proximal convoluted tubule, the filtrate is **isotonic** with the blood plasma.

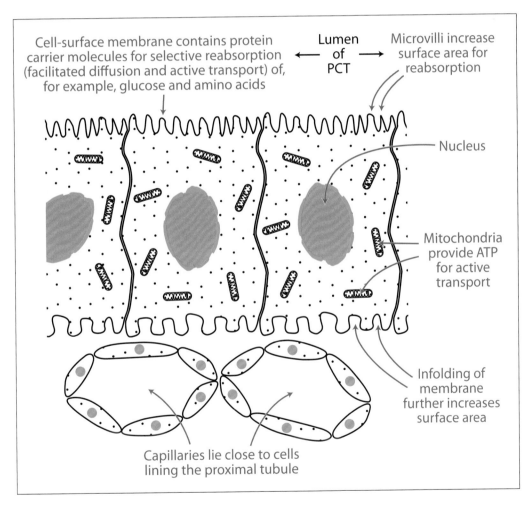

Cell-surface membrane contains protein carrier molecules for selective reabsorption (facilitated diffusion and active transport) of, for example, glucose and amino acids

Lumen of PCT

Microvilli increase surface area for reabsorption

Nucleus

Mitochondria provide ATP for active transport

Infolding of membrane further increases surface area

Capillaries lie close to cells lining the proximal tubule

Adaptations of the epithelial cells lining the proximal tubule

Further regulation of blood composition takes place in the **distal convoluted tubule**. The pH and ionic composition of the blood in the capillaries surrounding the tubule are adjusted and some toxic substances, for example, creatinine (a by-product from muscle metabolism), are secreted from the blood into the filtrate for disposal.

Kidney function 2 (osmoregulation)

Osmoregulation is a homeostatic process that controls water balance in the body. It does this through controlling water balance in the blood; consequently the water content of the tissue fluid and the cells is also controlled.

The collecting duct is where the water regulation takes place. Although **most water** is reabsorbed in the proximal convoluted tubule, the process is passive and the exact amount of water reabsorbed back into the blood cannot be controlled. However, reabsorption in the collecting ducts can be controlled by varying the permeability of the collecting duct walls – this is where the fine control of water balance takes place. The **antidiuretic hormone (ADH)** is crucial in this process as it can control the degree of permeability of the collecting duct walls.

The role of the antidiuretic (ADH) hormone

ADH is *produced* in the **hypothalamus** (part of the brain just above the junction with the spinal cord) and then secreted into the **posterior lobe** of the **pituitary body** where it is *stored*. The solute potential of the blood is monitored by **osmoreceptors** (specialised cells) in the **hypothalamus**.

What happens if the blood becomes too concentrated? Blood can become too concentrated, ie a more negative solute potential, for many reasons, for example, sweating after exercise or on a hot day, not drinking enough water or eating a very salty meal. If this happens:

- the solute potential of the blood becomes *more* **negative** and this is detected by the osmoreceptors in the hypothalamus.
- the posterior lobe of the pituitary body releases *more* **ADH** into the blood.
- this causes the walls of the distal convoluted tubules and the collecting ducts to become *more* **permeable** – special channel proteins (aquaporins) open which helps make the walls of the collecting ducts more permeable.
- therefore *more* **water is reabsorbed** from the collecting ducts back into the blood.
- the net result is that the solute potential of the blood returns to normal (becomes less negative) and a smaller volume of *more* **concentrated (hypertonic) urine** is produced.
- this process exemplifies **negative feedback**. As the blood concentration changes it sets in train a process (as described above) that returns the solute potential back to normal; as the blood concentration returns to normal the release of ADH reduces, returning to normal levels.

What if the blood is too dilute? This is most likely to happen when drinking (hypotonic) liquid. In this situation the opposite happens: the blood develops a higher solute potential (becomes less concentrated) and this is detected by the osmoreceptors in the hypothalamus, *less* ADH is released, the walls of the collecting ducts become *less* permeable and *less* water is reabsorbed back into the blood (large quantities of **dilute (hypotonic) urine** are produced).

The role of the Loop of Henle

The Loop of Henle is the part of the nephron that enables mammals to produce a **hypertonic urine** and plays a significant role in water reabsorption from the collecting ducts.

As the isotonic renal fluid leaves the proximal tubule and enters the Loop of Henle it passes down the descending limb and back up the ascending limb. A critical process in terms of osmoregulation is the passage of sodium (Na^+) and chloride (Cl^-) ions from the ascending limb into the surrounding medulla tissue. The ascending limb is impermeable to water so water will not follow the sodium and chloride ions by osmosis.

The effect of the addition of salt to the interstitial region between the two limbs of the Loop of Henle is to create a **more negative solute potential** in the **medulla** of the kidney. This negative solute potential creates the water potential gradient that allows water to be drawn from the collecting ducts (which pass through the medulla) by osmosis.

> **Note 1:** The cuboidal cells in the ascending limb are rich in mitochondria. The mitochondria provide the ATP necessary to pump the salt into the medulla.

> **Note 2:** The descending limb of the Loop of Henle is permeable to water, allowing some water to leave the nephron in this region and enter the blood by osmosis (due to the more negative water potential in the medulla). However, it is the collecting duct that is mainly responsible for the fine control of water reabsorption.

> **Note 3:** There is a positive correlation between the length of the Loop of Henle and the ability to reabsorb water and concentrate the liquid in the collecting duct (liquid that will become urine) and conserve water in a species. Some desert living mammal species such as the kangaroo rat and the camel have very long Loops of Henle as an important adaptation in their ability to conserve water. The longer the Loop of Henle, the more water that can be absorbed. This is largely because a longer Loop allows the medulla to have an even more negative solute potential.

The kidneys are a very effective filter but equally effective in osmoregulation. All the blood in the circulatory system passes through the kidneys every five minutes with over 99% of the material (mainly water) filtered being reabsorbed with less than 1% ending up as urine.

Exam questions

1. In an experiment to investigate the functioning of the mammalian kidney, samples were taken by micropipette from different regions. The diagram below shows the sample sites, labelled 1 to 6.

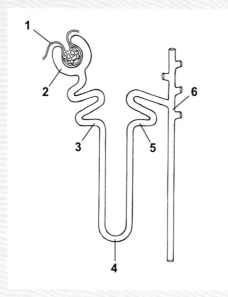

Each sample was analysed to determine the concentration of glucose, protein, urea and sodium ions. The flow rate was also measured at each of the sample sites. The results are shown in the table below.

Sample sites within the kidney	Concentration/g dm^{-3}				Flow rate /cm^3 min^{-1}
	Protein	Glucose	Sodium ions	Urea	
1. Plasma in afferent arteriole	80	1.2	34	0.3	600.0
2. Filtrate in Bowman's capsule	0.5	1.2	34	0.3	125.0
3. End of proximal convoluted tubule	0	0	34	1.6	25.0
4. Bottom of loop of Henlé	0	0	70	1.8	1.5
5. Beginning of distal convoluted tubule	0	0	30	1.8	1.5
6. Beginning of collecting duct	0	0	45	2.2	1.3

Use the information in this table and your own understanding to answer the following questions.

(a) Explain the changes in the composition of proteins and glucose between the plasma in the afferent arteriole (sample site 1) and the end of the proximal convoluted tubule (sample site 3).

- Protein
- Glucose [4]

(b) Comment on the changes in sodium ion concentration in the different sample regions. [4]

(c) Explain the changes in urea concentration as it moves along the nephron. [2]

(d) Suggest an explanation for the fall in the flow rate as fluid moves from the plasma into and then along the nephron. [2]

(e) The experiment described on page 14 was carried out at 37 °C. When the experiment was repeated at 30 °C, the glucose concentration at the end of the proximal convoluted tubule was 0.15 g dm^{-3}. Suggest an explanation for this result. [3]

Question taken from CCEA's Biology Assessment Unit A2 1, Physiology and Ecosystems, January 2010, © CCEA 2013

2. (a) In an experiment on kidney function, a student drank 700 ml of water. After drinking the water the student produced a sample of urine at 30 minute intervals for a period of 3 hours. The volume of each sample of urine and the mass of solute in each sample were measured. The results are shown in the graph.

    (i) Using the information in the graph, determine which sample was the most concentrated. [1]

    (ii) Compare the samples taken after 60 minutes and 120 minutes and determine which of the two samples has the lower solute potential. Explain your answer. [2]

(b) Explain the process of osmoregulation in the body after drinking a large volume of water. [4]

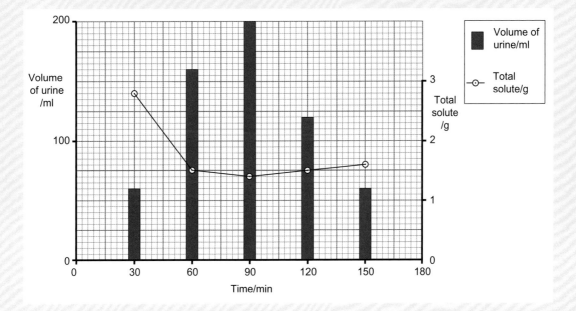

Question taken from CCEA's Biology Assessment Unit A2 1, Physiology and Ecosystems, May 2010, © CCEA 2013

3. (a) Photographs A and B are from different regions of the kidney. Photograph B is at a higher magnification than photograph A.

    (i) Identify the structures labelled X in Photograph A. [1]

    (ii) Identify the kidney regions that the photographs are taken from. [2]

Photograph A

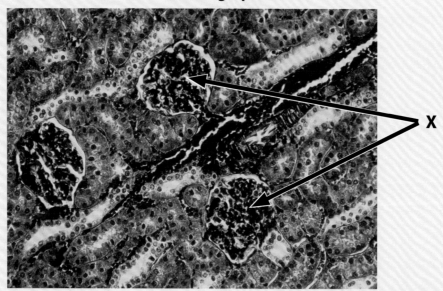

X

© *Manfred Kage / Science Photo Library*

Photograph B

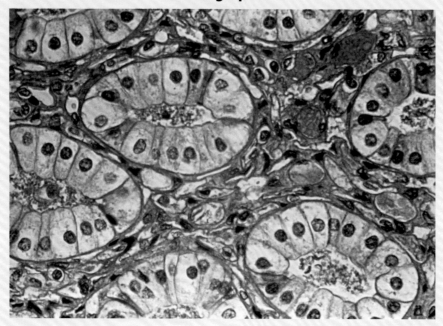

© *CRNI / Science Photo Library*

(b) The hormone ADH is involved in water reabsorption in the kidney. However, most of the water reabsorption in the kidney takes place independently of ADH being present.

   (i) State precisely where ADH is produced in the body. [1]

   (ii) State where most water reabsorption takes place in the kidney. State also the process by which this water is reabsorbed. [2]

(c) The following graph shows the level of ADH in a student's blood over a three hour period after drinking 0.5 litres of water.

With reference to the process of osmoregulation, explain fully the changes in ADH concentration. [4]

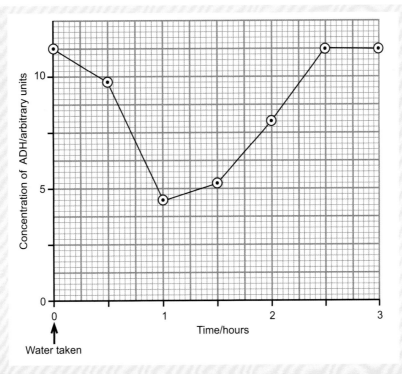

Question taken from CCEA's Biology Assessment Unit A2 1, Physiology and Ecosystems, January 2012, © CCEA 2013

4. In humans, the process of osmoregulation is an example of homeostasis and involves:
    • the release of antidiuretic hormone (ADH) which controls water loss.
    • a thirst response which controls water uptake through drinking.

The following graphs show how ADH levels and the intensity of a person's thirst are affected by changing plasma solute concentration.

(a) Using the information in Graph A and your understanding of how ADH is released into the plasma, explain the effect of changing plasma solute concentration on plasma ADH levels. [4]

(b) Describe and explain the effect of increasing ADH levels on urine production. [3]

(c) With reference to Graph B, describe and explain the relationship between a person's thirst and the plasma solute concentration. [2]

(d) Plan an investigation which tests the following hypothesis.
    "Drinking isotonic solutions instead of water reduces urine production"
    (There is no need to include a plan for statistical analysis.) [4]

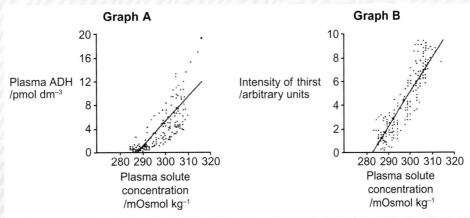

Question taken from CCEA's Biology Assessment Unit A2 1, Physiology and Ecosystems, January 2011, © CCEA 2013

5. Medium- and long-distance runners often use isotonic sports drinks before, during, and after their events.

A typical male runner can have around 90 g of stored glycogen reserves in the liver and a further 350–400 g stored in the muscles at the start of a race. During a race, up to 4 g of this reserve can be used up each minute. In addition, distance runners lose considerable quantities of sweat, rich in sodium, potassium, calcium, magnesium and other ions.

The isotonic drink *Powerade* provides the following nutritional information.

Nutrition Information – typical values per 100 ml			
Energy	70 kJ	Fat	0 g
Protein	0 g	Of which saturates	0 g
Carbohydrate	3.9 g	Fibre	0 g
Of which sugars	3.9 g	Sodium	0.05 g
Other added nutrients per 100 ml			
Potassium 12.5 mg Calcium 1.3 mg Magnesium 0.6 mg			

Figures from Powerade – The Coca Cola Company

Isotonic drinks have many advantages. They replace ions lost in sweat and can reduce the depletion of glycogen reserves. The uptake of the ions into the cells also reduces dehydration.

(a) (i) How does the data for *Powerade* suggest that sodium is the principal ion lost in sweat? [1]

(ii) Suggest why all the carbohydrate in *Powerade* is in the form of sugars. [1]

(b) Explain why the uptake of ions into the body cells reduces dehydration in these cells. [2]

Many manufacturers claim that drinking an isotonic drink during a race, as opposed to drinking water only, reduces the need for runners to go to the toilet (to urinate) while running.

(c) Explain the reasoning for this claim. [3]

(d) The absorption of the sugars in the isotonic drinks takes place in the ileum.

(i) Describe the process of sugar absorption in the ileum. [2]

The process of absorption is aided by the presence of villi and microvilli.

(ii) Give one similarity and one difference between villi and microvilli. [2]

Question taken from CCEA's Biology Assessment Unit A2 1, Physiology and Ecosystems, May 2012, © CCEA 2013

6. Quality of written communication is awarded a maximum of 2 marks in this section. [2]

Give an account of:

(a) the kidney and excretion. [11]

(b) osmoregulation and the kidney. [5]

Question taken from CCEA's Biology Assessment Unit A2 1, Physiology and Ecosystems, May 2011, © CCEA 2013

Chapter 2 – Immunity

Pathogens and immunity

Most microorganisms are harmless or even beneficial (for example, the many types of bacteria and fungi involved in decay and decomposition are essential for life on Earth). However, a small percentage of microorganisms, including some bacteria, fungi, protoctists and viruses (although technically viruses are not classified as living organisms) can cause disease or be **pathogenic**.

If a **pathogen** gains entry to the body it could cause significant harm or even death, therefore the body's **first line of defence** against pathogens is to try to **prevent entry**.

If pathogens do enter the body, the subsequent defence mechanisms can be grouped into two types.

- **Non-specific** – these defence mechanisms are not specific to individual types of pathogens. **Phagocytosis** is an example of a non-specific defence mechanism.
- **Specific immune response** – this type of response does distinguish between individual pathogens and the response is tailored to the pathogen involved. Specific immune responses take **longer to work** but tend to provide **long term immunity**. Specific immune responses involve **lymphocytes**, a specialised type of white blood cell.

Natural barriers to pathogen entry

Barriers preventing the entry of pathogens in humans include:

- **An outer protective covering (skin)** – the skin provides a tough physical barrier that most pathogens cannot penetrate. The skin only ceases to be an effective barrier to most pathogens if it is punctured, for example, a wound or cut, or if it is not in its normal healthy condition.
- The enzyme **lysozyme** – is contained in many body secretions including **tears**, **saliva** and **sweat.** Lysozyme is anti-bacterial as it is able to digest (hydrolyse) their cell walls. Tears can also wash away debris and pathogens from the front of the eye which is delicate and easily damaged.

- **Epithelial lining** covered in **mucus**, such as in the respiratory tract – The mucus traps pathogens (and other foreign particles) and prevents them penetrating the underlying membranes. **Cilia,** tiny hairs that line the respiratory tract, sweep the mucus and its trapped pathogens, back up the trachea.
- **Hydrochloric acid** in the **stomach** – This kills most pathogens that are in the food we eat or the liquids we drink. It is effective as it provides a very low pH that denatures the enzymes of the pathogens.

However, despite these (and other) barriers to pathogen entry, many do invade our body. The next line of defence is **phagocytosis**.

Phagocytosis

Phagocytosis is non-specific but has the advantage of being rapid. Phagocytosis is carried out by a number of types of white blood cell, collectively known as **phagocytes**.

As part of an **inflammatory response** following infection, the capillaries in the area affected become leaky, allowing plasma to seep into the surrounding areas. Inflamed parts of the body tend to become swollen with phagocytes, dead pathogens and cell debris, collectively known as pus. Inflamed areas appear red due to the increased blood flow to that area.

> **Note:** Inflammation also involves the affected part of the body becoming hot (as well as swollen). The raised temperature helps reduce infection by denaturing enzymes in the pathogen.

Phagocytes including **polymorphs** (the most common and first to arrive) and **macrophages** (develop from monocytes in the blood, they are larger but much longer lived than polymorphs) are able to squeeze through the capillary walls and engulf the pathogenic bacteria and surrounding cell debris at the site of the infection. The process of phagocytosis is summarised below.

- The phagocyte moves towards the pathogen, **attracted by the chemicals** it produces.
- As it does so the **phagocyte membrane invaginates** to begin to enclose the pathogen.
- As the pathogen is **engulfed**, the invaginated phagocyte membrane forms a vesicle (**phagosome**) around the pathogen.
- Lysosomes move towards the phagosome and fuse with it.
- Hydrolytic **enzymes** within the lysosome are released into the phagosome, onto the pathogen. These enzymes **hydrolyse** the pathogen.
- The soluble digested products are absorbed into the cytoplasm of the phagocyte.

Phagocytosis

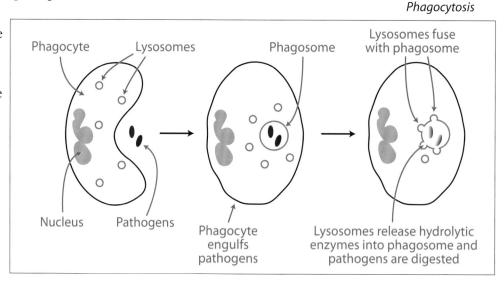

The specific immune response

Specific immune responses are associated with **lymphocyte** white blood cells. The responses are triggered by the body being able to recognise 'foreign' cells, linked to the concept of self and non-self tissue.

Self and non-self – Foreign (non-self) cells are cells not recognised by the body, if detected they will produce an immune response. In reality, it is specific molecules, or clusters of molecules, that form part of the cell-surface membrane that are recognised as foreign. These molecules are often protein, but can be other substances, for example, polysaccharides, glycoprotein, glycolipid, and are collectively referred to as **antigens**. Different pathogens have different antigens, consequently the immune response is specific to these antigens. This specific response is due to the lymphocyte having a receptor on its cell-surface membrane that is *complementary* in shape to the antigen. Antigen and lymphocyte fit together like substrate and enzyme in the lock and key model of enzyme action.

> **Note:** Antigens can be defined as chemicals capable of producing a specific immune response.

How do lymphocytes know what is self and non-self? – There are many million different types of lymphocytes, each having receptors with a complementary shape to a potential antigen. In the foetus, these lymphocytes frequently make contact with other foetal (self) cells. Lymphocytes that are complementary in shape with foetal cells are 'switched off' so by the time the baby is born the functional lymphocytes that remain are those that are not complementary to self cells. However, because there are many million functional lymphocytes remaining there are only a few of each type. This is part of the reason why the specific immune response is relatively **slow**.

Types of lymphocyte – There are two types of lymphocyte, each of which has a specific but different type of response. The two types, **B-lymphocytes (B-cells)** and **T-lymphocytes (T-cells)** are summarised in the following table.

Type of lymphocyte	Where formed	Site of development (maturation)	Name of immune response	Nature of immune response
B-lymphocytes	Formed from stem cells in the bone marrow	Mature in bone marrow	**Antibody-mediated** (humoral) immunity	Produce **antibodies** which respond to antigens found in **body fluids** (for example, blood and tissue fluid). Respond usually to bacterial or viral infection.
T-lymphocytes	Formed from stem cells in the bone marrow	Mature in thymus gland (lymph gland in the neck)	**Cell-mediated** immunity	Respond to antigens attached to **body cells**. Respond usually to body cells affected by viral infection.

Lymphocyte activation – Once infection occurs, a specific immune response requires an antigen to come into contact with its complementary lymphocyte – a process that may take some time due to the small numbers involved. When this happens the lymphocytes become **sensitised** or **activated**. However, the process is different in the two types of lymphocytes.

In **B-lymphocytes**, certain genes are activated to set in motion a process that eventually leads to the production of **antibodies**. In **T-lymphocytes**, a number of types of **T-cells** are produced, each type having different roles in the battle against infection. In both B and T-cells, sensitised lymphocytes are **cloned** (involving division by **mitosis**). The products of the cloned B and T-cells will be investigated in the next two sections covering cell-mediated and antibody-mediated immunity.

Cell-mediated immunity

In an immune response, the production of **T-cells** is stimulated by the body's **own** cells that have been changed due to the presence of non-self material within them. These cells are referred to as **antigen-presenting cells**. Examples include:

- macrophages (phagocytes) that have engulfed and broken down a pathogen and '**present**' some of the pathogen's antigens on their own cell-surface membrane.
- any type of **body cell** that has been invaded by a virus – again some of the viral antigens are presented on the cell-surface membrane of the body cell (remember, viruses cannot live on their own, they must live inside other cells).
- cancer (tumour) cells, as many type of cancer cells present abnormal antigens on their cell-surface membranes.

The **antigen-presenting** cells bring about a response as summarised by the diagram below.

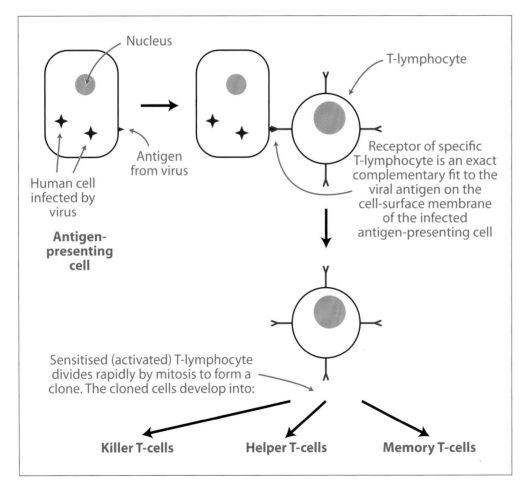

The development of a range of T-cells in cell-mediated immunity

The cloned T-cells produced from this response can:

- develop into **killer T-cells**. Killer (**cytotoxic**) T-cells destroy infected cells by attaching to the antigens on the cell-surface membrane and producing chemicals (for example, the protein perforin which punches holes in the cell-surface membrane, nitric acid or other chemicals) that destroys the cell.

- develop into **helper T-cells**. These cells stimulate other cells involved in the immune response, for example, they stimulate B-cells to divide (and produce the plasma cells that produce antibodies – see next section) and promote the process of phagocytosis through their effect on phagocytes. Phagocytosis is a slow process without the activating role of the helper T-cells. They also attach special chemicals (**opsonins**) to the pathogens that mark them out for the attention of phagocytes. Helper T-cells also secrete the protein interferon that helps limit the ability of viruses to replicate.

- develop into **memory T-cells**. These cells circulate in body fluids and can respond rapidly to future infection by the same pathogen (presenting the same antigen(s)). If a subsequent infection occurs, as the memory cells are already sensitised they can very rapidly produce a large clone of T-lymphocytes.

Antibody-mediated immunity

This type of response targets microorganisms (usually bacteria or viruses) that are found in the **body fluids** (for example, blood and tissue fluid), rather than in body cells. As its name suggests, antibody-mediated immunity defends the body through the production and action of **antibodies**.

The development of plasma cells and memory cells in antibody-mediated immunity

Note:
Antibodies can be defined as globular proteins which are complementary to specific antigens and which can react with the antigens (microbes) leading to their destruction.

Specific antigens sensitise specific **B-lymphocytes** that have receptors that match the pathogen's antigens. Therefore, following infection by a particular

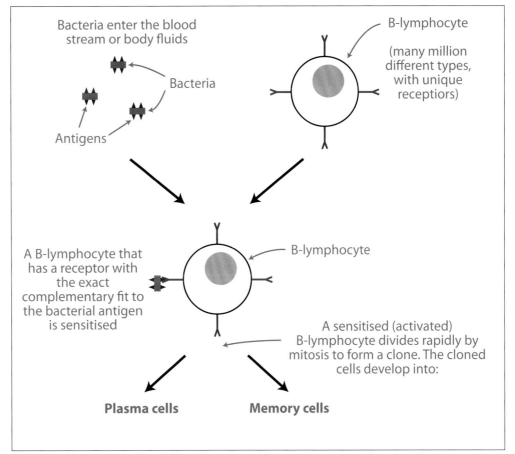

Bacteria enter the blood stream or body fluids

Bacteria

Antigens

B-lymphocyte

(many million different types, with unique receptiors)

A B-lymphocyte that has a receptor with the exact complementary fit to the bacterial antigen is sensitised

B-lymphocyte

A sensitised (activated) B-lymphocyte divides rapidly by mitosis to form a clone. The cloned cells develop into:

Plasma cells   **Memory cells**

pathogen, a particular type (or types) of B-lymphocyte becomes cloned. In common with T-cells, sensitised B-cells produce different types of cell, in the case of B-cells, plasma cells and memory cells.

However, most cloned B-cells become plasma cells. **Plasma cells** are short lived (a few days) but each produces very large numbers (many millions) of antibodies. The antibodies neutralise the pathogens as a consequence of **antigen-antibody reactions**.

The action of antibodies – The antibodies produced as a consequence of a specific antibody-mediated response will have a complementary shape to the antigens of the invading bacteria. The antibodies latch on to the bacterial antigens clumping the bacteria together. Typically, the build up of antibodies in the body fluids will enable a sufficient number to be present to immobilise the bacteria (or other pathogens) causing their **agglutination** or clumping as an **antigen-antibody complex**. In due course the antigen-antibody complex (clump of bacteria and antibodies) is engulfed by polymorphs and other phagocytes.

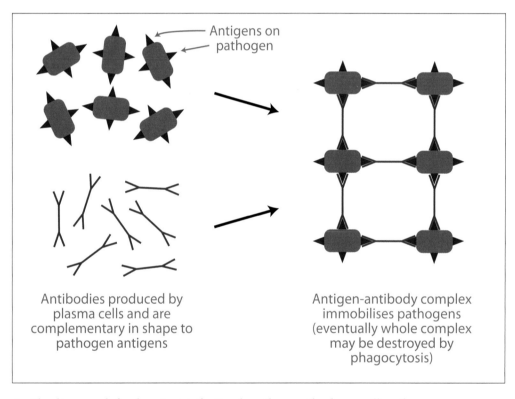

The action of antibodies in forming an antigen-antibody complex

Antigens on pathogen

Antibodies produced by plasma cells and are complementary in shape to pathogen antigens

Antigen-antibody complex immobilises pathogens (eventually whole complex may be destroyed by phagocytosis)

Antibodies can defend against infection by other methods as well as the process described in the diagram above. Other methods include the destruction of the invading cells directly. Antibodies can also act as opsonins by attaching to pathogens and marking them for phagocytosis.

Note 1: Antibodies are **globular proteins**. Protein is the ideal molecule as small changes in the sequence of amino acids in the primary structure can produce the millions of different three-dimensional shapes required to be **complementary** in shape to the range of antigens that exist.

Note 2: The receptor on the sensitised B-lymphocyte and the part of the antibody that attaches to the antigen are exactly the same shape (and both are complementary in shape to the antigens on the invading pathogen).

In contrast, the **memory cells** produced by B-cells can live for many years (sometimes for life) in the body fluids. These cells remain inactive unless stimulated by the presence of the same antigen (pathogen) again. If this happens, the memory cells **divide rapidly** (they are already sensitised) and produce **vast numbers** of plasma cells as there are more memory cells than there were 'correct' B-cells at the start of the primary response. The plasma cells produce the antibodies necessary to destroy the pathogen while the memory cells provide a guarantee of further long term protection. This is known as the **secondary immune response**. The **primary immune response** is the initial response to the antigen when meeting it for the first time.

> **Note 1:** Pathogens can contain many different types of antigen. Each antigen can produce an immune response with a different type of B-lymphocyte. Therefore, for any one type of pathogen there may be many different antigen-antibody reactions taking place at the same time.

> **Note 2:** No one individual is immune to all potential pathogens and diseases. However, individuals can be immune (protected against) to specific diseases.

Active and passive immunity

Immunity can be active or passive. **Passive immunity** is when the individual receives antibodies from another source (ie from outside the body). **Active immunity** is produced when the individual achieves immunity through the production of antibodies by his/her own body.

Passive immunity – can develop by a number of methods. These include:

- antibodies passing from mother to baby across the **placenta** and in the **mother's milk** (colostrum). The passive immunity that this produces is crucial in the very early stages of life, a time when the baby's immune system is still developing.
- antibodies made in another individual, which are harvested and **injected** into another person as a serum. The antibodies can be obtained from individuals recovering from illness (they will have high levels of the required antibody in their blood). An older method of obtaining antibodies involved immunising animals, for example, horses, with attenuated pathogens or their inactivated toxins. This caused the animal to produce the antibodies required and serum from the animals was given to individuals requiring rapid immunity.

> **Note:** Serum is blood plasma with all blood clotting substances removed.

The methods of obtaining antibodies for medical use from other live sources (described above) is now largely superseded by **monoclonal antibody production**. This involves the removal of sensitised and cloned B-lymphocytes from a mouse that has been infected with a particular antigen. The mouse B-lymphocytes are hybridised with cancer cells to produce long lived lymphocytes that can produce the required antibodies in a fermenter, conveyer-belt style over a long period.

Monoclonal antibodies have many advantages. Compared to obtaining antibodies from horses or other large mammals they:

- can be produced in large quantities in the laboratory.
- can produce a single type of antibody (antibodies obtained from horses usually come as a range of types, together with other chemicals that can potentially cause allergies).

Passive immunity provides **rapid** immunity as the processes of B-lymphocyte sensitisation and plasma cell production do not need to take place first. It is especially effective if someone becomes infected with a particularly harmful pathogen when it is probable that they have no defence against it (for example, a 'new' disease encountered in a foreign country or when suffering from a snake bite).

However, passive immunity is only **temporary** as in time the antibodies are broken down and the individual's immune system is not programmed to make more.

Active immunity – This can develop through **having had the disease**. The individual becomes ill but recovers as a consequence of the primary response to the infection. Should a subsequent infection occur, involving the same pathogen, the secondary response is so rapid and strong that the immune system may destroy the pathogen(s) so quickly that individuals may not even be aware that they were infected. In contrast, the primary immune response is **slow** to develop and the individual usually suffers the disease symptoms for a period of time (it may take 4–5 days before antibody levels reach a high enough level to be effective in a primary response, due to the time involved in activating the specific B-lymphocyte and producing plasma cells) but once in place it is **long lasting**.

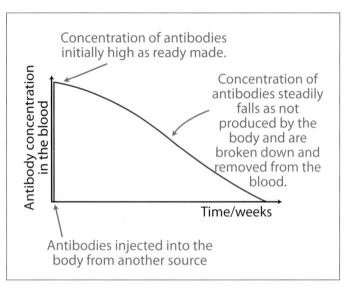

Changes in the concentration of antibodies during passive immunity

The very **strong** and **rapid secondary response** (relative to the primary response) is due to there being many more memory cells than there were specific B-lymphocyte cells at the start of the primary response (strength) and the fact that the memory cells are already sensitised (speed).

> **Note:** Some antibodies can last in the blood for a considerable time. However, the fact that active immunity is long lasting is primarily due to the presence of memory cells and their ability to respond quickly and effectively if a subsequent infection occurs.

Vaccinations also produce active immunity. In the UK, vaccination programmes are in place for many diseases, for example, measles and mumps. Most vaccinations are given early in childhood and their function is to stop individuals being infected by potentially common and harmful infectious diseases. Vaccinations trick the immune system into thinking the body has been infected by a particular pathogen; consequently the primary immune response is triggered and the immune system is equipped to produce a secondary response if required. Due to the speed and strength of the secondary response, vaccinations render the individual immune.

Vaccinations normally contain one of the following:

- Killed or **weakened** (attenuated) **pathogens** – These pathogens contain the antigens required to produce an immune response but they will not cause the disease itself (however, mild symptoms may sometimes appear).

- Modified **toxins** produced by the pathogen – With some pathogens it is their toxins that can produce the immune response. The toxins must be modified and made harmless but not changed so much they do not produce an immune response.
- Isolated **antigens** separated from the pathogen itself – For some pathogens the antigens can be made by genetic engineering.

Sometimes vaccinations require subsequent **booster** injections. These produce a secondary immune response, similar to the response produced when catching a particular disease for a second time.

The characteristics of active immunity are highlighted in the following diagram.

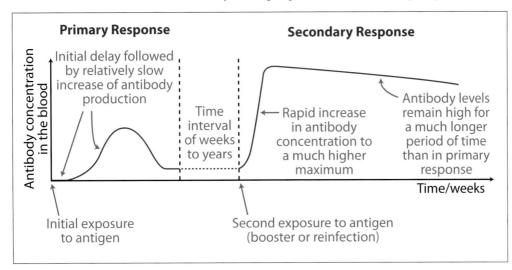

Changes in the concentration of antibodies during active immunity

The different types of immunity can be summarised in the following flow diagram.

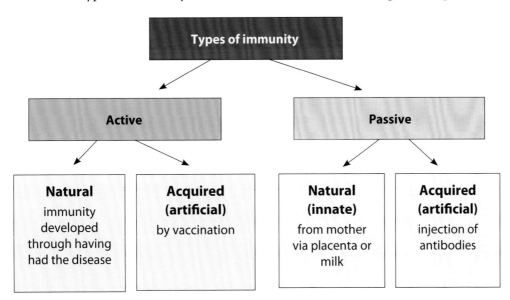

Transplanting tissue

As discussed in the previous section, the body will produce an immune response to the presence of any non-self antigens. Normally this response occurs as a consequence of infection. However, transplanted organs, for example, kidneys, or tissue (such as skin grafts), will also produce an immune response as the transplanted organs/tissue will contain non-self antigens if they come from someone else. Exceptions are if the tissue is transplanted within the same person, as can happen with skin grafts or if tissues/ organs are transplanted between identical twins (identical twins are genetically identical therefore they have identical antigens).

Transplant rejection – However, most organ transplants do not take place between identical twins, therefore the risk of transplant rejection exists. Transplant rejection is the main reason for many organ transplants failing.

The process of rejection involves the following steps:

- **T-lymphocytes** are stimulated (sensitised) by the non-self antigens present in the transplanted tissue.
- These T-cells are cloned by mitosis to produce **killer T-cells** (and the range of other T-cells associated with cell-mediated immunity).
- The killer-T cells destroy the transplanted cells.

Note: Transplant rejection can also involve the action of B-lymphocytes and antibodies. For example, if the blood of a donor and a recipient is different this can produce an immune response involving antibodies (see next section). Normally, tissue matching is accurate so rejection by B-lymphocytes in this situation is unlikely to occur.

As organ transplants may be a last resort in saving a life or even in providing a better quality of life for a patient, considerable scientific endeavour has gone into devising strategies for reducing transplant rejection.

These include:

- **tissue typing** – This is the term that describes the process of matching the donor and recipient cell-surface markers (antigens) so that there is as good a match as possible, ie there is as small a difference as possible between the self and non-self antigens. Generally, the best tissue matching will take place between close relatives. The best possible transplant will be between identical twins, which will have identical antigens therefore the transplant is much less likely to be rejected.
- **immunosuppression techniques** – such as the use of **drugs to inhibit DNA replication** and therefore the cloning of lymphocytes (and the production of killer T-cells) will slow down or stop rejection processes. For many types of transplant, the immunosuppression drugs have to be taken for a very long time (for the life of the transplant and therefore often for life).
- **X-rays** – can also be used to inhibit the production of lymphocytes through the irradiation of bone marrow or lymph tissue. Unpleasant side effects can result and the use of X-rays is usually a backup to immunosuppressant drugs rather than a first course of action.

Immunosuppression (whether by drugs or X-rays) will **compromise the recipient's immune system**. This makes the individual susceptible to infection, as immunosuppression depresses the immune system in general (not just its response to the antigens involved in the transplanted tissue). A number of additional strategies are used to help support the transplant patient against subsequent infections including anti-viral drugs, anti-bacterial mouth rinses and the use of monoclonal antibodies to help target and reduce the effect of the T-cells involved in rejection.

Nonetheless, there is a delicate balance between reducing the risks of rejection and restricting the side-effects that are linked to the use of immunosuppressant technologies.

Blood transfusion

Erythrocytes (red blood cells) also have **antigens** (markers) on their cell-surface membrane. The blood of any one individual will not have antibodies that correspond to the antigens on his/her red blood cells as this would trigger an immune reaction. As with other B-lymphocytes that correspond with self-antigens, the lymphocytes responsible for these blood antibodies are switched off during very early development.

The delicate balancing act between risk of transplant rejection and use of immunosuppressant agents

However, the type of antigens on the erythrocytes of different people varies. In the **ABO** system there are four different types of blood group (A, B, AB and O) and everyone belongs to one of these groups. This is an example of **polymorphism** – a situation where there are several distinct categories or forms.

When giving a **blood transfusion** to an individual (for example, following surgery, an accident or when treating some illnesses), it is important that the transfusion is compatible. Take the following two examples:

- Blood **can** be donated from an individual with blood **group A (the donor)** to another individual with blood **group A (the recipient)**. This is because the recipient has no antibodies (no anti-a antibodies) that correspond to the antigens on the donor's erythrocytes.

- Blood **cannot** be donated from a donor with blood **group A** to a recipient with blood **group B**. This is because the recipient has anti-a antibodies in his/her plasma. The presence of both antigen A and anti-a antibodies causes an antigen-antibody reaction. The anti-a antibodies cause the blood, containing red blood cells with antigen A, to **agglutinate** or clump. This agglutination could block capillary networks and lead to organ failure and death.

Note: An individual with blood group B will have anti-a antibodies as they had no A antigens in early development; therefore, A antigens were not identified as self antigens and the lymphocytes responsible for producing antibody-a were not 'switched off'.

The antigens and antibodies of the ABO blood group system are shown in the following table.

Blood group	Antigens on erythrocytes	Antibodies in plasma
A	A	anti-b
B	B	anti-a
AB	both A and B	neither anti-a nor anti-b
O	neither A nor B	both anti-a and anti-b

Using the information in the previous table, it is possible to work out which blood can be transfused into which other types(s). Donated blood does not have to be the same type as the recipient but it is important that the donated blood type does not lead to an antigen-antibody reaction and subsequent agglutination.

Safe (no reaction) and unsafe (agglutination occurs) transfusion combinations

Blood group of donor	Blood group of recipient			
	A	B	AB	O
A	no reaction	agglutination	no reaction	agglutination
B	agglutination	no reaction	no reaction	agglutination
AB	agglutination	agglutination	no reaction	agglutination
O	no reaction	no reaction	no reaction	no reaction

As blood of group O does not have either A or B antigens, blood of group O can be transfused into any of the four blood groups. Consequently, blood group O is referred to as the **universal donor**. Blood group AB lacks both anti-a and anti-b antibodies, therefore this is referred to as the **universal recipient**, as people with blood group AB can receive blood from any group.

> **Note:** A key point when working out transfusion compatibility is that donated blood is mainly red blood cells and that the amount of donated plasma is insignificant. The table above indicates that blood group A can be donated to a recipient with blood group AB. This is only because none, or a very insignificant number of, anti-b antibodies in blood group A will be transfused into the recipient with blood group AB.

Why do we have an ABO system? It is thought that the different antigens (groups) evolved as a consequence of mutations. Currently, none of the blood groups appears to give individuals a selective advantage (ie the mutations are neutral). However, it is possible that in our evolutionary past some of the mutations gave selective advantage against specific diseases – this would explain why the different groups have persisted through time. The ABO is only one of a number of many blood group systems in humans, although it is the most important in clinical practice. Another very important blood group system is the **rhesus system**.

The rhesus system – This system is based on the presence or absence of an antigen (the rhesus antigen or antigen D) on the cell-surface membranes of the red blood cells. Around 85 % of the population have this antigen and are described as **rhesus positive** (Rh⁺). **Rhesus negative** (Rh⁻) individuals do not have the antigen. Unlike the antibodies for the ABO system, antibodies against the antigen D marker, (anti-D antibodies) do not occur naturally in the plasma. An individual who is rhesus positive will not produce anti-D antibodies (relevant B-lymphocytes are 'switched off' when the rhesus positive marker is recognised as self during development).

Rhesus negative individuals do not normally have the antibodies either, **but** can produce anti-D antibodies if their blood becomes contaminated with blood containing antigen D as can happen in the following situations:

- Blood transfusion between a rhesus positive donor and a rhesus negative recipient. In reality, this is unlikely to occur with modern blood matching techniques.

- When a **rhesus negative mother** has a **rhesus positive baby**. The typical sequence of events is explained in the following flow diagram.

> During birth (or late in pregnancy) some foetal red blood cells (rhesus positive so contain antigen D) leak into the mother's circulation.

> This causes the rhesus negative mother's immune system to produce anti-D antibodies. By the time the antibodies are produced in significant numbers by the mother the baby will have been born therefore there is no threat to the developing foetus.

> However, during subsequent pregnancies, if the foetus is rhesus positive, the relevant B-lymphocytes in the mother are already sensitised and large numbers of anti-D antibodies can be produced immediately if any foetal blood cells enter the maternal circulation. The anti-D antibodies can cross the placenta and cause agglutination of foetal red blood cells, a condition known as haemolytic disease of the newborn.

Foetal death, or serious illness, due to haemolytic disease of the newborn seldom occurs today as rhesus negative mothers are treated during pregnancy (around 30 weeks) by being given an injection of anti-D antibodies. These attach to any antigen D-containing foetal red blood cells fragments that may pass across the placenta and enter the mother's circulation before the mother's B-lymphocytes are stimulated to produce anti-D antibodies. Following birth, if the baby proves to be rhesus positive, another injection of anti-D antibodies is given within 72 hours.

However, if medical screening and intervention is bypassed and the condition does occur, the baby can be treated by blood transfusion.

Exam questions

1. The human body has different lines of defence against bacteria and viruses. These range from natural barriers preventing their entry to specific reactions once entry is gained.

   (a) (i) Describe how tears act as a barrier to entry. [1]

   (ii) Antibodies are produced which specifically react with the type of bacterium or virus which has entered the body. Antibodies are made of protein. Using your understanding of protein structure, explain why protein is suitable for this role. [3]

   (b) In the winter of 2010–2011, many of the patients occupying hospital intensive care beds were suffering from swine flu (a viral infection). Most of these patients were young while it appeared that many older people were less affected. It is suggested that many older people have gained immunity through coming into contact with similar viruses many years ago.

   Suggest how previous infection with similar viruses may have made older people immune to swine flu, so preventing them becoming ill. [4]

Question taken from CCEA's Biology Assessment Unit A2 1, Physiology and Ecosystems, May 2011, © CCEA 2013

2. The diagram below summarises the process of phagocytosis.

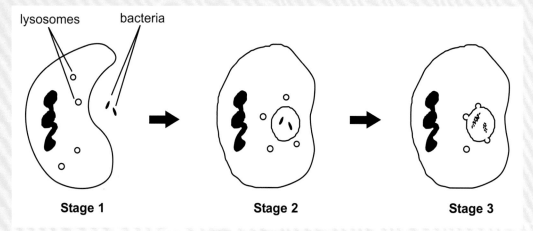

Stage 1	**Stage 2**	**Stage 3**

   Describe what is happening between:

   (a) stages 1 and 2. [1]

   (b) between stages 2 and 3. [2]

Question taken from CCEA's Biology Assessment Unit A2 1, Physiology and Ecosystems, January 2012, © CCEA 2013

3. Many people have an immunity to measles as a result of either infection or vaccination. Measles vaccination starts with infants at 15 months.

   The measles antibody levels were measured in a group of babies during the first 24 months of life. The results for mean antibody levels are shown in the following graph.

   (a) Explain the high levels of the measles antibodies in babies at birth and for the first six months. [2]

   (b) Explain the low levels of the antibody in babies after 12 months. [2]

   (c) Explain why a measles vaccine would not be successful if given within the first six months. [1]

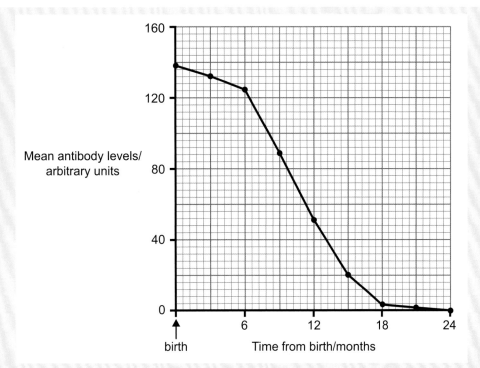

Question taken from CCEA's Biology Assessment Unit A2 1, Physiology and Ecosystems, January 2010, © CCEA 2013

4. The ABO blood grouping system is based on the presence of certain antigens.

    (a) (i) Describe the precise location of the blood antigens. [1]

    (ii) State the antigen present when the blood plasma contains antibody b. [1]

    (iii) Describe the process of agglutination. [3]

    (b) Antibodies to the ABO system are used to identify different blood groups. The table below shows the results of testing for four different blood groups. The first one, blood group A, has been identified. Identify the other three blood groups and name them in the spaces provided. [3]

Blood Group	Antibody added to the sample of blood	
	Antibody a	Antibody b
A	Agglutination	No agglutination
	No agglutination	Agglutination
	Agglutination	Agglutination
	No agglutination	No agglutination

Question taken from CCEA's Biology Assessment Unit A2 1, Physiology and Ecosystems, May 2010, © CCEA 2013

5. Quality of written communication is awarded a maximum of 2 marks in this section. [2]

    Give an account of the various immune responses following the entry of bacteria and viruses into the blood at the site of a wound. [16]

Question taken from CCEA's Biology Assessment Unit A2 1, Physiology and Ecosystems, January 2011, © CCEA 2013

6. Quality of written communication is awarded a maximum of 2 marks in this section. [2]

An immune response is the way in which the body responds to invasion by a specific antigen. Modern medicine has further developed procedures to influence the body's ability to respond to invading antigens.

(a) With reference to antibody-mediated immunity, acquired naturally and artificially, describe how humans are protected against disease. [10]

(b) Tissue to be transplanted (eg donor kidneys) contain antigens which may promote an unwanted immune response. Outline the process of transplant rejection and discuss the strategies used to reduce rejection. [6]

Question taken from CCEA's Biology Assessment Unit A2 1, Physiology and Ecosystems, May 2012, © CCEA 2013

Chapter 3 – Coordination and Control in Plants

Students should be able to:

4.3.1 Understand the role of phytochromes in the control of flowering in long-day and short-day plants

4.3.2 Understand the role of plant growth substances (hormones) in stem elongation

4.3.3 Understand the role of auxins in phototropism

As complex living organisms, plants are able to respond to many stimuli in the environment including gravity, water, chemicals and light. The effect of light on plant growth and development is easily demonstrated, and historically, much studied. One example of the effect of light on plant growth and development involves the phytochrome system.

Phytochrome and flowering in plants

Phytochrome is a pigment system found in the **leaves** of flowering plants. It is primarily involved in the timing of flowering in many species. While in some species, the flowering process is initiated when average temperatures reach a certain level, for example, tomatoes, for most British species the trigger is the **duration of light** or day length (**the photoperiod**).

For species sensitive to day length there are two categories of plants:

- **Long-day plants** (LDPs), for example, cabbage, petunia. These species flower only if the day length **exceeds** a certain minimum length.

- **Short-day plants** (SDPs), for example, chrysanthemum, strawberry. These species only flower if the days are **shorter** than a critical value (or the nights exceed a minimum length).

Phytochrome as the photoreceptor

Phytochrome pigments act as the **photoreceptor**. Phytochrome is sensitive to light and its suitability for this role is linked to its ability to exist in two inter-convertible forms:

- P_{660} (P_R) absorbs **red light** (light from the red part of the spectrum) with a absorption peak of 660 nm.

- P_{730} (P_{FR}) absorbs **far red light** with an absorption peak of 730 nm.

Due to the differences in absorption peaks, the two forms of phytochrome are known as P_{660} and P_{730} respectively. If subjected to red light the P_{660} is rapidly converted to the P_{730} form and if P_{730} is subjected to far red light it is rapidly converted to P_{660}.

Additionally, in darkness, (as P_{730} is much less stable than P_{660}), P_{730} will slowly convert to the P_{660} form.

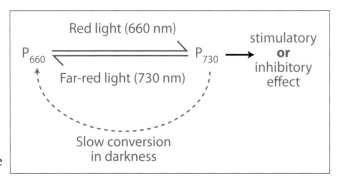

The inter-convertible forms of phytochrome

Two key points:

- As **daylight contains more red than far red light**, P_{660} is converted to P_{730} during the day. Consequently, as day length gets longer in spring/early summer the proportion of phytochrome that exists in the P_{730} form increases. In LDPs, as day length increases, the amount of P_{730} eventually reaches a critical level that initiates flowering. The *intensity* of light is also important as the conversion is quicker in high light intensities.

- Furthermore, it is the **P_{730} form** that is the **physiologically active** form, whether it is that sufficient P_{730} has accumulated to promote flowering in LDPs or that there is too much P_{730} to allow flowering to occur in SDPs. In SDPs the inhibitory effect of high levels of P_{730} must be removed before flowering can take place.

The following table summarises the effect of different photoperiods on LDPs and SDPs.

Photoperiod 0 ---------- 24 hours	Type of plant	Phytochrome response	Effect
short day – long night	LDP	P_{660} converted to P_{730} during the day but the night (dark period) is long enough for sufficient P_{730} to be slowly converted back to P_{660} to prevent the P_{730} reaching the critical level needed for flowering.	No flowering
long day – short night		Long day length allows P_{660} to be converted to P_{730} in high concentrations. The night (darkness) is too short for enough P_{730} to be converted back to P_{660}. P_{730} builds up to critical level.	Flowering
short day – long night	SDP	P_{660} is converted to P_{730} during the day. The dark period is long enough for a sufficient level of P_{730} to be converted to P_{660} to remove the inhibitory effect of P_{730}.	Flowering
long day – short night		P_{660} is converted to P_{730} during the day but the dark period is not long enough for a sufficient level of P_{730} to be converted to P_{660} to remove the inhibitory effect of P_{730}.	No flowering

Note: it is the length of the dark period that is critical in determining whether flowering occurs in both LDPs and SDPs as it determines how much P_{730} can be converted back to P_{660}.

Manipulating the photoperiod

Commercial plant growers need to have flowering plants available at the times of the year when sales are likely to be highest, for example, roses for St Valentine's Day and a wide range of flowers for Christmas. Most species will not naturally flower at these times of the year but manipulation of the photoperiod (the light regime) can ensure that supply and demand are matched.

Manipulating Long Day Plants – the onset of flowering in LDPs is stimulated by increasing day length (and reducing the period of darkness) – although there can be a time interval between the *stimulation* of the flowering process and the actual *appearance* of flowers, ie in some British LDPs the flowers may not appear until July/August, by which time the days are getting shorter!

In **LDPs** the flowering period can be brought forward or delayed by manipulating the photoperiod, for example, by using artificial lighting in glasshouses or by using screens to reduce the light period.

Interpretation of diagram – In light regimes **1** and **2** the length of day is not long enough to build up P_{730} to sufficiently high levels to initiate flowering. In **3** flowering is initiated as the period of light is sufficient to build up P_{730} to the critical level (and the period of darkness is not long enough to break down the P_{730} and keep it below the critical level). In light regime **4** the period of darkness that interrupts the light period does not reduce the P_{730} level enough to inhibit flowering (there is still enough light to allow the P_{730} to reach the critical level).

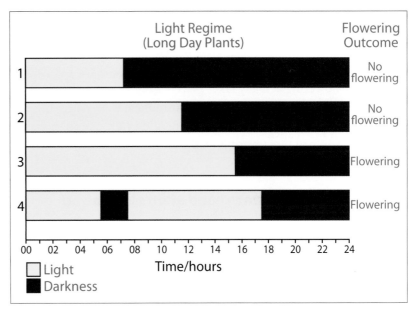

The relationship between light regime and flowering in Long Day Plants

Note: In the LDP exemplified by the diagram above, flowering is initiated by a light period of a critical length somewhere between about 11.5–15.5 hours. Based on the evidence in the diagram it is impossible to be any more specific.

In **SDPs** flowering times can also be adjusted by manipulating the photoperiod.

Interpretation of diagram – In light regime **1** the period of darkness is not long enough to remove the inhibitory effects of high levels of P_{730}. In light regime **2** the period of darkness is long enough to allow enough P_{730} to be converted back to P_{660} (thus removing the inhibitory effect of high levels of P_{730}). In light regime **3** the short flash of light during the dark period is enough to inhibit flowering, as during the short flash of light P_{660} will be rapidly converted to P_{730} therefore not allowing a sufficiently long continuous period of darkness for enough P_{730} to be converted to P_{660}.

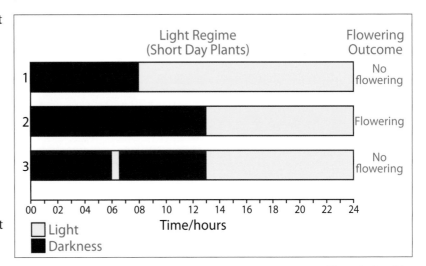

The relationship between light regime and flowering in Short Day Plants

Note 1: In SDPs the critical period of darkness must be **continuous** (uninterrupted) – this is because a short flash of light will rapidly convert P_{660} to P_{730} whereas the conversion of P_{730} to P_{660} in darkness is slow.

Note 2: In the SDP exemplified by the diagram above, flowering is initiated by a continuous dark period of critical length somewhere between 8–13 hours.

While light duration is perceived by phytochrome, it has been widely assumed that the photoperiod response is brought about by the action of a **hormone**. There are many reasons why this has been suggested, including the fact that there must be some form of communication between where the light stimulates the phytochrome (the leaves) and where flowering actually takes place – a considerable distance apart in some plants. However, as yet no 'flowering' hormone has been identified but a number of **plant growth substances** (hormones) and their functions in plants have been identified. Some of these plant growth substances and their functions will be reviewed in the next section.

Plant growth substances and stem elongation

Plant growth substances control many aspects of plant growth with their influence on the growth of the stem being particularly widely studied. Growth in stem or shoot tips is very similar to the growth in root tips (as discussed when covering mitosis at AS). In plants, unlike most animals, growth is localised in specific zones at the tips of roots and shoots called **apical meristems**. In these meristems, **cell division** (mitosis) takes place to produce **more cells**. This is not the whole story as much of the actual growth that takes place is due to the extra cells produced by mitosis **elongating**. Stem and root tips have clearly identified **zones of division** and **zones of elongation**. In most plants the majority of their growth is due to this division and elongation of cells at their tips.

The photograph (right) shows a cactus with a clearly defined (lighter) region of growth at the shoot tip. This region represents the growth during the year in which the photograph was taken.

In many plants, additional growth can take place in the **internodal** regions. These are the parts of the stem between the nodes (points at which leaves develop).

The clear differentiation between new and old growth in a cactus

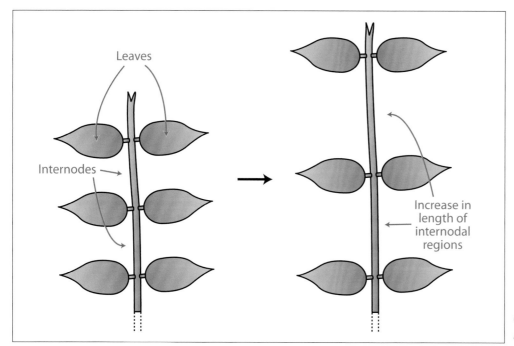

Growth of shoot internodes

The three main groups of plant growth regulators that affect growth in stems are **auxins**, **cytokinins** and **gibberellins**. Each stimulates growth in different ways, as summarised in the following table.

Plant growth substance	Site of production	Main functions
auxins	produced in the tip and move down the stem – the concentration of auxin decreases as it moves down the stem	promotes growth by increased **cell elongation** (in the zone of elongation)
cytokinins	produced in meristematic (actively dividing) tissues in zone of division	promotes growth by increased **cell division** in the apical meristems (zone of division)
gibberellins	produced in leaves (and in other parts of the plant)	promotes growth by **cell elongation** (in the internodes)

Note: these plant growth substances interact and seldom act in isolation, for example, cytokinins promote cell division only in the presence of auxins.

Phototropism

Auxin is also involved in the process of phototropism. **Phototropism** is the bending of shoots in the direction of light. Shoots are positively phototropic in that they bend towards the light (roots are negatively phototropic in that they grow away from light). The advantages of this response in plants are obvious. By bending in the direction of the light stimulus, the shoots (and leaves) will get more light energy and therefore photosynthesise more and grow more.

Before studying the phototropic response in detail it is worth investigating how auxin carries out its primary function – the elongation of cells.

The action of auxin

Cells in the zone of division have a characteristic appearance: they are small, cuboidal, have a large nucleus/cell size ratio and do not have the large vacuole characteristic of most mature plant cells. These features are not surprising as these cells are continually dividing – they get little opportunity to elongate and mature. However, as more and more cells are produced the zone of division (and the tip above it) moves upwards causing growth. The 'older' cells in the zone become more removed from the tip as more and more new cells are produced. These 'older' cells imperceptibly merge into the zone of elongation as they increase in size. It is in this process of elongation that auxin has its principal effect.

How does the auxin cause the elongation? – The auxins are produced in the apical meristem (where *division* is taking place) but diffuse or are actively transported down into the zone of elongation. After binding to auxin receptors on the cell-surface membrane of the newly formed cells, the auxin causes the cell-surface membrane to pump hydrogen ions out into the surrounding cellulose cell wall. The hydrogen ions acidify parts of the wall and loosen or break the bonds between adjacent cellulose microfibrils. This allows the walls to become more flexible.

Once the walls have become more flexible, the driving force for elongation is the uptake of water by osmosis. As the cells take in more water, the hydrostatic pressure causes

39

each cell to expand. At this stage the large permanent vacuole, typical of plant cells, develops through the accumulation of much of the water that has entered the cell.

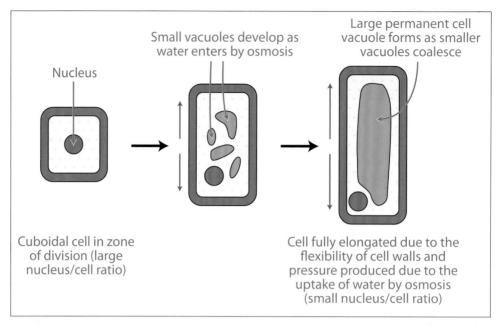

Small vacuoles develop as water enters by osmosis

Large permanent cell vacuole forms as smaller vacuoles coalesce

Nucleus

Cuboidal cell in zone of division (large nucleus/cell ratio)

Cell fully elongated due to the flexibility of cell walls and pressure produced due to the uptake of water by osmosis (small nucleus/cell ratio)

Cell elongation

Auxin and phototropism

The previous section shows how auxin causes elongation. However, for phototropism to occur the auxin must act differentially, ie it cannot act evenly across the stem otherwise the stem would continue to grow straight up.

Phototropism occurs if there is directional light – uneven light intensity reaching the shoot from different sides. This difference in light intensity is perceived at the shoot or stem tip where the auxin is produced. As auxin is produced it moves down the shoot but more moves down, or is deflected towards, the less illuminated (shaded) side. This causes **differential growth** as there is a positive correlation between auxin concentration and degree of elongation of cells in the zone of elongation. This differential growth causes curvature of the shoot in the direction of the light.

The principle of auxin action is as described earlier when explaining its role in the zone of elongation – the only difference with phototropism is that the auxin action is not uniform across the width of the shoot.

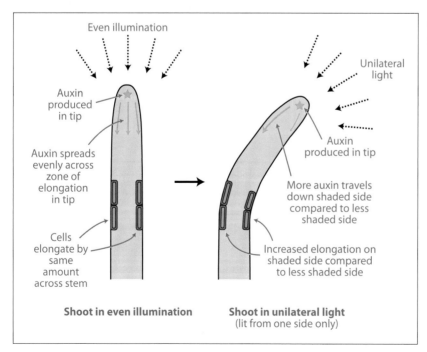

Auxins and phototropism

Even illumination

Auxin produced in tip

Auxin spreads evenly across zone of elongation in tip

Cells elongate by same amount across stem

Unilateral light

Auxin produced in tip

More auxin travels down shaded side compared to less shaded side

Increased elongation on shaded side compared to less shaded side

Shoot in even illumination

Shoot in unilateral light (lit from one side only)

Experimental evidence for the role of auxin in phototropism

A number of scientists carried out pioneering investigations on phototropism many decades ago. The scientists involved included Charles Darwin, Boysen-Jensen and Fritz Went, and their experiments demonstrated excellent examples of good scientific deduction and the ability of scientists to develop theories building on the work of others.

Darwin – Charles Darwin of course is most famous for his work on natural selection and evolution. However, he was a prolific research worker who investigated many areas of biology including phototropism.

In **1880** he demonstrated **phototropism** occurring in oat coleoptiles (the protective sheath that tightly surrounds emerging seedlings in some species, such as oat and wheat. The coleoptile provides protection as the shoot tip grows through and emerges from the soil. Some time later, the coleoptile stops growing and the seedling penetrates through the coleoptile and continues growing. Young seedlings that have a protective coleoptile still present are referred to as coleoptiles).

Darwin also demonstrated that phototropism **did not occur if the tip was removed** or if it was **covered** (with an opaque cap).

Darwin was able to conclude that light is perceived at the tip and some form of stimulus moves from the tip to the zone of elongation. Furthermore, the phototropic response is caused by cells on the shaded side of the shoot elongating more that those on the side that receives most light.

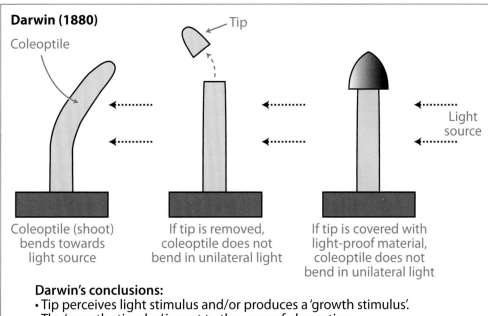

Darwin's experiments on phototropism

Darwin (1880)

Coleoptile

Tip

Light source

Coleoptile (shoot) bends towards light source

If tip is removed, coleoptile does not bend in unilateral light

If tip is covered with light-proof material, coleoptile does not bend in unilateral light

Darwin's conclusions:
• Tip perceives light stimulus and/or produces a 'growth stimulus'.
• The 'growth stimulus' is sent to the zone of elongation.
• Differential growth (phototropism) is caused by cells on the shaded side elongating more than the cells on the non-shaded side.

The experiments of Boysen-Jensen

Boysen-Jensen – Experiments in **1913** showed that materials impermeable to water, such as mica, can prevent the normal phototropic response in some situations but materials permeable to water, such as gelatin, do not change the expected response.

Boysen-Jensen (1913)

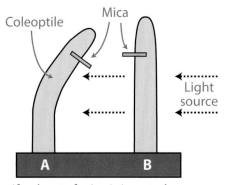
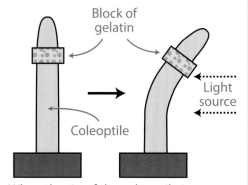

If a sheet of mica is inserted on the non-shaded side (A), the phototropic response occurs. If inserted on the shaded side (B), no bending takes place.

When the tip of the coleoptile is removed and replaced on a block of gelatin, the phototropic response is unaffected.

Boysen-Jensen's conclusions:
The impermeable mica pevented the 'growth stimulus' (later identified as auxin) passing down the shaded side in (B), as the mica was inserted on the shaded side. However in (A) auxin passes down the shaded side as normal.

As the gelatin is permeable, the auxin is able to diffuse through it and bring about the bending as normal in unilateral light. Further evidence that the 'growth stimulus' (auxin) is a chemical.

Went's experiments

Went – in experiments carried out in **1928**, Fritz Went was able to provide further evidence that phototropism is due to a chemical diffusing from the tip and that there is a positive correlation (up to a limit) between the concentration of the chemical and the degree of curvature in phototropism.

Went (1928)

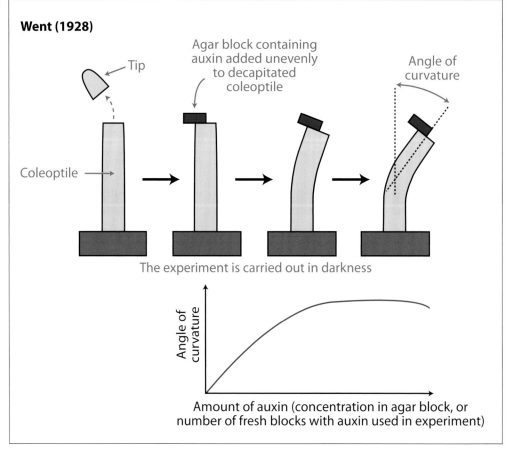

Exam questions

1. The importance of the photoperiod in the control of flowering has been known since the early 1900s and phytochrome, the plant pigment responsible, was eventually discovered in 1960. Phytochrome exists in two interchangeable forms P_{660} (P_R) and P_{730} (P_{FR}). The conversion between the two forms is illustrated below.

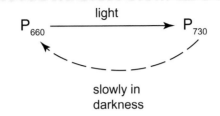

(a) (i) State one other treatment that would cause the conversion of P_{660} to P_{730}. [1]

(ii) State which of the two forms of phytochrome is the active form. [1]

(iii) Describe in detail how phytochrome controls flowering in a long-day plant. [3]

Experiments were designed to investigate whether it is the leaves or the apical bud which are sensitive to the photoperiod. In each experiment, the entire plant or a portion of the plant was placed in a light-proof box which allowed the period of light and darkness to be controlled. The plants used were short-day plants.

The experiments are shown in the diagram together with the results obtained.

Experiment one	Experiment two
• Entire plant receives a short-day light treatment within the box	• Leaves receive a short-day light treatment within the box • Apical bud receives a long-day light treatment outside the box
apical bud leaves	
Result: plant flowers	Result: plant flowers

(b) (i) How do the results of Experiment Two suggest that the photoperiod is perceived by the leaves and not the apical bud? [3]

(ii) What is the purpose of Experiment One in this investigation? [1]

The results suggest that a chemical messenger is involved in flowering.

This is supported by the fact that plants, given light treatments to inhibit their flowering, can be caused to flower by grafting or attaching leaves from plants that are already flowering.

(c) How do such grafting experiments suggest that a chemical messenger is involved? [2]

Question taken from CCEA's Biology Assessment Unit A2 1, Physiology and Ecosystems, May 2010, © CCEA 2013

2.   (a) Flowering in many plants will only take place when the photoperiod (relative length of day and night) is appropriate. It is controlled by a photoreceptor pigment.

      (i) Name the photoreceptor pigment which is involved in the control of flowering in plants. [1]

      (ii) In which part of the plant is the photoreceptor pigment located? [1]

The outcome for flowering in chrysanthemum plants when exposed to four different light regimes is shown in the following diagram.

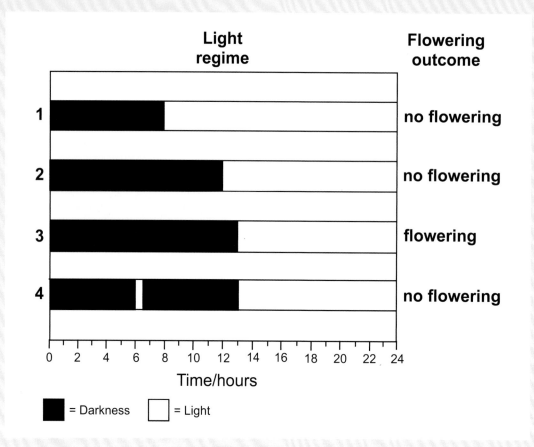

    (iii) Using the information in the diagram, determine whether the chrysanthemum is a short-day or long-day plant. Explain your answer. [2]

    (iv) Using your understanding of the phytochrome system, explain the difference in flowering outcomes in light regimes 3 and 4. [3]

(b) Two plant hormones, A and B, were applied to decapitated shoots.
The effect of each hormone, after five days, on the relative size of the cells within the shoots is shown in the diagram below.

    (i) Describe the effect of each hormone and identify hormones A and B. [3]

    (ii) Suggest an appropriate control for this experiment. Explain why a control is necessary. [2]

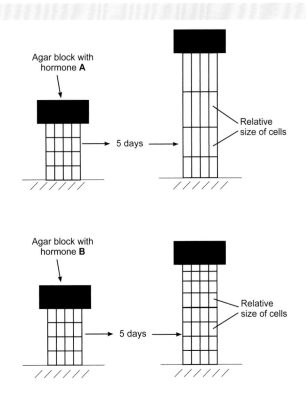

Question taken from CCEA's Biology Assessment Unit A2 1, Physiology and Ecosystems, May 2011, © CCEA 2013

3.   (a) Auxins and gibberellins are both plant growth substances which promote cell elongation in different parts of the stem. State which parts of the plant stem are stimulated by
- Auxins
- Gibberellins [1]

(b) Growth in plants involves the division of cells which subsequently increase in length.

In an experiment, the effects of two "growth substances" on both cell division and cell elongation were compared with an untreated control plant. Each treatment resulted in longer stems than the untreated control. The specific effects on cell division and cell elongation are shown in the table below.

	Untreated Control	Treatment with an artificial growth substance	
		1-naphthaleneacetic acid (NAA)	2,4-dichlorophenoxyacetic acid (2,4-D)
Cell division – average number of new cells produced /cells day $^{-1}$	3.9	3.8	5.9
Cell elongation – average increased length of each new cell/µm	30	48	24

Using the information in the table, explain the increase in stem elongation produced by each treatment. [3]

Question taken from CCEA's Biology Assessment Unit A2 1, Physiology and Ecosystems, January 2011, © CCEA 2013

4. (a) The table below concerns two plant hormones and their functions.
        Complete the table. [2]

Hormone	Function
Cytokinin	
	promotes elongation of internodal regions

(b) Many people grow plants in pots on window ledges. The plants will only grow straight if they are turned frequently.

A particularly fast-growing plant was placed on a window ledge and turned occasionally. It did not grow straight but developed a 'corkscrew' appearance as shown in the diagram below.

Suggest an explanation for the corkscrew appearance. [3]

Question taken from CCEA's Biology Assessment Unit A2 1, Physiology and Ecosystems, May 2012, © CCEA 2013

5.   (a) The concentration of phytochrome P_{730} in the leaves of a species of commercially grown, glasshouse plants was measured between June and December. The change in the level of P_{730} is shown in the graph below. The graph also shows that flowering is initiated in October and that flowering continues for a 6 week period.

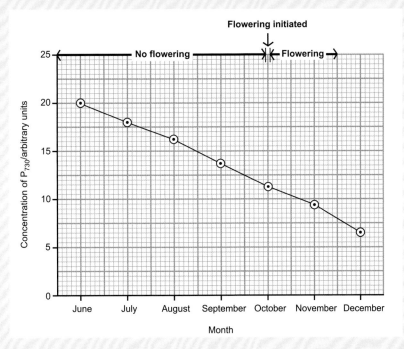

(i)   Explain how the results indicate that the plant species investigated is a short-day plant. [1]

(ii) It is commercially important that fresh flowers are available at Christmas time. Describe how the photoperiod should be manipulated to ensure flowering is delayed until December. Explain why this would be effective. [2]

(b) Fritz Went was one of the scientists who investigated plant growth hormones. In 1928 he carried out the following experiment.

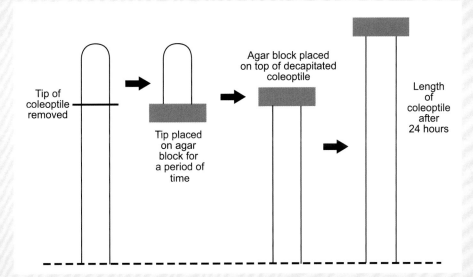

(i)   Explain the change in the length of the coleoptile after 24 hours. [2]

Such experiments have indicated that the increased length of decapitated coleoptiles is dependent on the length of time that the coleoptile tip was left on the agar block. The results are shown on the graph below.

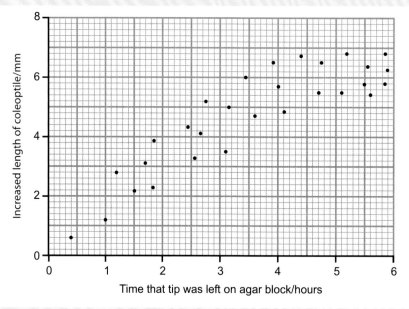

(ii) Describe and explain fully these results. [3]

(iii) Suggest one reason to account for the high degree of variability in the results. [1]

Question taken from CCEA's Biology Assessment Unit A2 1, Physiology and Ecosystems, January 2012, © CCEA 2013

6. An oat seedling has a protective sheath (the coleoptile) which is frequently used as convenient plant material for experiments on phototropism.

   An experiment was carried out in which the tips of oat coleoptiles were removed and placed on blocks of agar. The agar blocks underneath each coleoptile were divided by thin sheets of metal. The tips of the coleoptiles were either illuminated evenly from above or from the right during this initial treatment period.

   The experiment set-up is shown in the diagram below.

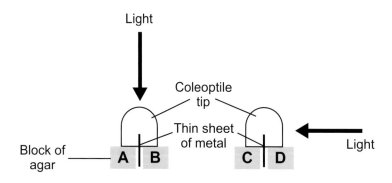

After the treatment outlined above the agar blocks then were placed on decapitated coleoptiles. The diagram below shows the height of the coleoptiles, initially (just after placement of the agar blocks) and finally (after 48 hours).

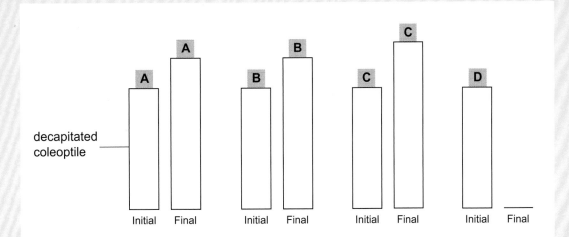

(a) Make a copy of the diagram above and complete it by drawing a result for agar block D. [1]

(b) Explain the changes in height of the four coleoptiles. [4]

(c) Explain the reason for the inclusion of blocks A and B in the experiment. [1]

Question taken from CCEA's Biology Assessment Unit A2 1, Physiology and Ecosystems, January 2010, © CCEA 2013

Chapter 4 – Neurones and Synapses

4.3.4	Describe the structure of a neurone
4.3.5	Understand the generation and transmission of nerve impulses
4.3.6	Describe the structure and functioning of a synapse

Coordination in animals, as in plants, involves hormones (called plant growth substances in plants). However, animals also have a **nervous system**. The nervous system is based on a system of **neurones** (nerve cells) that transmit electrical **nerve impulses** throughout the body. Fine control and integration is provided through a system of **synapses** (junctions) between neurones that can control the nerve pathways involved.

Note: Do not confuse neurones with nerves – nerves are bundles of neurones (nerve cells) grouped together (analagous to how individual electrical wires are grouped in electrical cabling).

In general, nervous control is **faster** and more **precise** than hormone action.

Nervous control usually involves **receptors** and **effectors** with an interlinking **coordinator**. Receptors are found in, for example, the eye, ear and nose, and each type of receptor is sensitive to a particular type of **stimulus**. Using the examples in the previous sentence, a stimulus is something we see, hear or smell. **Effectors** are parts of the body that produce the **response**; in mammals effectors are often muscles. Coordination invariably involves the **central nervous system (CNS)** comprising the brain and the spinal cord. Consequently, many of the neurones in the body travel **to** the CNS from receptors and **from** the CNS to effectors.

Neurones

There are three main types of neurone:

- **Motor neurones** – carry impulses from the CNS (brain or spinal cord) to effectors (muscles or glands).
- **Sensory neurones** – carry impulses from receptors to the CNS.
- **Connector** (relay, association or intermediate) neurones – connect neurones within the CNS.

Each type of neurone has the same function – to conduct **nerve impulses**. However, the three types differ in location as outlined above. Furthermore they have different shapes and sizes as seen in the following diagram.

Note: Neurones are much longer than they appear in the diagram. Some neurones can have a thousand or more Schwann cells along the length of the axon.

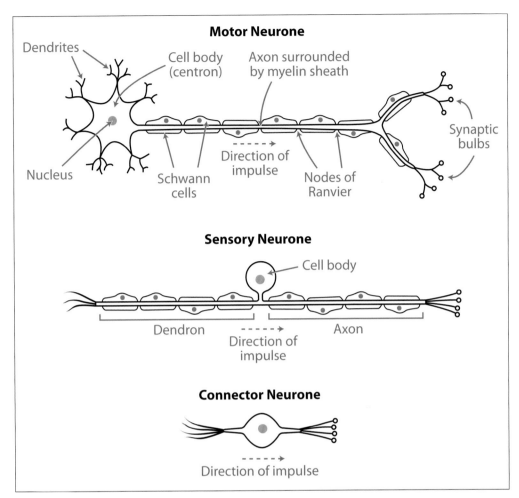

Motor, sensory and connector neurones

As seen in the diagram, neurones have a cell body and an extended nerve fibre. The **cell body** (**centron**) contains a nucleus, mitochondria and other organelles as well as Nissl's granules (large groups of ribosomes).

Terminology surrounding the **nerve fibre** depends on whether the part involved carries impulses to the cell body or away from it. If it transmits impulses away from the cell body, it is referred to as an **axon** – in motor neurones the entire fibre is an axon. However, if a part of the fibre is carrying impulses to the cell body (as in sensory neurones) it is called a **dendron** – **dendrites** are very small (and numerous) extensions that can conduct impulses into a dendron (for example, a sensory neurone) or into the cell body directly (for example, a motor neurone). Axons terminate in **synaptic bulbs** (knobs). Nerve fibres can range in length from less than a millimetre (some connector neurones) to over a metre.

In mammals, many nerve fibres (but not all) are **myelinated**. This means that their dendrons and axons are covered with an insulating **myelin sheath**. The myelin sheath, rich in the lipid myelin, is formed from the greatly extended cell-surface membrane of **Schwann cells** repeatedly being wrapped round the axon (or dendron). The Schwann cells (each about 1 mm in length) are arranged at intervals along the nerve fibre with small gaps between each cell called **nodes of Ranvier**. At these nodes the dendron or axon is exposed. The myelin sheath is both protective in function and also serves to speed up nervous conduction.

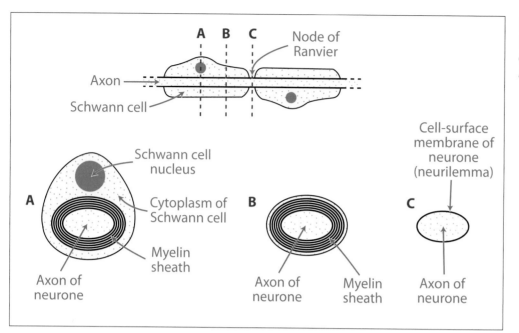

Transverse sections (TS) through different parts of a myelinated axon

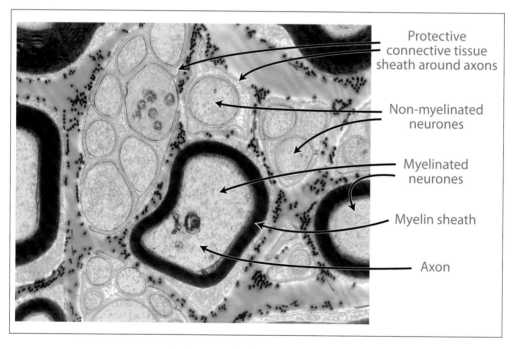

TEM through a nerve showing myelinated and non-myelinated neurones

Note: Nerves are bundles of neurones protected within an outer protective layer. Nerves can contain sensory neurones only, motor neurones only, or can be mixed and contain both types.

The nerve impulse

The resting potential – Being able to conduct electrical impulses, neurones are highly specialised cells. They have a potential difference across their cell-surface membranes called a **resting potential**, ie the neurones are **polarised** as there is an electrochemical gradient across the membrane. This potential difference is caused by there being an excess of positively charged ions (Na^+) outside the membrane compared with inside. At rest, the outside of the neurone is positive relative to the inside (or the inside is negative relative to the outside) with a potential difference of around **70 mV** (millivolts). This differential can be maintained as the cell-surface membrane is **impermeable to the flow of ions** when not conducting an impulse (an important feature as if it was permeable, the positive ions would diffuse into the neurone down the concentration gradient).

The action potential – When a neurone is stimulated the cell-surface membrane becomes **permeable** to ions. With an excess of positive ions outside the neurone relative to inside, they diffuse into the neurone down the concentration gradient. As the potential difference across the cell-surface membrane decreases, a point is reached (the outside + 40 mV relative to the inside) where a number of gated ion channels open, rapidly increasing the rate of diffusion of ions leading to **depolarisation** of the neurone.

Axon in transverse section

Outside of membrane positive relative to inside

The resting potential

As positive ions flood in, the inside becomes positive relative to the outside, reaching a potential difference of around 40 mV. This depolarisation and reversal of potential difference in neurones is called an **action potential**, a sequence of events that takes about 1 millisecond.

At the peak of the action potential (inside of neurone + 40 mV relative to outside) the recovery phase starts and the positive ions both **diffuse** and are **pumped out** of the neurone. This rapidly restores the resting potential and the cell-surface membrane becomes impermeable again. During this recovery phase (**refractory period**) a further impulse cannot occur as the gated ion channels are closed and the resting potential has not been fully restored. The entire electrochemical sequence of events associated with an action potential takes about 4 milliseconds.

Changes in the potential difference across the axon membrane as an action potential occurs

Explanation of diagram

1. Resting potential with inside of axon – 70 mV relative to outside (another way of saying outside of membrane is + 70 mV relative to inside).

2. Membrane becomes permeable and positive ions diffuse into the axon – membrane is starting to become depolarised.

3. At – 40 mV (inside relative to the outside) gated channels open and positive ions flood in at an

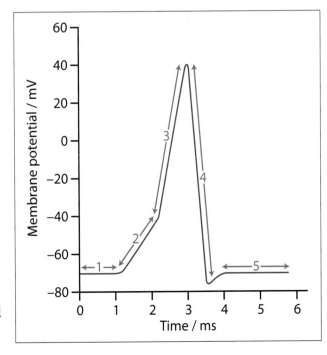

even more rapid rate. Rapid depolarisation of the membrane takes place and the inside becomes + 40 mV relative to the outside – the action potential.

4. Positive ions diffuse out and are also pumped out of the axon. This stage is called the refractory period as the membrane cannot be depolarised again until the resting potential is restored. At the end of this stage there is a slight 'overshoot' as the inside of the axon membrane becomes slightly more negative than in the normal resting potential (hyperpolarisation).

5. The resting potential is restored and the axon can conduct another nerve impulse if stimulated.

Note: The sequence of events in the diagram representing the action potential describes the sequence as it occurs at one point on the axon over a very short period of time (a few milliseconds).

The **refractory period** has a number of functions.

• It ensures that the action potentials are propagated in one direction only. This is important as axons are physiologically capable of transmitting an impulse in either direction.

• It also limits the number of action potentials that can be fired and ensures that each action potential is a discrete entity.

The threshold stimulus and the all-or-nothing-law

Two more important features about nerve impulses:

• The **threshold stimulus** refers to the level of stimulus a neurone requires before an action potential is produced, for example, a small degree of depolarisation in the cell-surface membrane of the neurone can occur without resulting in an action potential but at a critical point (the threshold potential) an action potential will result.

• The **all-or-nothing-law** refers to the principle that once the threshold stimulus is reached the action potential results, ie an action potential either occurs or it does not; different intensities of action potential do not occur – they are all the same.

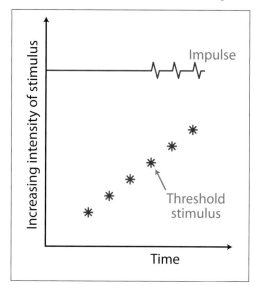

Once an action potential occurs it sweeps along the neurone as a **nerve impulse**. The propagation of the nerve impulse is discussed in the next section.

Propagation of the nerve impulse – Action potentials 'move' very rapidly along neurones. In reality a wave of depolarisation moves rapidly along the neurone. Just as quickly the region immediately behind the depolarised zone becomes repolarised. As one part of the membrane becomes depolarised it sets up **local (electrical) circuits** with the areas immediately adjacent on either side. Positive ions from the depolarised zone pass along the inside of the membrane towards the polarised zone immediately in front. A similar effect occurs on the outside of the membrane, where positive ions move back

Local circuits and nerve impulse propagation

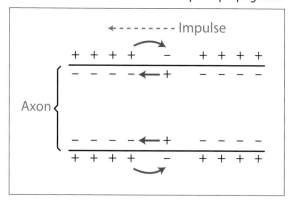

from the (as yet) still polarised zone into the depolarised zone. It is these processes occurring continuously that creates a wave of depolarisation that moves rapidly along the neurone. Similar circuits enable the resting potential to be restored directly behind the action potential.

Factors affecting the speed of the nerve impulse – The speed of the nerve impulse is affected by a number of factors including the presence or absence of a myelin sheath and the thickness of the axon.

The **myelin sheath** acts as an electrical insulator in myelinated neurones. As an insulator it prevents depolarisation in that part of the neurone. However, every 1–2 mm along the neurone the sheath is disrupted – these breaks are the junctions between adjacent Schwann cells. At these points, called **nodes of Ranvier**, depolarisation can take place. The local circuits form between the nodes only, allowing sections of the neurone to be bypassed. The action potentials 'jump' from one node to the next in a process called **saltatory conduction**.

The **diameter of the axon** also affects the speed of impulse. In general, the thicker the axon the faster the impulse. This is because there is proportionally less 'leakage' of ions in a neurone with a larger diameter. If there is too much leakage, as can happen in axons with very small diameters, it makes it very difficult to maintain the potential gradients required to form resting and action potentials.

Note 1: The zone of depolarisation is the part of the neurone where polarity is reversed, ie the inside is positive relative to the outside.

Note 2: Many textbooks refer to the propagation of the nerve impulse as being analogous to a 'Mexican wave' moving around a sports arena.

Saltatory conduction in myelinated neurones

In myelinated neurones, there are relatively few ion channels under the fatty myelin sheath (they are concentrated at the nodes of Ranvier). Consequently myelination tends to overcome the problems presented by neurones of small diameter, in addition to producing the faster speeds associated with saltatory conduction, for example, up to 100 m s^{-1}.

As with many metabolic processes, the speed of nerve impulse is affected by **temperature**. As temperature affects the rate of diffusion of ions involved in neurone action it affects the speed that neurones can conduct impulses.

Synapses

Synapses are junctions between the axon of one neurone and the dendrite (or dendron/centron) of an adjacent neurone. Synapses also occur between neurones and muscle – these specialised neuromuscular junctions will be discussed in the next chapter, in the section on muscle.

Structure of synapses – Impulses are transmitted from one neurone to another by chemicals called **neurotransmitters** that diffuse across a very small gap, **the synaptic cleft**, which is 20–30 nm wide. Both the **pre-synaptic neurone**, the neurone that releases the transmitter, and the **post-synaptic neurone**, the adjacent neurone that receives the diffusing neurotransmitter, are specialised for their roles in synaptic transmission.

The end of the pre-synaptic neurone is thickened into a **synaptic bulb (knob)**. Synaptic bulbs contain large numbers of mitochondria (important in manufacturing the neurotransmitter) and **synaptic vesicles** in which the neurotransmitter is stored.

The post-synaptic membrane contains **receptors** complementary to the type of neurotransmitter involved in that particular synapse. In general, the principle is that the neurotransmitters that pass across the synaptic cleft will cause depolarisation in the post-synaptic neurone allowing the nerve impulse to continue from one neurone to the next.

Note: A synapse includes the synaptic bulb, the synaptic cleft and the post-synaptic neurone membrane. If you get a question about synaptic transmission you will probably be expected to account for what takes place in each of these areas.

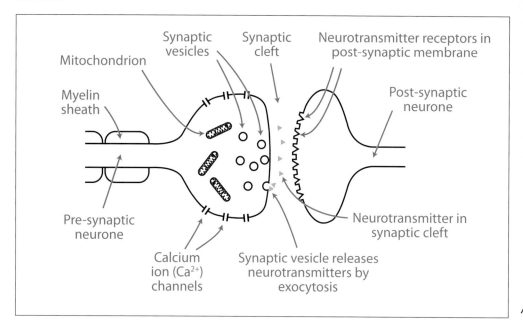

A typical synapse

Transmission at synapses

1. When an impulse arrives at the end of a neurone (synaptic bulb), calcium ion (Ca^{2+}) channels open allowing **calcium ions** to diffuse into the synaptic bulb.

2. The calcium ions cause the **synaptic vesicles** to move towards the pre-synaptic membrane.

3. The vesicles fuse with the pre-synaptic membrane, releasing the neurotransmitter (typically **acetylcholine**) by **exocytosis** into the synaptic cleft.

4. The acetylcholine diffuses across the synaptic cleft and binds to acetylcholine **receptors** in the post-synaptic membrane.

5. This causes the opening of ion (Na^+) channels in the membrane of the post-synaptic neurone. As positive ions diffuse in, the membrane becomes gradually depolarised and an **excitatory post-synaptic potential (EPSP)** is generated.

6. If sufficient depolarisation takes place (dependent on the number of neurotransmitter molecules filling receptor sites) the EPSP will reach the **threshold** intensity required to produce an **action potential** in the post-synaptic neurone.

7. The enzyme **acetylcholinesterase** (attached to the post-synaptic membrane) breaks down the acetylcholine. The breakdown products, **choline** and **ethanoic acid** (acetyl), are released into the cleft. It is very important that the acetylcholine is broken down and does not continually remain in a receptor – this prevents it continuously generating a new action potential in the post-synaptic neurone.

8. The breakdown products diffuse across the cleft and are reabsorbed into the synaptic bulb. They are subsequently **resynthesised** into **acetylcholine** which is stored in the synaptic vesicles to be used again. The ATP required is produced by the **mitochondria**.

Function of synapses – The diffusion of chemicals across a short gap is necessarily slower than the conduction of an impulse along myelinated neurones. However, due to the very short distances involved it is still very fast! Nonetheless, the presence of synapses gives the nervous system many advantages.

- They ensure **unidirectionality** – Nerve impulses can only pass from the pre-synaptic neurone to the post-synaptic neurone as the neurotransmitter is only made in the pre-synaptic neurone and neurotransmitter receptors are only in the membrane of the post-synaptic neurone.

- They **prevent** the **overstimulation** of effectors (for example, muscles) – Too many impulses passing along the same neurone in a short period of time will exhaust the supply of the neurotransmitter more quickly than it can be built up – the synapses **fatigue**.

- They provide **integration** – This may involve a number of pre-synaptic neurones forming junctions with one post-synaptic neurone. In effect, synapses provide **flexibility** – if there were no synapses, nervous activity would be little more than a series of reflexes with a particular stimulus producing an automatic and never-changing response. Integration is aided through the process of summation, which is discussed in the next section.

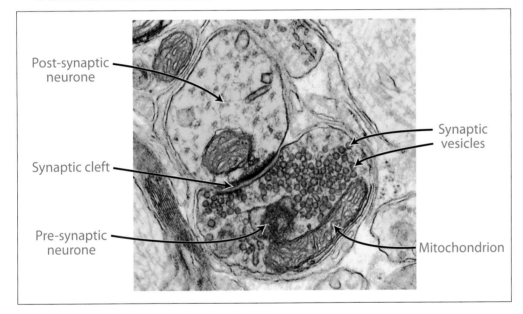

TEM of a synapse in the brain

Note 1: In the TEM (transmission electronmicrograph) the axons of the two neurones extending beyond the synapse are not evident. This is because they were in different planes to the very thin section chosen for this photograph.

Note 2: A2 examinations will test synoptic knowledge, ie AS knowledge important in understanding A2 content. For example, you could be asked for the evidence that shows that the image is a transmission electron micrograph rather than a SEM (scanning electronmicrograph).

Summation is important in providing the complexity and flexibility that synapses demonstrate. For example, an infrequent action potential reaching a synapse may not be sufficient to cause an action potential in the adjacent post-synaptic neurone. However, a series of impulses travelling along the same neurone or a number of pre-synaptic neurones operating in unison, each releasing neurotransmitter chemicals, may be enough to cause a sufficient EPSP to trigger an impulse in the post-synaptic neurone.

The two types of summation just described are spatial and temporal summation. In **spatial summation** a number of different pre-synaptic neurones can together release enough neurotransmitter to produce an EPSP above the threshold level to produce an action potential in the post-synaptic neurone, whereas one on its own may not.

In **temporal summation**, a single pre-synaptic neurone releases neurotransmitter several times over a short timeframe (as a consequence of a series of action potentials passing along the neurone). Each pulse of neurotransmitter contributes to the depolarisation of the post-synaptic membrane, although any one action potential on its own may not be enough. As with spatial summation, if the EPSP reaches the threshold potential, an action potential is produced.

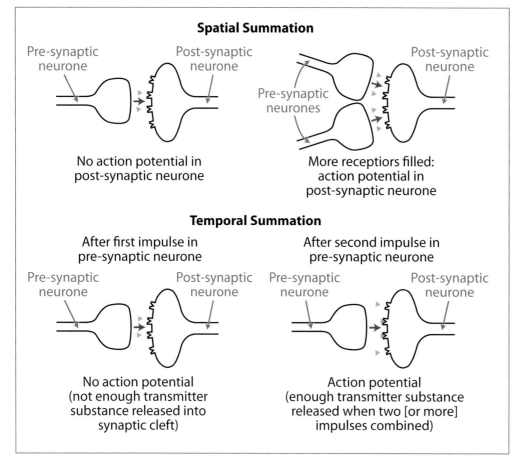

Spatial Summation

Pre-synaptic neurone   Post-synaptic neurone

No action potential in post-synaptic neurone

Post-synaptic neurone

Pre-synaptic neurones

More receptiors filled: action potential in post-synaptic neurone

Temporal Summation

After first impulse in pre-synaptic neurone

After second impulse in pre-synaptic neurone

Pre-synaptic neurone   Post-synaptic neurone

Pre-synaptic neurone   Post-synaptic neurone

No action potential (not enough transmitter substance released into synaptic cleft)

Action potential (enough transmitter substance released when two [or more] impulses combined)

Spatial and temporal summation

Note: In the diagram, for explanatory purposes, each pre-synaptic neurone produces two molecules of neurotransmitter each time a nerve impulse reaches the synaptic bulb – in reality many more are produced.

The synapses discussed so far refer to **excitatory synapses** – neurotransmitter chemicals are released with the function of causing an EPSP and a subsequent action potential. **Inhibitory synapses** have the function of making it more difficult for synaptic transmission to take place. The neurotransmitter they release makes it more difficult for an EPSP to form in the post-synaptic membrane. Neurotransmitters in inhibitory synapses can, for example, lead to an influx of negative ions in the post-synaptic membrane, making the inside of the membrane even more negative (hyperpolarisation) than normal resting potential values. Consequently, this makes it more difficult than normal for excitatory synapses to produce an EPSP that reaches threshold level.

Whether an impulse will actually take place in the post-synaptic neurone depends on the relative contribution excitatory and inhibitory synapses make in promoting or inhibiting depolarisation.

Why have inhibitory synapses? They can help by reducing the input of background stimuli that would clutter up the nervous activity in the brain or may prevent some reflex actions.

The effects of summation and the action of inhibitory synapses provide integration and fine control through the synapse **integrating** all the different inputs (there may be hundreds) at synaptic junctions. Synapses also have an important role in filtering out low-level background stimuli thus preventing overload and overstimulation.

Neurotransmitter substances

Acetylcholine is the primary transmitter substance in the central nervous system (CNS) of vertebrates, although **noradrenaline** (typically used in involuntary nervous control, for example, the regulation of gut movements) is one of several other types. However, each synaptic bulb only produces one type of neurotransmitter.

Many drugs work by stimulating the development of more action potentials, for example, through being similar in shape to the 'normal' transmitter or causing the production/release of more neurotransmitter at synapses. Others work by restricting the number of action potentials produced, for example by preventing the release of neurotransmitter or by blocking receptor sites. Three examples are given in the table below.

Substance	Effect
Nicotine	Stimulates the release of acetylcholine and other neurotransmitters making action potentials more likely.
Curare	Blocks receptors (at neuromuscular junctions) preventing synaptic transmission – loss of muscle function.
Opioids	Block the calcium channels in the pre-synaptic neurone. Less transmitter substance is released and action potentials less likely. Opioids and related compounds can provide pain relief by reducing impulses coming from the pain receptors.

Note: Many examination questions involve drugs that either stimulate, or are antagonistic to, neurotransmitters. The questions often provide information concerning the function of the drug involved (as in the table above) and you would be expected to deduce the effect they would have on synaptic transmission.

Exam questions

1. The diagram below represents the structure of a neurone.

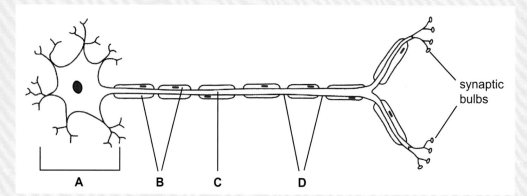

(a) Identify the structures labelled A to D. [3]

(b) Make a copy of the diagram above and draw an arrow to indicate the direction of a nerve impulse travelling along the neurone. [1]

(c) Explain why the neurone shown above might be expected to have a high speed of impulse conduction. [2]

Question taken from CCEA's Biology Assessment Unit A2 1, Physiology and Ecosystems, January 2010, © CCEA 2013

2. (a) (i) The diagram below shows two adjacent neurones at a synapse, as seen using an electron microscope. Three important features of the synapse are labelled A, B and C.

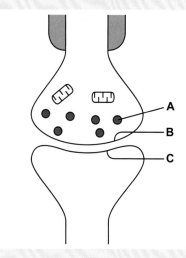

The table below lists four statements describing functions of certain features of a synapse.

Number	Statement
1	stores acetylcholine
2	location of acetylcholine receptor sites
3	provides energy for the re-synthesis of acetylcholine
4	location of exocytosis of acetylcholine

Make a copy of the following table and complete it by matching the labelled feature with the number of the most appropriate statement. [3]

Feature	Statement number
A	
B	
C	

(ii) Make a copy of the diagram in 2 (a) (i) and mark the following:

– with X, the location of an excitatory post synaptic potential.

– with Y, a structure necessary for saltatory conduction. [2]

(b) Explain why transmission between neurones is unidirectional. [1]

Question taken from CCEA's Biology Assessment Unit A2 1, Physiology and Ecosystems, May 2011 © CCEA 2013

3. (a) The photograph below is a photomicrograph that shows part of a motor neurone cell.

(i) Identify the features labelled X and Y. [2]

(ii) Suggest which part of the body this photomicrograph was taken from. [1]

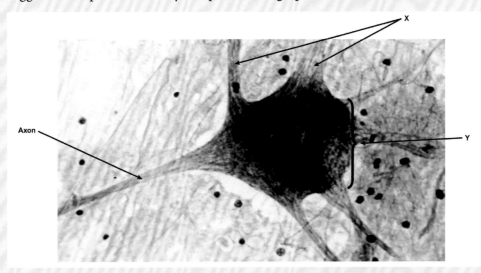

© Science VU, Visuals Unlimited / Science Photo Library

(b) Attention-deficit disorder (ADD) is relatively common and is caused by a malfunctioning in neurotransmitter action. Recently it has been widely accepted that this disorder is genetic in origin as opposed to being a consequence of an individual's environment. Research published in *The Lancet* in October 2010 indicated that patients who had been given a clinical diagnosis of ADD were over twice as likely to have abnormalities in chromosome 16 compared with individuals without the condition. The data used in the research was based on 366 patients diagnosed with ADD with a control group of 1000.

(i) Outline the role of neurotransmitters in the functioning of the nervous system. [2]

(ii) State one reason why the conclusions of this research could be considered reliable. [1]

Research in scientific journals is 'peer-reviewed'. This means that other scientists working in the same field review the procedures used and the conclusions derived from the research.

(iii) Explain the importance of peer review in reviewing scientific research. [2]

Question taken from CCEA's Biology Assessment Unit A2 1, Physiology and Ecosystems, May 2012 © CCEA 2013

4. Almost all drugs taken by humans, including nicotine and alcohol, affect the nervous system, especially synapses.

(a) The drug nicotine, found in the leaves of the tobacco plant, binds to the acetylcholine receptor sites in synapses. After binding to these receptor sites, nicotine acts in a similar way to acetylcholine.

(i) Using your understanding of the nerve synapse, describe precisely where nicotine would bind. [1]

(ii) Describe and explain the effect of nicotine on the nervous system. [3]

(iii) Unlike acetylcholine, nicotine is not broken down within the synapse. Suggest one possible consequence of nicotine remaining in the synapse. [1]

(b) The drug alcohol, binds with gamma aminobutyric acid (GABA) receptors in synapses. After binding, alcohol acts in a similar way to GABA – the inside of the neurone membrane becomes more negative, a state known as hyperpolarisation.

(i) Suggest one way in which alcohol causes the inside of the membrane to become more negative. [1]

(ii) Alcohol is known to inhibit the nervous system. Suggest how this inhibition may be brought about. [2]

(iii) Suggest one consequence of alcohol inhibition of the nervous system. [1]

Question taken from CCEA's Biology Assessment Unit A2 1, Physiology and Ecosystems, January 2011 © CCEA 2013

5. Quality of written communication is awarded a maximum of 2 marks in this question. [2]

Give an account of the generation of an action potential, impulse transmission along an axon and subsequent transmission to a post-synaptic neurone. [16]

Question taken from CCEA's Biology Assessment Unit A2 1, Physiology and Ecosystems, May 2010 © CCEA 2013

Chapter 5 – The Eye and Muscle

The mammalian eye

The mammalian eye is a complex sense organ. Only a very small section of the eye contains the photoreceptors that are sensitive to light. The rest of the eye contains structures that ensure that the receptors in the retina at the back of the eye receive focused light rays at the correct intensity to form an image.

Structure of the eye

The diagram below represents a cross-section of the mammalian eye.

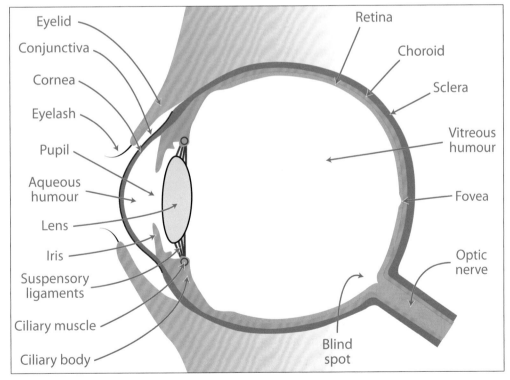

The structure of the eye

The following table summarises the functions of the main parts of the eye.

Part of eye	Description	Role
conjunctiva	thin transparent membrane covering the cornea	protects the cornea from damage
sclera	tough opaque connective tissue covering the eye – replaced by transparent cornea at front	protects against damage; site of attachment of eye muscles
cornea	front transparent part of sclera	transparent and most refraction (bending) of light occurs here
aqueous humour	transparent watery fluid between cornea and lens	maintains the shape of the front part of the eye
iris	muscular layer with both circular and radial muscle; contains pigment that absorbs light	adjusts the size of the pupil to control the amount of light entering the eye
pupil	gap within the iris	the area through which light reaches the lens and enters the centre of the eye
ciliary body	contains a muscular ring of (ciliary) muscle around the eye; suspensory ligaments extend from the ciliary body and hold the lens in place	adjusts the shape of the lens to focus light rays
suspensory ligaments	ligaments that connect the ciliary body to the lens	transfers tension in the wall of the eyeball to make the lens thinner; important when focusing on distant objects
lens	transparent biconcave structure with refractive properties	refracts light and focuses light rays on the retina
vitreous humour	transparent, jelly-like material between the lens and the back of the eye	maintains the shape of the rear part of the eye and supports the lens
retina	inner layer of the eyeball containing the light sensitive receptor cells (rods and cones)	when stimulated the rods and cones initiate impulses in associated neurones
fovea	region in the centre of retina that is particularly rich in cones and does not contain rods	part of eye that gives the clearest daylight colour vision
choroid	a layer of pigmented cells between the retina and the sclera	contains blood vessels that supply the retina; prevents reflection of light back through the eye
optic nerve	bundle of sensory nerve fibres that leave the retina	transmits impulses from the retina to the brain
blind spot	part of the retina where the sensory neurones that unite to form the optic nerve leave the eye	contains no light sensitive cells so is not sensitive to light

Function of the eye

Obtaining a focused image – As light rays enter and pass through the cornea, some bending (refraction) of light automatically takes place. In reality, most of the refraction takes place in the cornea. Further bending takes place as the light passes through the lens. By adjusting the thickness of the lens, light rays can be focused on the retina, irrespective of their angle as they enter the eye. The diagram below shows how the lens focuses light on distant and close-up objects.

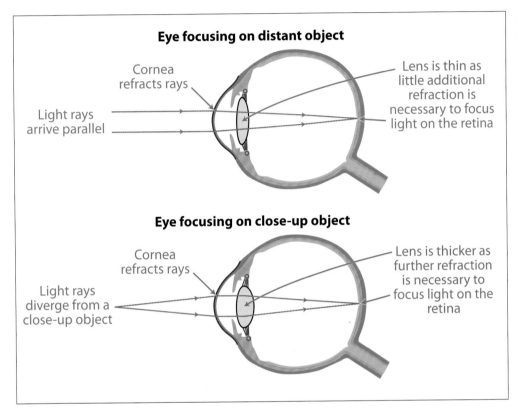

Focusing on distant and close-up objects

The **ciliary body** contains a ring of muscle (**ciliary muscle**) running around the inside of the eyeball and surrounding the lens. The lens is attached to the ciliary body by **suspensory ligaments** that resemble small pieces of nylon thread. If the ciliary body relaxes the tension in the wall of the eyeball is transferred through the suspensory ligaments to the lens (in effect, the ciliary body springs out to form a bigger diameter pulling the suspensory ligaments taut). When this happens the suspensory ligaments pull the lens into a thinner shape that has less refractive power.

The opposite happens to make the lens fatter when a greater degree of refraction is required. The ciliary muscle contracts to form a tighter circle with a smaller diameter. The suspensory ligaments are not pulled taut so relax and with less pressure on the lens it is able to spring back to its 'normal' thicker shape.

The adjustment of lens thickness to ensure that the light rays are focused on the retina, irrespective of the angle of light rays reaching the eye, is called **accommodation**.

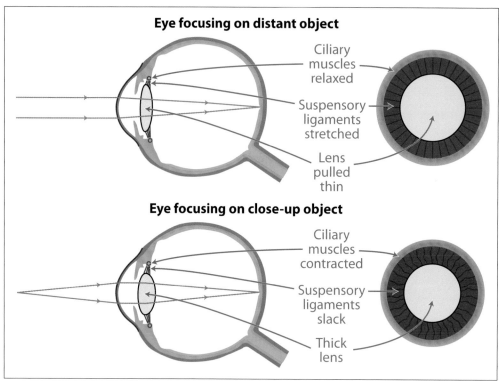

Eye focusing on distant object

Ciliary muscles relaxed

Suspensory ligaments stretched

Lens pulled thin

Eye focusing on close-up object

Ciliary muscles contracted

Suspensory ligaments slack

Thick lens

The role of the ciliary muscles and suspensory ligaments in accommodation

Note: ligaments are tough and flexible but they do not stretch. Not being stretchable is important as this ensures that the suspensory ligaments pull the lens thin when the ciliary muscle relaxes.

Controlling the amount of light that enters the eye – It is important that the correct **intensity of light** enters the eye and reaches the retina. Too little or too much light will prevent an image being formed. In addition, too much light can damage the sensitive light receptor cells in the retina. In low light intensities a large **pupil** diameter allows as much light as possible to enter the eye to ensure that there is sufficient light to stimulate the photoreceptors in the retina. In bright light the pupil is reduced to a small size to restrict the amount of light entering. The size of the pupil is a direct consequence of the size of the iris.

The muscles of the **iris** can contract or relax to change the size of the pupil. The iris consists of two types of muscle – **radial** and **circular**. Radial muscles are like the spokes of a wheel moving out from the edge of the pupil through the iris, and circular muscles form rings within the iris around the pupil.

Note: Accommodation and the control of the amount of light entering the eye are both examples of reflex action. They are automatic responses not under voluntary control.

- In **low light** intensities the **radial muscles contract** (and the circular muscles relax) – this makes the pupil larger.

- In **bright light** the **circular muscles contract** (and the radial muscles relax) – this makes the pupil smaller.

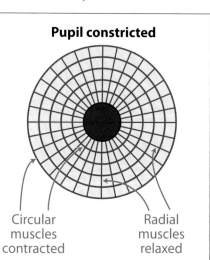

Pupil dilated

Pupil constricted

Iris

Pupil

Circular muscles relaxed

Radial muscles contracted

Circular muscles contracted

Radial muscles relaxed

Adjusting the size of the pupil

The retina in detail

The retina contains millions of light sensitive cells and the neurones with which they synapse. **Rod** and **cone** cells are specialised **photoreceptors** (photosensitive cells) in that light energy brings about change in the level of polarisation of their membranes – they act as transducers converting a light stimulus to a nerve impulse in their associated neurones.

Rod cells – In rods the light sensitive pigment **rhodopsin** is packed into an array of membranes in the outer part of the rod cell. Rhodopsin is formed from a protein **opsin**, combined with a light absorbing compound called **retinal** which is derived from vitamin A. When stimulated by light the rhodopsin breaks down into its retinal and opsin components. This changes the membrane potential of the rod cell and creates a **generator potential**. If a **threshold level** is achieved, this can cause the adjacent linking neurone (bipolar neurone) to become depolarised to the extent that it will conduct an action potential.

> **Note:** A generator potential is the degree of depolarisation a stimulated receptor can produce. Only if the generator potential reaches a threshold level will it produce an action potential in the neurone.

The membranes in the inner segment of the rod cell are rich in mitochondria, important in producing the ATP needed for the re-synthesis of rhodopsin from retinal and opsin following light stimulation.

Rods are adapted for vision in **low light intensities**. They have **high sensitivity** as the rhodopsin will break down readily in low light levels requiring only a small amount of light energy. However, this can lead to the phenomenon of **dark adaptation**. In bright light virtually all the rhodopsin is broken down (bleached) and it takes time for it to be re-synthesised. This explains why if we move from a well lit area into a dark room our vision in the low light environment is very poor initially but gradually improves. In effect, our eyes have changed from being light-adapted (when in bright light) to being dark-adapted, ie adapted for functioning in low light intensities.

Cone cells – The same general principles apply to the functioning of **cone** cells. However, in cones a different pigment, **iodopsin**, is situated in the membranes of the outer segment. The iodopsin is less readily broken down and will only produce a generator potential in bright light.

While rods are not sensitive to colour and provide monochromatic vision, **cones** provide **colour vision**.

Iodopsin exists in three different forms with each form being sensitive to different wavelengths of light. The absorption peaks of the three types of cone (each with a different type of iodopsin) correspond to the colours **blue**, **green** and **red** (the **trichromatic theory of**

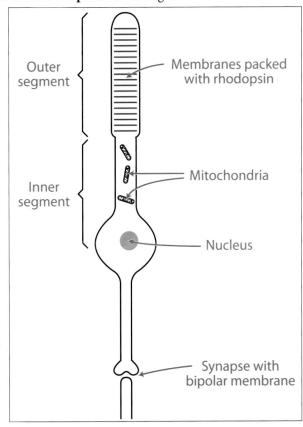

A rod cell

Outer segment

Membranes packed with rhodopsin

Inner segment

Mitochondria

Nucleus

Synapse with bipolar membrane

colour vision). Pure blue light will only break down the 'blue' iodopsin but of course most light is not pure blue, green or red. In effect, it is the degree of stimulation of each type of cone that determines colour vision.

The arrangement of rods and cones in the retina – It is not only the differences in the structure and sensitivities of rod and cone cells that are important in their functioning. Their distribution across the retina and the different ways in which they are arranged with linking neurone cells is also crucial.

As the following diagram shows, the rods and cones form a layer immediately inside the choroid. A layer of **bipolar neurones** lies immediately inside the photosensitive cells and beyond the bipolar neurones there is another layer of sensory cells (**ganglion cells**). It is the axons of the ganglion cells that group together to make up the optic nerve that carries the impulses from the retina to the brain.

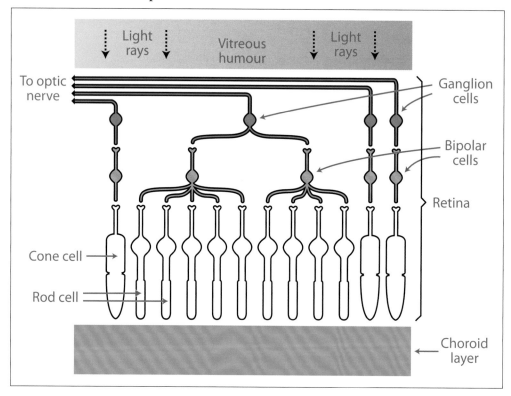

Section through the retina showing photoreceptor cells and their associated neurones

Note 1: The different properties of rods and cones, and their retinal arrangement, explains why we can see detailed colour vision during the daytime (the light intensity is sufficient to break down iodopsin) but can only see less detailed black and white image during the night (light intensity sufficient to break down rhodopsin but not iodopsin).

The diagram also shows that each cone cell can synapse individually with its own bipolar neurone, ie each provides its own discrete image in vision. This is the basis of **high visual acuity** – the ability of cones to provide highly precise (colour) vision of high resolution – enabling the brain to distinguish between two points that are very close together. However, the rods show **retinal convergence**. This involves a number of rods having a common bipolar neurone (and a number of bipolar cells having a common ganglion cell). Retinal convergence allows the generator potentials from individual rods to combine together (**summation**) and reach the threshold required for producing an action potential in a bipolar neurone.

Allied to the ability of rhodopsin (in rods) to break down more easily than iodopsin (in cones), retinal convergence is the basis of the **sensitivity** that rods show. The light energy reaching any one rod is not enough to stimulate the bipolar cell sufficiently but stimulation of a group of rods provides enough generator potential to produce an impulse in the bipolar neurone. This of course also explains another feature of rods –

their **lack of visual acuity** or high resolution as the individual rods in each 'convergence unit' only provide as much detail as one cone cell.

Note 2: Do not confuse sensitivity with visual acuity. Sensitivity is the ability to operate in very low light intensities – not the ability to provide precision vision.

Note 3: If you look again at the arrangement of photosensitive cells and neurones in the retina you will note that the light rays have to pass through layers of neurones before reaching the light sensitive cells. This 'inverted' arrangement appears to be less efficient than if it was the opposite way round with the photosensitive cells being on the inside with the neurone 'cabling' behind. Perhaps, but the arrangement in mammals is a consequence of the evolutionary development of the eye.

The following diagram shows how the cones and rods are distributed across the retina. The distribution explains phenomena such as the blind spot and why we can distinguish shapes but not colour at the periphery of our vision, ie when the light rays are focused on the edge of the retina.

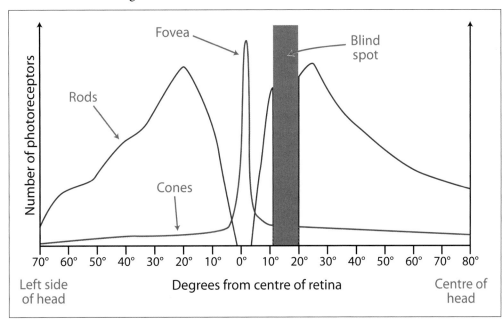

The distribution of rods and cones across the retina of the human left eye

Note: The diagram above showing the distribution of cones and rods across the left eye shows that there are more rods at the right side of the retina (closer to centre of head) compared to the left. This facilitates peripheral vision on the left side of the head – the converse arrangement exists in the right eye.

Binocular vision

The presence of two eyes in mammals provides **binocular** or stereoscopic vision. If the two eyes create a single image it allows accurate **judgement of distance**. **Stereoscopic vision**, the ability to form **three-dimensional images** is also possible.

In humans and other primates and also in most predatory species, the eyes are positioned on the front of the head. This facilitates excellent judgement of distance and 3D vision as discussed above. Many prey species, such as rabbits, have their eyes positioned on the side of their heads rather than at the front. This provides a wider field of view, a greater priority for prey aiding the detection of potential predators rather than 3D vision.

Muscles

Muscles are specialised effectors that bring about movement through contraction. The main type of muscle in the body is skeletal muscle, muscle that is attached (via tendons) to the skeleton. Skeletal muscle is **voluntary** muscle in that it is under conscious control.

Structure of skeletal muscle

Skeletal (voluntary) muscle can vary considerably in size, for example, compare the triceps and biceps muscles with the muscles controlling the eyeball. However, the basic structure of all skeletal muscle is the same.

Skeletal muscle consists of many **muscle fibres** bunched together. Muscle fibres are **multinucleate** and each fibre is surrounded by a cell-surface membrane (**sarcolemma**). Each fibre is multinucleate with the nuclei typically arranged just inside the sarcolemma. The fibre, which is effectively a very specialised 'cell', contains the cell organelles typically found in any cell, but is particularly rich in **mitochondria**. At intervals the sarcolemma folds deeply inwards to form **transverse tubules** or **T-tubules**.

The bulk of the muscle fibre is filled with highly specialised contractile units called **myofibrils**. Muscle fibres are very large structures and can be up to many centimetres long.

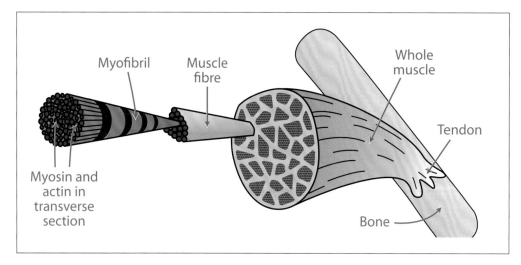

Muscle, muscle fibres and myofibrils

The ultrastructure of myofibrils – The myofibril consists largely of two types of protein, myosin and actin. **Myosin** forms **thick** filaments around 15 nm in diameter and **actin** forms **thin** filaments about 7 nm in diameter.

Myosin filaments lie in the central region of each contractile unit and are linked together by a thin disc (the **M-line**) that runs perpendicular to the orientation of the myosin filaments. The actin filaments slot between the outer edges of the myosin filaments and they are also held together by a thin disc called the **Z-line**. A section of myofibril between two Z-lines (ie the basic contractile unit) is called a **sarcomere**.

Note: Be clear that you can distinguish between the terms muscle, muscle fibre, myofibril and sarcomere.

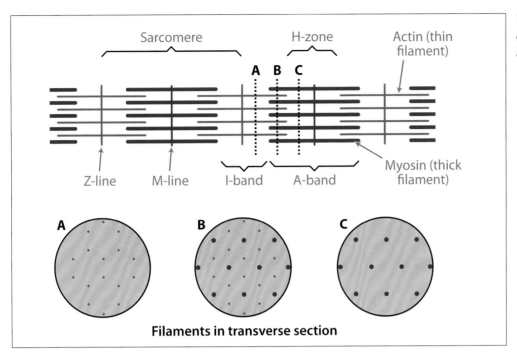

The arrangement of myosin and actin in a myofibril

The thicker myosin filaments form denser or darker striations or bands and the thinner actin filaments form less dense or lighter regions between them as seen in the figure above. It is this alternating pattern of myosin and actin that forms the **striated (banded)** pattern of voluntary (striated) muscle as seen in electronmicrographs.

TS of A-band (through region where myosin and actin filaments overlap)

The part of the myofibril containing myosin is referred to as the **A-band** (or **anisotropic band**). The A-band includes those areas where the thinner actin penetrates between the myosin filaments. The **I-band (or isotropic band)** is the part of the myofibril that is actin only. The **H-zone** is the zone in the centre of the A-band where there is myosin only (the area beyond the ends of the actin filaments).

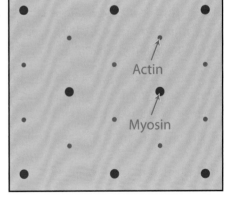

Furthermore, the relationship between the overlapping actin and myosin is very regular with each myosin filament being surrounded by six actin filaments in a regular hexagonal pattern as highlighted in the enlarged image on the right.

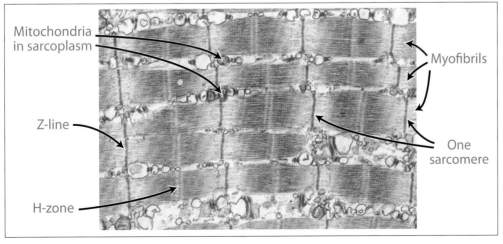

TEM of striated muscle showing series of myofibrils running left to right

Muscle contraction

The basic principle of muscle contraction is that the myosin and actin filaments slide past each other so reducing the overall length of the sarcomere (and muscle). The process is called the **sliding filament mechanism.**

Before considering the mechanics of the sliding filament process it is important to revisit the structure of the myosin and actin protein molecules. Although mainly a long fibrous molecule, the myosin also has small bulbous heads that protrude at intervals as shown in the diagram opposite. The thinner actin filaments have small binding sites into which the bulbous heads of the myosin fit.

When not contracting the actin binding sites are blocked by another ancillary protein (tropomyosin) to prevent binding.

The process of muscle contraction can be summarised in the following steps:

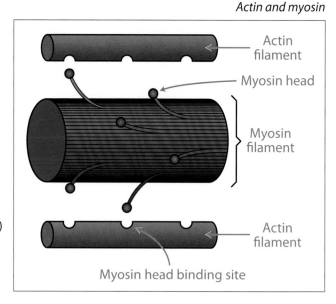

Actin and myosin

- An action potential stimulates the muscle fibre as it travels through its extensive system of **T-tubules**.

- The action potential causes the calcium ion channels in the **sarcoplasmic reticulum** (the name given to the specialised endoplasmic reticulum of muscle cells) to open.

- This causes the **calcium ions** (Ca^{2+}) that have been stored in the sarcoplasmic reticulum to diffuse into the **sarcoplasm** (the cytoplasm of muscle cells) down a concentration gradient.

- The calcium ions cause **ancillary protein** (tropomyosin) that normally covers the binding sites on the actin filaments to be moved so enabling the myosin bulbous heads to link with the actin binding sites (forming **actomyosin** bridges).

- Once attached, the myosin heads change their angle (rotate or 'rock' back to an angle about 45°) and pull the actin filaments over the adjacent myosin filaments (by about 10 nm).

- An **ATP** molecule attaches to each myosin head and the energy released from its hydrolysis enables the myosin head to detach from the stationary actin binding site and return to its original position.

- The detached myosin heads repeat the process so that the **cycle of attachment, rotation and release** is repeated in a type of ratchet mechanism with each cycle occurring about five times each second.

- The cycle continues as long as the muscle fibre receives nervous stimulation (and has calcium ions present).

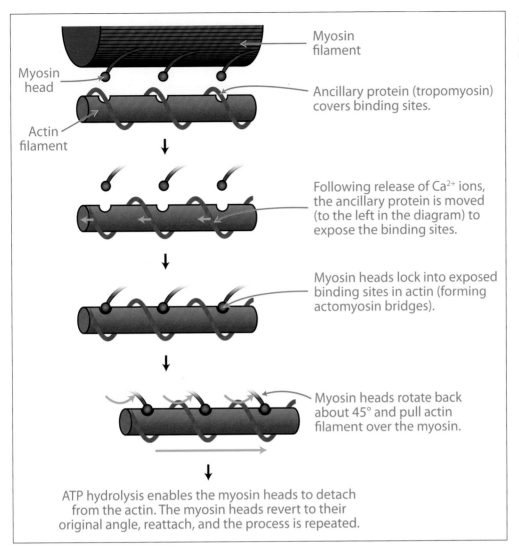

Myosin filament

Myosin head

Actin filament

Ancillary protein (tropomyosin) covers binding sites.

Following release of Ca²⁺ ions, the ancillary protein is moved (to the left in the diagram) to expose the binding sites.

Myosin heads lock into exposed binding sites in actin (forming actomyosin bridges).

Myosin heads rotate back about 45° and pull actin filament over the myosin.

ATP hydrolysis enables the myosin heads to detach from the actin. The myosin heads revert to their original angle, reattach, and the process is repeated.

The sliding filament mechanism of muscle contraction

The diagram on the right shows that as contraction takes place the arrangement of the myosin and actin filaments in each sarcomere changes as summarised below:

- The sarcomere shortens (distance between Z-lines decreases)

- The H-zone becomes shorter

- The I-band becomes shorter

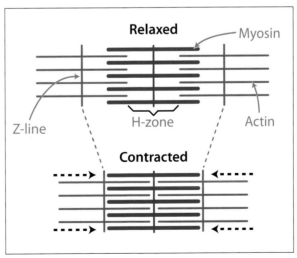

Relaxed

Myosin

Z-line

H-zone

Actin

Contracted

A sarcomere in a relaxed and contracted state

Note: myosin filaments in adjacent sarcomeres are not shown for clarity.

Note 1: With each sarcomere being microscopic in size (approx 2.5 μm) it is obvious that the contraction caused by each sarcomere shortening is almost negligible. However, with many sarcomeres lined end to end in a muscle fibre, and all contracting at the same time, the overall muscle contraction can be considerable.

Note 2: The power of muscle contraction is due to the many parallel myofibrils lined side by side in a muscle fibre (and many fibres in a single muscle) all contracting at the same time.

The neuromuscular junction – Skeletal muscle is voluntary muscle and requires nervous input for contraction. Skeletal muscle contracts as a consequence of stimulation by the motor (effector) neurone(s) that supply it.

The synapses between neurone and muscle are specialised and are called **neuromuscular junctions**.

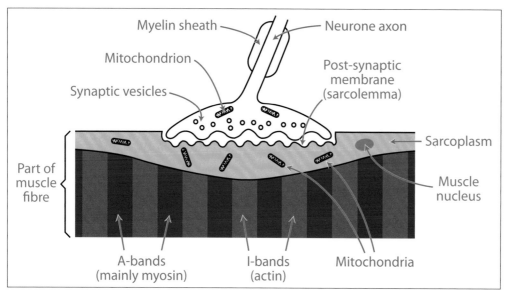

A neuromuscular junction

Note 1: The specialised infolded part of the muscle fibre that forms a synapse with the motor neurone is called a **motor end plate**.

Note 2: The infolding of the post-synaptic membrane (motor end plate) at a neuromuscular junction provides a larger surface area for more neurotransmitter receptors.

In each muscle fibre there are many neuromuscular junctions spread along the fibre. This is important to ensure that the whole muscle contracts at once rather than a wave of contraction gradually spreading across it. Often one motor neurone (with its many branches) services a number of muscle fibres (and even a whole muscle) to ensure that synchronised contraction takes place.

Note 3: The strength of muscle contraction depends on a number of factors including for how long the muscle is stimulated but also how many muscle fibres are actually stimulated and contracting. Although one motor neurone may control contraction in an entire muscle, not all the fibres may be contracted at the one time.

Skeletal muscle, although the most obvious in terms of size and extent, is not the only type of muscle in the body. Smooth and cardiac muscles also contract and bring about movement but are different in appearance and have different functions to skeletal muscle.

The three main types of muscle are summarised in the following table:

	Skeletal	**Smooth**	**Cardiac**
Appearance	Striated (banded). Multinucleate fibres	Discrete uninucleate cells are spindle shaped. Non-striated	Striated but branched with intercalated discs (seen as discrete lines) between cells
Distribution	Attached to bone throughout the body (most of the muscle in the body)	Lining gut and blood vessels Iris and ciliary body in eye	Wall of heart
Nervous control	Voluntary (conscious) control	Involuntary or automatic (for example, reflex action)	Myogenic and involuntary control

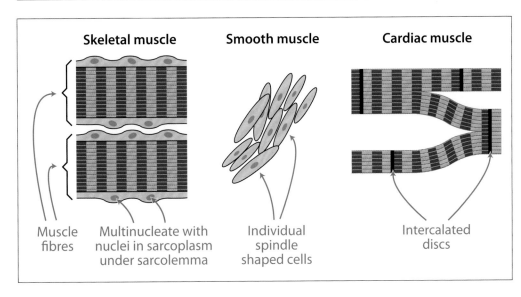

The three types of muscle

Exam questions

1. The photograph below shows the eye of a young mammal with the eyelids closed.

   (a) Identify the structures labelled A to D. [4]

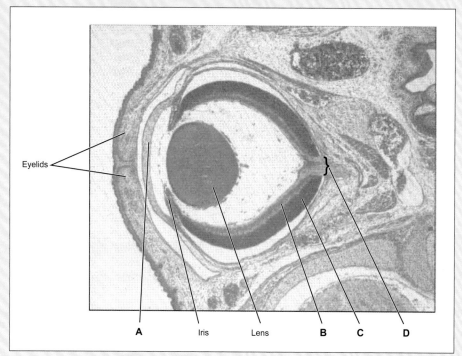

Eyelids

A   Iris   Lens   B   C   D

© Lutz Slomianka 1998-2009 by permission Dr Ron Swann, School Manager, School of Anatomy and Human Biology – The University of Western Australia

   (b) Describe the operation of the iris in bright sunlight. [2]

   (c) The diagrams E and F below show eyes with different lens thicknesses and so adapted differently for the accommodation (focusing) of light.

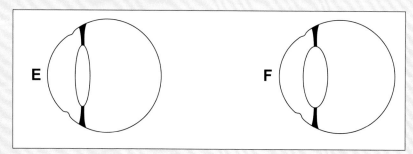

E   F

   (i) State which of these shows an eye adapted for accommodation of light from a near object. Explain your answer. [1]

   (ii) Explain how the lens shape in E is produced within the eye. [2]

Question taken from CCEA's Biology Assessment Unit A2 1, Physiology and Ecosystems, May 2010, © CCEA 2013

2. (a) Photoreceptor cells (rods and cones) are not distributed evenly across the retina. The diagram below shows the distribution of rods and cones across the retina of the human left eye.

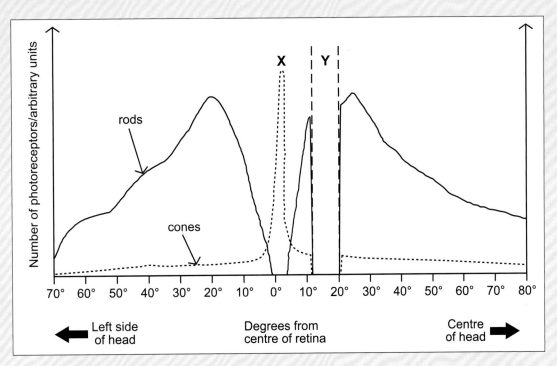

(i) Name regions of the retina represented by X and Y. [2]

(ii) The diagram shows that there are more photoreceptor cells (rods and cones) at the edge of the retina closest to the centre of the head compared to the edge closest to the side of the head. Suggest a reason for this. [1]

(iii) Peripheral vision can be described as vision at the limits of our field of view. With reference to both rods and cones, explain why peripheral vision has reduced visual acuity. [2]

(b) The ability of the eye to focus on near and distant objects is called accommodation. Describe and explain the events that occur in the eye when accommodating a distant object. [3]

Question taken from CCEA's Biology Assessment Unit A2 1, Physiology and Ecosystems, January 2012, © CCEA 2013

3. Quality of written communication is awarded a maximum of two marks in this section. [2]

Give an account of the functioning of the mammalian eye to include the role of the following:

- the iris
- the lens
- rods
- cones [16]

Question taken from CCEA's Biology Assessment Unit A2 1, Physiology and Ecosystems, January 2010, © CCEA 2013

4. Skeletal (voluntary) muscle makes up a large proportion of our body weight and is essential for movement. Skeletal muscle is also called striated muscle as it has alternating light and dark bands.

(a) Explain precisely what causes the alternating light and dark band pattern in skeletal muscle. [2]

(b) Muscle is also important in the functioning of the eye.

(i) Suggest one difference between the control of muscle in the iris and skeletal muscle in the arm.[1]

(ii) Describe the role of muscle in the functioning of the iris. [3]

(iii) Name one other muscle in the eye that is important in producing a clear image. [1]

Question taken from CCEA's Biology Assessment Unit A2 1, Physiology and Ecosystems, May 2012, © CCEA 2013

5. (a) The photograph below shows a photomicrograph of a section through skeletal muscle.

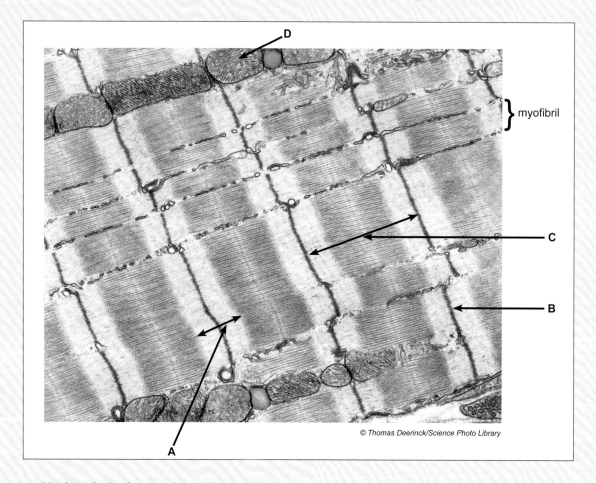

} myofibril

© Thomas Deerinck/Science Photo Library

(i) Identify the features labelled A to D. [4]

(ii) The H-band (H-zone) is not very obvious in the photograph. What does this suggest about the state of the muscle at the time the photograph was taken? [1]

(b) What is the role of calcium ions in muscle contraction? [1]

Question taken from CCEA's Biology Assessment Unit A2 1, Physiology and Ecosystems, May 2011, © CCEA 2013

6. (a) The diagram shows a representation of part of a myofibril in cross-section.

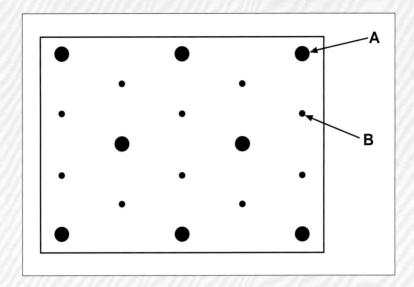

   (i) Name the type of protein found in the structures represented by A and B. [2]

   (ii) Name the region (band) of the myofibril the section represents. [1]

   (iii) Describe the sliding filament mechanism of muscle contraction. [3]

(b) Neuromuscular junctions are specialised synapses that link neurones to muscle fibres. Each motor neurone subdivides into several branches, each with its own neuromuscular junction, as shown in the diagram below.

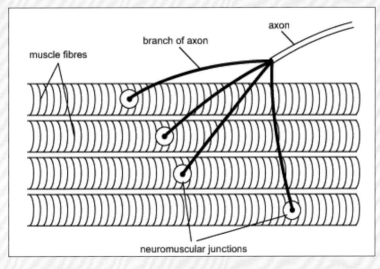

© CCEA

   (i) In terms of outcome, identify the main difference between neuromuscular junctions and neurone to neurone synapses in the nervous system. [1]

   (ii) The diagram shows that the axon of one motor neurone branches to supply a number of muscle fibres. Suggest a reason for this. [1]

Question taken from CCEA's Biology Assessment Unit A2 1, Physiology and Ecosystems, January 2012, © CCEA 2013

7. Photographs A, B and C show three mammalian muscle types.

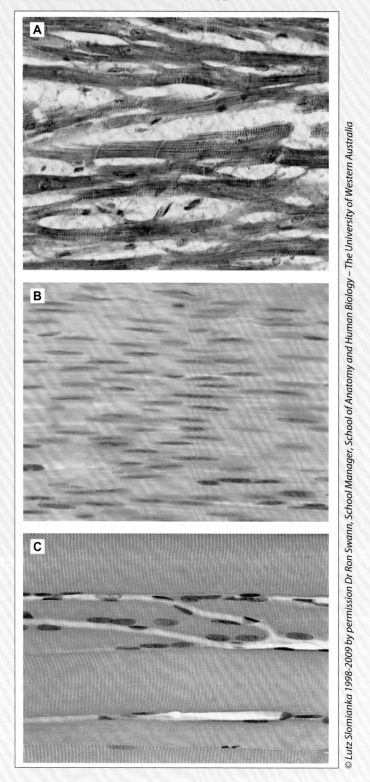

(a) Identify the muscle types in each photograph and state one identifying feature for each. [6]

(b) (i) Name the two protein filaments present in muscle fibres. [1]

(ii) Describe the arrangement of these protein filaments in the myofibrils of a muscle fibre. [2]

Question taken from CCEA's Biology Assessment Unit A2 1, Physiology and Ecosystems, January 2010, © CCEA 2013

Chapter 6 – Populations and Communities

Populations

A **population** is a group of organisms of the **same species** living in a particular area. Population numbers can remain relatively stable or can grow or decline over time. Factors influencing population growth include birth and death rates, immigration and emigration. Some of the main types of population growth are discussed in the following sections.

Population growth

One of the most studied examples of population growth is the growth of bacteria (or yeast) in nutrient medium in **closed conditions**, for example, in a beaker or conical flask. The diagram below shows the characteristic pattern of population growth typically seen in these circumstances. Population growth (or decline) is measured as the change in **number of organisms** – in bacteria increase occurs when a bacterium divides (splits) to produce two new daughter cells.

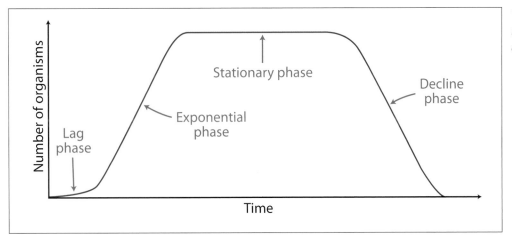

The growth of bacteria in closed conditions

The pattern of growth evident in the diagram can be divided into four distinct phases, the lag phase, the exponential (or log growth) phase, the stationary (or stable) phase and the decline phase.

1. **Lag phase** – In this phase there will be a very slow increase in number (numbers may even decrease for a time). This is a stage when **nutrient assimilation** takes place – this may involve the bacteria activating genes and producing the appropriate enzymes to metabolise a particular food substrate.

2. **Exponential (log) phase** – The bacteria divide **exponentially**. There is **no restriction to growth** (for example, abundant resources present and insignificant waste accumulation) and the bacteria can divide to produce new bacteria at the maximum rate. Bacteria can divide to produce two new bacteria as often as once every 20 minutes and consequently the increase in numbers can be exponential.

3. **Stationary (stable) phase** – In this stage food supplies may begin to become limiting so the number of new individuals produced falls. Waste products and toxins also may have accumulated to a level that restricts growth. During the stationary phase the 'birth' and death rates approach equilibrium.

4. **Decline phase** – The death rate exceeds the birth rate and the population declines, sometimes very rapidly in a population 'crash'. In the bacterial population in the diagram this can be due to the accumulation of toxic waste and/or the nutrient supply running out.

Note: The **sigmoidal** (S-shape) growth curve comprising the lag, exponential and stationary growth phases in the diagram on page 81 applies to the populations of many species in particular circumstances, such as when colonising a new area. The same principles apply but other factors can contribute to particular parts of the growth curve, for example, the lag phase can be due to the time taken for egg or larval production or the gestation period or even the time to grow and reach sexual maturity. However, most natural populations are most likely to remain in the stable phase rather than progress into the decline phase – a phase typically associated with 'closed' conditions.

Some key terms describing population growth are discussed below.

- **Biotic potential** – The maximum rate of growth of the population as seen in the exponential phase reflects the population's **biotic potential** – the reproductive potential (rate) of a population under optimum environmental conditions with unlimited resources.

- **Environmental resistance** – The environmental restrictions on population growth, for example, as evident in the stationary phase, create what is described as an environmental resistance. **Environmental resistance** is the restriction by the environment on the population reaching its maximum growth rate and its biotic potential. Environmental resistance can be due to many factors including nutrient shortage or accumulation of waste (as discussed above) but also climate, competition from other organisms, predation and disease. The factors that influence populations can be grouped into two main categories. **Abiotic factors** are factors in the chemical or physical environment and loosely referred to as non-living; examples include water, nutrient, light or oxygen availability. **Biotic factors** are the effects of other organisms whether the same or other species, for example, food supply or predation.

- **Carrying capacity** – The **carrying capacity** is the maximum number that the population can support. The carrying capacity is very much determined by the amount of **resources** available. In our example of bacterial growth, if extra resources were provided – for example, a larger volume of medium which would have additional nutrients (and which also would dilute the waste/toxins produced) – there would be a higher carrying capacity.

Renewable and non-renewable resources – The characteristic flattening out in the stationary phase and rapid fall of the decline phase in our bacterial example is due to the resources being **non-renewable**. The nutrients that were there at the start of the investigation were not replaced (as well as the waste not being removed).

If resources are **renewable**, as in a broadleaved, deciduous woodland where trees shed their leaves each year and provide food for earthworms, the earthworm population tends to remain in a stationary or stable phase.

Some other growth curve examples

The diagram below shows the growth of an algal (planktonic protoctistan) population over the course of a year; a **J-shaped** growth curve that is characteristic of many protoctistan species.

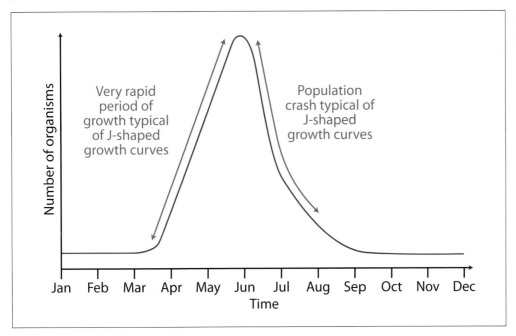

A J-shaped growth curve

The graph shows that there is a very rapid period of growth in spring as there is abundant nutrient availability in the water, both temperature and light levels are increasing and there are relatively few herbivores in the water at this time of the year. However, in mid-summer the population often 'crashes' (with no stationary phase) and rapidly falls largely because the nutrient supply becomes exhausted but also because herbivores (zooplankton) increase in number and because wastes accumulate. In this example, **resource availability** is again a key determinant of the growth pattern.

Note: The human population growth curve is a J-shaped curve with very rapid and increasing growth over the last 200 years. The big difference with the algal populations is that, as yet, there has been no crash!

Competition between organisms – When different organisms are competing for the same resource. **Competition** is also an important factor in providing environmental resistance and influencing the carrying capacity. Competition can be either **intraspecific**, between members of the same species as in our example of bacterial growth, or **interspecific**, between members of different species. The diagram below summarises a very famous investigation involving interspecific competition carried out by the Russian zoologist G.F. Gause over 80 years ago.

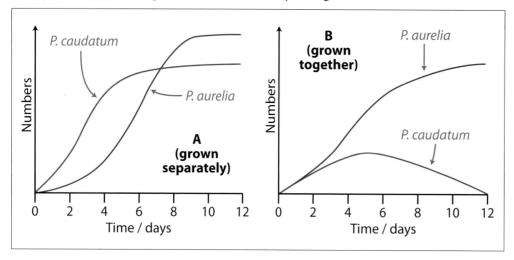

Population growth curves for two species of Paramecium when grown separately (A) and when grown together (B).

Gause investigated competition between populations of two species of *Paramecium* – *P. aurelia* and *P. caudatum*. When cultured separately in the laboratory and fed on bacteria the *P. aurelia* reached a higher final density compared to *P. caudatum* as shown above in **A**. However, when cultured together in the same conditions (**B**) the *P. aurelia* population increased at only a slightly reduced rate compared to when grown separately. However, the *P. caudatum* was eliminated as a consequence of being losers in the competition for the food resource. Clearly, the smaller *P. aurelia* was better adapted for utilising the food resources available.

This example highlights a point made during the AS course, in that no two species occupy the identical ecological niche. When this happens one species loses out as a consequence of the **competitive exclusion principle**.

Predator-prey interaction

Predator-prey interaction – The oscillating growth curves produced as a consequence of predator-prey interactions with alternating peaks and troughs are shown in the diagram (right).

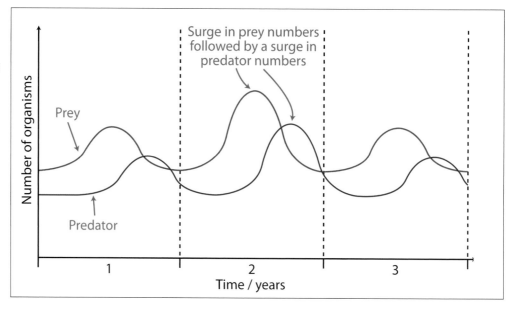

If there are large numbers of prey there will be more food available for predators so their numbers will increase. In due course the increased numbers of predators will cause the numbers of prey to decrease which in turn will cause the number of predators to decrease and so on. The types of growth curve shown opposite demonstrating the classical predator-prey interaction tend to have a number of features in common:

- The predator peaks and troughs **lag behind** the prey peaks and troughs – the time lag depends on a number of features including the rate and time involved in which the predators can produce offspring.

- Although lagging behind, the **length** of the predator cycle is usually similar to the length of the prey cycle.

- The number of predators is normally significantly **lower** than the number of prey individuals at equivalent points on the cycle.

Note: Predator-prey relationships such as the one in the diagram (opposite, bottom) are only as obvious as this when the predator relies on one particular prey. In reality, most predators have more than one prey species so the growth curves often have a smoother pattern and there is less of a correlation between any one prey and any one predator.

Population dynamics

As the growth curves show, the number of individuals making up populations fluctuates over time. However, the change in size of any population is determined by the birth and death rate and any migration that takes place.

Population growth = (births – deaths) + (immigration – emigration)

This equation holds true whether the population is increasing or decreasing and can be applied to any example we review. In the lag-exponential-stationary-decline growth pattern of bacteria cultured in a laboratory, migration is not a factor so the different stages are dependent on the balance between 'births' and deaths. The rapid increase in the populations of migratory bird species throughout spring and summer is a combination of both immigration and a high birth rate.

The example of migratory birds highlights another feature of populations in general. In many species there is a very obvious **seasonal** effect on population size. Thousands of migrant birds may be all too obvious during spring and summer but in contrast there may be no local population during the winter. For most species the seasonal effect on population size is not a migration effect but is determined by the balance between births and deaths. Many species of animals give birth in spring or early summer so there are large populations at this stage when temperatures are high and food resources are plentiful. Seasonal effects can often be represented by survivorship curves which show the percentage of individuals surviving over **a year** as the seasons progress. Survivorship curves can also be used to show the number of individuals of a particular species surviving over a **period of years**. The diagram on page 86 shows a typical survivorship curve for tawny owls over their first five years of life – the percentage survival values represent the number of chicks from one particular year that survive over successive years as they age.

Population sizes can also change from **year to year.** This can be for many reasons including being part of a normal predator-prey cycle, changes in food supply or abiotic factors such as a colder winter.

r- and K-selected species (r- and K-strategists) – The characteristics of the species itself influences the population dynamic. Most species can be broadly grouped into either r- or K- selected species.

r-selected species tend to be '**opportunistic**' and grow both very quickly as individuals and increase the population number very rapidly when conditions are ideal. Their numbers also decline very rapidly when conditions are less favourable. They tend to exhibit '**boom and bust**' patterns of growth as the emphasis is on reproduction and the colonisation of new areas rather than survival. Examples of r-selected species typically include bacteria, protoctistans and annual plants (many species of weeds).

Represents the number of chicks hatched in the first year

Survivorship curve for tawny owls over their first five years

K-selected species have more **stable** populations and the population size usually remains at or close to the **carrying capacity** for the species. In K-selected species the emphasis is more on survival and dominance rather than expanding the population or colonising new areas. K-selected species include many large mammals such as humans and many species of trees. The table below shows features of typical r-selected and K-selected species.

r-selected (r-strategists)	K-selected (K-strategists)
Small body size	Large body size
Short lived	Long life cycle – usually number of years before mature and able to produce offspring
Reproduce rapidly with usually many offspring	Few offspring
Very little parental care	Large amount of parental care – high investment in young – few young produced so important that they have high chance of survival
Able to disperse rapidly and colonise new habitats	Low dispersal ability – colonisation of new habitats less frequent
Population size (density) very variable	Population size (density) more constant
Low competitive ability – unlikely to become dominant	High competitive ability – may be a dominant species in the ecosystem
Not specialised so adaptable to change in environment – can evolve rapidly, for example, antibiotic resistance in bacteria	Tend to be highly specialised so less resistant to environment change – prone to becoming endangered or extinct in changing environment, for example, polar bears and global warming
Often inhabit unstable or short-lived habitats, for example, weeds colonising a ploughed field	Typically occur in stable habitats that remain relatively undisturbed for many years, for example, oak trees in a forest

Note 1: r is the designation for the **intrinsic rate of natural increase** (the biotic potential). r-strategists as indicated in the table have short life cycles and reproduce very rapidly and therefore have a high value for r – they approach the biotic potential.

Note 2: In population growth curves **K** represents the **carrying capacity**. Consequently K-strategists have population sizes that remain close to the carrying capacity (K).

Population interactions – winners and losers

We have already seen how predator and prey populations can interact. This is only one example of how the populations of two **different species** can interact and influence each other.

Predator-prey interactions are an example of a + / − interaction where one species gains and the other loses. Herbivores **grazing** on plants is a similar type of + / − interaction where one species (the cow) gains and another (the grass) loses.

Parasitism is a third type of + / − interaction. The parasite gains at the expense of the host.

Parasites can be defined as organisms that live in or on another organism (the host) benefiting from it and causing it harm over an extended period of time.

Cows grazing in a field, a + / − interaction

The differences between a predator-prey relationship and a parasite-host relationship can often be very subtle and difficult to distinguish with no clear demarcation. However, as a general rule, parasites differ from predators in four ways:

- The parasite lives in or on the host.

- The parasite causes harm to the host over an extended period of time.

- The parasite is usually smaller than the host.

- The parasite seldom kills the host (or if it does it is a very slow process).

Examples of parasites include the flea, the human tapeworm and the malarial parasite *Plasmodium* that is transferred between humans by female mosquitoes. Examples of parasites are not restricted to the animal kingdom; the common tar spot fungus is an example of a fungal parasite that infects sycamore leaves and mistletoe is an example of a plant parasite that infects trees across much of north-west Europe. The amount of harm that parasites cause varies considerably – normally a flea is little more than an irritation but malaria is often fatal.

Tar spot fungus in sycamore

Mistletoe

Mistletoe has evergreen leaves and forms dense spheres that hang from the host tree – the photograph on page 87 was taken in March before the tree leaves opened making the mistletoe even more obvious. The mistletoe can photosynthesise to produce its own carbohydrate but produces special structures to penetrate the tree and absorb water and minerals for its needs – it has no roots as such that reach the ground.

There are also – / – interactions, where both species suffer. This is often the case with **competition**. If you revisit the growth curves of *Paramecium aurelia* and *P. caudatum* on page 84 you will observe that when the two species are grown together neither species grows as well as it does when growing on its own. The graphs also show another common feature of competition, the loser is often eliminated by competitive exclusion.

Although this example of competition shows that the species with better competitive ability can lead to the elimination of another **species**, in nature there is as much competition between members of the same species (intraspecific competition) as there is between different species (interspecific competition). For example, the oak seedlings growing around an oak tree are competing with each other (and with the parent tree). Over time, fewer and fewer **individuals** survive due to competition for resources such as space, light, water and minerals.

Mutualism is the interaction where **both partners benefit** (a + / + interaction). Mutualistic relationships can be complex and often have evolved to the extent where at least one of the species cannot survive on its own.

Lichen growing on a tree trunk

Lichens are an example of an obligate mutualistic relationship between fungi and green algae. The fungi provide the supporting framework and absorb water and nutrients (as well as sheltering the algae and protecting them from desiccation) and the algae photosynthesise thus providing carbohydrates and other organic compounds, some of which are available to the fungi.

Mutualistic **nitrogen-fixing bacteria** live in the nodules of the roots of legumes such as peas and beans. The nitrogen-fixing bacteria benefit through gaining carbohydrate from the plants and the plants benefit through gaining amino acids (or other nitrogen-containing compounds) from the bacteria.

Cellulose digestion in many herbivores is a consequence of mutualism between the herbivores and bacteria and/or protoctistans in the gut of the herbivore. In cows and other ruminants the bacteria possess the cellulases required to hydrolyse cellulose. The cows benefit as they can utilise a very abundant source of food not accessible to so many other animal species and their mutualistic partners gain a ready supply of food and are maintained at a relatively high and constant temperature ensuring rapid metabolic activity.

The biological control of pest species

Man often deliberately manipulates the relationship between other species for his own ends. This can be seen in the control of pests. Due to the harm caused by the use of chemical pesticides, the biological control of pest species is seen as an attractive alternative. But what exactly is a pest and what is biological control?

- **A pest species** can be defined as a species that damages a valuable/commercial crop species, causing economic damage.

- **Biological control** involves deliberately introducing predator (or parasitic or pathogenic) species that targets the pest.

Biological control will benefit the environment by reducing the need for chemical pesticides and the harm that they cause but are also used because 'broad-spectrum' pesticides (such as insecticides and herbicides) may not work particularly well. Broad-spectrum pesticides may kill many beneficial organisms including many natural enemies of the pest. The graph below shows an example of what can happen if a broad-spectrum insecticide is used to target a population of pest insects.

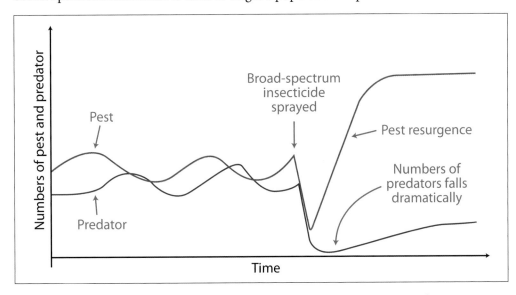

Pest resurgence following application of a broad-spectrum insecticide

The graph above shows that the pest can experience **pest resurgence** in that its numbers increase rapidly due to the elimination of a natural predator.

The graph below shows how **effective biological control** can reduce pest numbers below the threshold of economic damage.

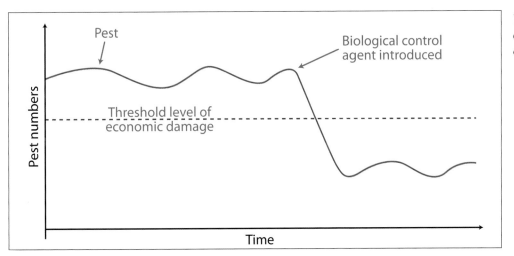

The potential of effective biological control

With effective biological control the introduced predator integrates naturally into the ecosystem, building a sustainable population and therefore does not need to be continually re-introduced. Effective biological control possesses the following **advantages**.

- There is **no chemical damage** to the environment with the risk of significant ecological harm and **bioaccumulation** in food chains.

- Biological control **targets only the pest species** – there is reduced collateral damage affecting other organisms.

- The development of **resistance** by the pests is unlikely (see note below).

- Pest resurgence is unlikely.

- Biological control if successful, needs **little additional action** and **saves money** on the continued use of pesticides.

Note: Insect **populations** treated with insecticides frequently develop resistance to the pesticide and it ceases to become effective. Before the pesticide is applied, a small number of **individuals** in a population will have resistance due to mutation. However, when the pesticide is used the non-resistant individuals are killed leaving only the resistant individuals (that survive and reproduce) resulting in the **population** becoming resistant.

Biological control has its **limitations** though and it is not always successful. For example, the pest will not be totally eliminated – its density is reduced (ideally to below the threshold for economic damage). Biological control will only work well if the biological control species can adapt and thrive in the ecosystem into which it is introduced – often an 'unnatural' crop ecosystem not found in the wild can be hostile to the introduced biological control species.

This section on populations has focused on how populations of individual species grow over time and how these populations interact with another (or small number of) species. The next section on communities addresses the relationships between many species as communities and ecosystems develop.

Communities

A **community** is the sum total of all the populations (species) in a particular area (habitat or ecosystem). A more complete definition is that it is the **biotic** component of an ecosystem involving interaction between the autotrophic and heterotrophic populations present.

An **ecosystem** is the community plus its physical environment – it consists of **both biotic** and **abiotic** components. In an ecosystem many of the species are interdependent on each other. For example, the abiotic environment, such as rock type and climate, will determine the type of community that can develop and the different species present will interact in areas such as energy flow, nutrient and gas exchange.

Succession (community development)

Ecosystems are constantly changing and **succession** is the term used to describe the changes over time in ecosystems. It is important to note that succession involves changes to both the community (the species present) and the abiotic environment and there is important interaction between these two components.

Primary succession

Primary succession occurs on newly formed, barren land that hasn't been previously colonised. This could be the lava fields produced after a volcanic eruption, the sudden appearance of a volcanic island or the exposed rock at the base of a disused quarry. A key point is that the exposed land (rock) provides a very harsh and hostile environment for life. There will be no soil present to support plants.

The first stage in the succession is usually the appearance of colonising **pioneer species**. Pioneer species such as **lichens** are able to survive the hostile conditions. The lichens can grow on the bare rock, tolerating desiccation. Over time the lichens begin to degrade the rock and help promote the weathering (aided by the climate, for example, frost action) that forms the embryonic **soil**. Initially the soil will accumulate in cracks in the rock. As the lichens die and decompose, the 'soil' will develop to a stage where it can support **mosses**.

Lichen

Lichens (and mosses) grow in shelter of rock crevices. 'Debris' containing moisture and nutrients from decomposed lichens and mosses accumulates in these crevices.

Lichens and mosses on a rock

Note 1: The communities present at each particular stage of the succession help to modify the abiotic environment thus creating the abiotic conditions necessary for the next stage, for example, the decomposing lichens and mosses form the embryonic 'soil', increasing nutrient availability.

Further successional stages

Note 2: The colonising plant species that succeed lichens and mosses in the early stages of succession are usually short lived r-strategists that have excellent dispersal mechanisms allowing them to rapidly colonise new areas.

Lichens colonise bare rock.

Mosses and plant species grow in rock crevices.

Soil accumulates and builds up in hollows between exposed rocks enabling a wider variety of plants and grasses to grow.

Typically with time as the succession develops **soil depth** and **fertility** increases so does the number of different plant species (although plant biodiversity often decreases again as the succession approaches maturity). The plant **biomass** also tends to increase as succession progresses, as seen in the graphs opposite.

Each stage in the succession is called a **sere** – the two photographs on page 91 could be regarded as representing successive seres in a succession. Eventually after a number of seres the climax community develops. The **climax community** is the stable end stage of a succession which is in equilibrium with the environment. In most of lowland Britain the climax community is mixed broadleaf deciduous forest dominated by oak and other common species. In harsher upland environments moorland is often the climax community.

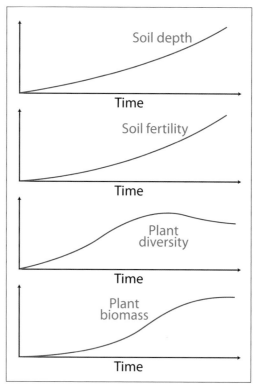

Features typical of primary succession

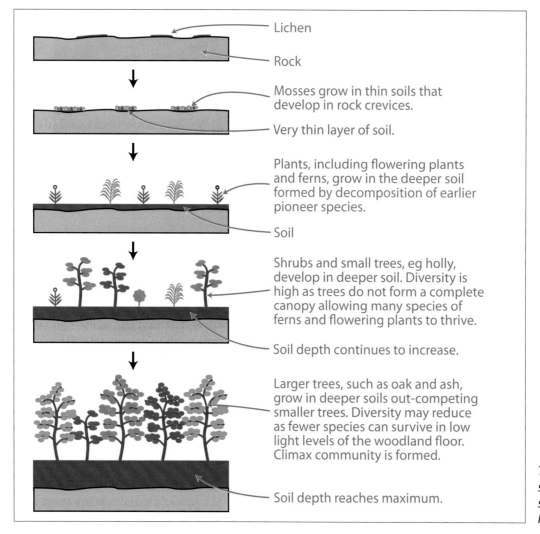

The typical sequence of succession in lowland Britain

If the composition of the climax community is determined by the climate (as in the examples described opposite) it is called a **climatic climax**. If it is determined by biotic factors, such as grazing, it is called a **biotic climax**.

Although the actual succession that will take place depends on a number of factors, including climate, all successions tend to have a number of features in common.

- They are **predictable** in pattern – pioneer species will always be the initial colonisers and a similar climax community will develop in the same conditions.

- The **abiotic environment becomes less hostile** as soil forms and the growth of plants provides shelter for the organisms in the later stages.

- The **height** and **biomass** of vegetation increases.

- Communities become **increasingly complex** with more complex food webs as a greater number of niches are provided for animals.

- There is **increased biodiversity** (at least until mid-succession).

- Communities in later stages of the succession are usually more **stable** than in earlier seres.

Case study

At any one time most successions will be at a particular stage or sere. If you visit a mature mixed deciduous woodland you will be in a climax community – a community that used to dominate most of Britain and Ireland but is much rarer now. You have to imagine what the pioneer stage was like many years ago as this type of succession will take several hundred years to develop.

Sand dunes are a particularly interesting type of succession in that they can demonstrate all the different seres at the same time. A sand dune ecosystem is continually developing as sand blown by the wind or carried by the force of the sea is forming new dunes close to the high tide mark. As dune renewal takes place at the hostile interface with the sea, there is a progression of increasingly older dunes further inland as conditions become more benign and the dune system becomes more stable and mature.

Young dune at edge of shore

In the **young dunes** at the shore edge, **marram grass** is the principal **pioneer species** and coloniser. The marram grass is highly specialised in a number of ways – it is a xerophyte and able to survive in the sand which is unable to effectively retain the (usually abundant) rain that falls in these ecosystems. The roots of the marram grass can rapidly penetrate through the sand and have a very important role in binding the sand together and stabilising the dunes.

Roots of marram grass bind the sand particles together

Just behind these young developing dunes, small areas of 'grassland' called **dune slacks** have a degree of protection and are rich in mosses and many other ground-hugging plant species such as birdsfoot trefoil and thyme. Animal species such as snails are also becoming more common as the food webs are becoming increasingly complex. Typically, these areas have the greatest biodiversity in the sand dune system. The continuing cycle of the growth and decomposition of the plants allows a thin soil to develop.

Dune slack immediately behind the young dunes

Further inland as the dunes are more **mature**, the ground is stable enough and the soil developed enough to allow shrubs such as **heather** to dominate. The increasing height of the plant community shades out many of the plants that dominated the ground cover in the previous sere. Not surprisingly, the biodiversity begins to fall although there is a significant increase in biomass at this stage.

Marram

Heather

Mature dune with heather and marram

This trend continues as we move inland and reach the **old dunes** – dunes that have been formed for hundreds of years. The old dunes are even more stable and are colonised by **bracken** and **gorse**. These species allow very little light to penetrate to ground level. Few species other than mosses are common under the bracken and gorse.

Gorse

Bracken

Old dunes with bracken and gorse

Further inland again, the heather and gorse community is often replaced by **woodland**.

Dune system merging into woodland

Reading through this example of sand dune succession you will note that it has all the typical characteristics of succession as listed in an earlier section of this chapter (page 93).

However, most successions that take place do not show the relatively slow sequence from bare land – usually rock but sand in the case of sand dune succession – to climax community. Instead, they are successions that take place when the normal primary succession is interrupted due to, for example, fire, flooding or as is often the case the activities of man (such as woodland clearance or ploughing land). This type of succession is called secondary succession.

Secondary succession

Secondary succession does not usually begin with the typical pioneer species such as lichen, as the **soil** is already formed and will contain the **seeds** of many species as well as other plant parts that can rapidly regenerate, for example, roots. Many other **soil organisms** such as nitrifying bacteria and detritivores are also usually present in the soil. As a consequence of all these factors, secondary succession is invariably much **quicker** than primary succession, with the climax community being reached in a much shorter time.

Foxglove – a common species early in a woodland secondary succession following clearance

A common secondary succession in Britain is the succession that takes place after woodland is cleared. Although some of the cleared land is often used for urban development, or for farming activity, some frequently remains untouched and has the opportunity to revert to climax community through secondary succession. The sequence of seres generally represents the sequence at the latter end of a primary succession but there are often some differences compared to the typical primary succession.

For example, some species are particularly adapted to the ecological niches associated with cleared woodland. They can either regenerate very rapidly from seed banks in the soil or colonise from surrounding areas.

For this reason, foxgloves are common plants in the years immediately following woodland clearing as shown in photograph (right).

The photograph opposite shows secondary succession taking place in an area of land that was formerly woodland. Many of the trees in the original woodland were destroyed by a very severe storm and the land is now largely covered by bracken. This photograph was taken about 15 years after the storm that destroyed the woodland.

Practical techniques

The haemocytometer

The haemocytometer is an instrument for counting cell numbers (density). As its name suggests it was originally designed for counting blood cells, but can also be used to count yeast or any type of cells that are large enough to be seen under the microscope.

The haemocytometer resembles a modified microscope slide with a grid (or grids) containing squares of known size. The design enables the central area (counting platform) containing the grid to be slightly lower by a fixed distance (0.1 mm) than the coverslip. This ensures that the squares in the grid represent not only a known area, but the liquid above them has a known volume.

The diagram below represents a haemocytometer.

Part of original woodland remaining after storm

Occasional tree left undamaged

Bracken growing as early sere in secondary succession

Secondary succession following woodland destruction

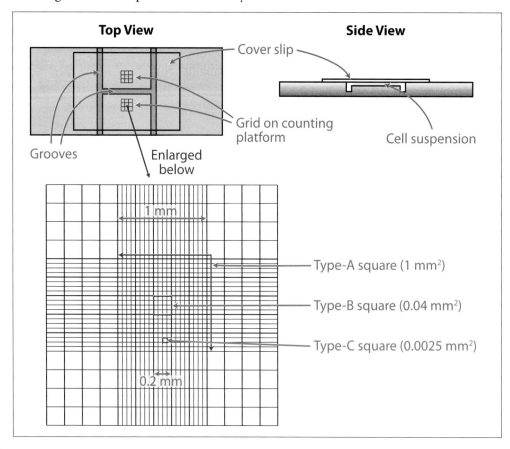

Top View

Side View

Cover slip

Grid on counting platform

Cell suspension

Grooves

Enlarged below

1 mm

Type-A square (1 mm²)

Type-B square (0.04 mm²)

Type-C square (0.0025 mm²)

0.2 mm

The volume enclosed (volume = area × depth [0.1 mm depth for all squares]) by the different size of squares is:

$$\text{type-A} = 1 \text{ mm}^2 \times 0.1 \text{ mm} = 0.1 \text{ mm}^3$$

$$\text{type-B} = 0.04 \text{ mm}^2 \times 0.1 \text{ mm} = 0.004 \text{ mm}^3$$

$$\text{type-C} = 0.0025 \text{ mm}^2 \times 0.1 \text{ mm} = 0.00025 \text{ mm}^3$$

Calculating cell density – A suspension containing the cells to be counted should be placed on the grid on the haemocytometer. Depending on the density of the cells a type-A, type-B or type-C square should be used. If there are very few cells in the sample, the type-A square should be used (as many type-B and most type-C squares will be empty). If there are so many cells in the sample that it would take too long to count all the cells in a type-B square, then a type-C square should be used.

When actually counting the cells in an investigation, many of the cells may lie over the grid lines of the square being counted. In this situation it is very important that cells are not counted twice or are not counted. Therefore one approach is to follow the 'north-west' rule. Cells touching (or lying on) the outer grid line at the top (north) and left (west) side of the square should be counted, but those touching or overlying the grid lines on the right hand side (east) or the bottom (south) should not be counted.

Worked example

Calculate the number of cells/mm^3 in the suspension shown in the type-B below.

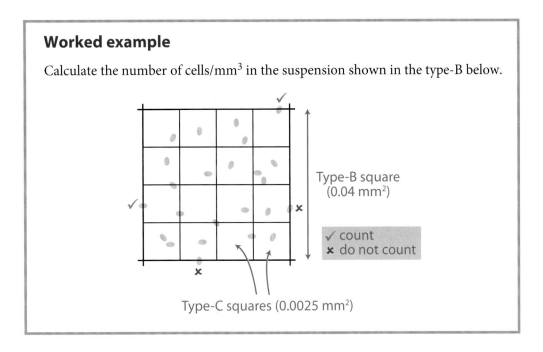

Type-B square (0.04 mm²)

✓ count
✗ do not count

Type-C squares (0.0025 mm²)

Note: For clarity and scale purposes the type-A square is not shown. In this diagram it is better to count the number of cells in the type-B square as there are too few cells in the type-C squares. For increased reliability, a good rule is to use the largest sized square that it is realistic to count.

Number of cells in the type-B square = 22 (using the north-west rule)

Volume of square = (0.04 mm^2 × 0.1 mm) = 0.004 mm^3

$$22 \times 250 = 5500 / \text{mm}^3$$

Using the haemocytometer – some important points

When carrying out investigations using the haemocytometer it is important to:

- mix the cell suspension thoroughly.

- if sampling from the 'natural' environment, for example, sampling phytoplankton from a lake, the retrieval of different samples should be taken from the same depth and if taken over a period of time may need to be taken at the same time of day.

- carry out an appropriate number of replicates for reliability.

When calculating the density of cells in some investigations there may be too many cells to be able to count them as discrete entities, even when using a type-A cell. If so, **serial dilution** will be necessary. Serial dilution involves diluting the suspension, usually by a factor of 10. For example, a 1 cm^3 of the original suspension could be added by pipette into 9 cm^3 of isotonic buffer and then the new solution examined under the microscope. If this first dilution is still too concentrated, the dilution process should be repeated and so on. However, it is very important that when calculating the number of cells/mm^3 the dilution factor is taken into account.

Also when investigating the growth curve of yeast (or other single-celled organisms) it will usually be impossible to distinguish living and dead cells without further analytical work. For this reason, the haemocytometer is a good tool for measuring increase in yeast density during the lag and exponential phases but less good for estimating numbers during the stationary and decline phases (as the counting of dead cells will suggest, the number may not be falling) unless additional work is done to distinguish between living and dead cells.

Estimating the size of an animal population using a capture-recapture technique

Population sizes of animals can be more difficult to estimate than plants due to the fact that animals move and many species spend considerable time in places where they are difficult to locate or observe, such as burrows.

The principle of the **capture-recapture** technique (also called the mark-release-recapture technique) is that a number of animals are trapped/caught and counted, marked and then released. After an appropriate time a number of the target species are caught in a second sampling process. At this stage the recaptured animals should contain a number of marked animals (ie caught on both occasions). The following formula (the **Lincoln index** or **Peterson estimate**) is used to estimate the population size.

$$\text{Estimated population size} = \frac{s_1 \times s_2}{r}$$

where s_1 = number caught in the first sample, s_2 = number caught in the second sample and r = number recaptured (ie caught in both samples)

Note: If the population is very small it is logical to assume that the second sample will contain a high number of marked animals. If the population is large it is probable that only a very small proportion of the recaptured animals in the second sample will be marked.

Detailed procedure for the capture-recapture technique

1. A **large sample** of the species is caught or trapped using an appropriate technique (for example, pitfall trap for beetles, sweep net for grasshoppers).

2. The caught animals are marked in a way that will last over the sampling period (the marking is **permanent** or **semi-permanent** using, for example, waterproof ink, correction fluid or bird ringing).

3. The marking should be done in a way that does not harm the animal or make it any more likely to be **predated** than other non-marked animals. This can be done by marking the animals on their underside which is out of sight to predators.

4. The marked animals are released. There must be sufficient time to allow the animals caught in the first sample to **mix** throughout the overall population.

5. The population is then **re-sampled** using the same trapping process as before and the population size estimated using the Lincoln index formula.

Assumptions: Estimating population size by this method makes a number of assumptions. These include:

- There are no significant gains or losses through immigration or emigration. This can be avoided through carrying out the sampling in a discrete area where mixing with other populations is less likely (for example, sampling the beetles in one wood rather than just part of the wood).

- There are no significant gains or losses through births or deaths.

- The trapping process (or subsequent marking) does not affect the animal in any way (for example, making it more wary of the trapping mechanism and reducing its possibility of being trapped in the re-sample or being more likely to be predated).

- The marked animals have mixed throughout the population by the time of the re-sampling period.

The mark-recapture technique works particularly well for small, mobile animals that are easily trapped such as beetles and grasshoppers.

Exam questions

1. Reindeer (*Rangifer tarandus*) have been introduced to remote oceanic islands to provide a source of meat for sailors on whaling ships.

   (a) On South Georgia, in the South Atlantic Ocean, reindeer were first introduced in 1909. The reindeer graze the lowland grass community of plants when this is not covered by winter snow. In the winter months the deer graze the lichen-rich banks, where less snow accumulates.

   The table shows the plant species present in the lichen-rich banks for an area where there are no reindeer (ungrazed) and where reindeer are present (grazed).

Plant species	Mean percentage cover/%	
	Area ungrazed by reindeer	Area grazed by reindeer
Vascular plants		
Acaena decumbens	9	5
Acaena tenera	4	–
Festuca erecta	17	–
Phleum alpinum	7.5	–
Rostkovia magellanica	5	40
Lichens		
Cetraria islandica	10	–
Cladonia balfourii	4	–
Cladonia carneola	–	2
Cladonia furcata	6	1
Cladonia rangiferina	10	–
Ochrolechia frigida	5	2
Pseudocyphellaria freycinetii	23	5
Psoroma hypnorum	5	3
Stereocaulon glabrum	5	–
Mosses		
Chorisodontium aciphyllum	21.5	40
Polytrichum alpinum	20.5	40
Tortula robusta	4	–

   (i) Comment on the effect of grazing on the diversity of the plant species. [3]

   (ii) It has been suggested that the reindeer population should be totally removed from the island. The killing of reindeer on South Georgia is controversial. Suggest the arguments that biologists might present to justify the killing of the reindeer population. [3]

   (b) A reindeer population was introduced to St Matthew Island in the North Pacific. The climate, with heavy winter snow falls, and the vegetation cover on St Matthew is very similar to that of South Georgia.

   A biologist undertook censuses of the reindeer population on the island in certain years. These showed a huge increase followed by a rapid decline: 29 deer in 1944; 1350 in 1957; 6000 in 1963; and finally only 42 in 1964.

   These population numbers are shown in the graph opposite. The dotted line is the biologist's assumption of the growth curve overall.

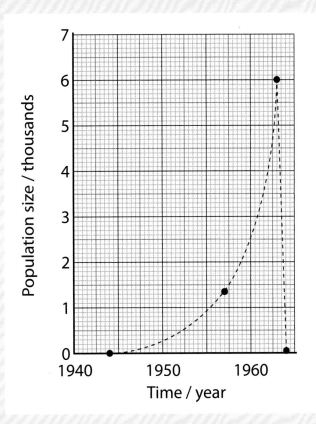

Note: For copyright reasons, this graph has replaced the one that appeared in the original exam paper. Data source: David R Klein 'The introduction, increase, and crash of reindeer on St Matthew Island' Alaska Cooperative Wildlife Research Unit, University of Alaska

(i) Suggest why the biologist chose an exponential curve to represent the growth of the reindeer population up to 1963. [2]

(ii) During the winter of 1963–64 exceptionally high levels of snow occurred. Suggest how the study in South Georgia, described in part (a), may explain the huge decline in the St Matthew population from 1963 to 1964. [2]

(iii) Suggest why these "boom and bust" population changes do not occur in reindeer populations on the mainland. [2]

Question taken from CCEA's Biology Assessment Unit A2 1, Physiology and Ecosystems, January 2011, © CCEA 2013

2. (a) According to their ecological role, plants may be grouped as 'competitors' or 'ruderals' or 'stress tolerators'. The features of each of these groups are summarised in the diagram below.

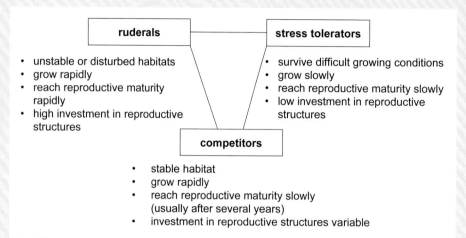

(i) State which group shows characteristics typical of r-selected species. [1]

(ii) Many crop plants, such as carrots and cabbages, are classed as competitors. Suggest why farmers would choose competitors as crop plants rather than ruderals or stress tolerators. [2]

(b) Most crop plants can be affected by pests.

(i) Define what is meant by a 'pest'. [1]

(ii) Describe two disadvantages of using broad spectrum, non-biodegradable pesticides to protect crops. [2]

(c) The use of pesticides can maximise profit for the farmer but will not increase the carrying capacity for a crop species in a particular environment.

Suggest one way in which the farmer can increase the carrying capacity for a crop species. [1]

Question taken from CCEA's Biology Assessment Unit A2 1, Physiology and Ecosystems, May 2011, © CCEA 2013

3. Copy out the following passage about the development of a community over a period of time and write the most appropriate word(s) in the blank spaces to complete the account.

The initial colonisation of bare rock is by _____ species.

Over time as the soil develops, more species colonise the area, a process known as

_____ succession. The final stable community is known as the

_____ community. If this final community is destroyed by fire a

more rapid _____ succession may take place. [4]

Question taken from CCEA's Biology Assessment Unit A2 1, Physiology and Ecosystems, January 2011, © CCEA 2013

4. In most of lowland Britain the natural climax community is broadleaf forest. In more mountainous regions it is mainly moorland.

(a) Define the term 'climatic climax community'. [1]

(b) When an ecosystem such as a forest is destroyed by fire or storm damage, the resulting regrowth is an example of secondary succession.

    (i) Suggest two reasons why secondary succession is usually a quicker process than primary succession. [2]

Secondary succession in a wood destroyed by fire has been investigated over the 20 years immediately following the fire. The table below shows the biomass of a range of plant species (recorded as kg in a 25 m² section of woodland). The species were grouped as herbs, shrubs or trees.

Species	Group (herb, shrub, tree)	Biomass/kg 25 m^{-2} over time			
		5 yr	10 yr	15 yr	20 yr
Birch (*Betula spp.*)	Tree	0.7	5.2	8.9	14.8
Cow parsley (*Anthriscus sylvestris*)	Herb	1.2	0.4	0.2	0.1
Dandelion (*Taraxacum officinale*)	Herb	0.4	0.2	0.1	0.1
Goose grass (*Galium aparine*)	Herb	0.3	0.2	0.1	0.1
Gorse (*Ulex europaeus*)	Shrub	1.3	3.6	2.2	1.4
Hazel (*Corylus avellana*)	Tree	0.9	2.0	2.9	4.3
Heather (*Calluna vulgaris*)	Shrub	0.8	2.9	1.4	0.6
Lords and Ladies (*Arum maculatum*)	Herb	0.5	0.4	0.2	0.2
Nettle (*Urtica dioica*)	Herb	1.4	0.7	0.2	0.2
Rhododendron (*Rhododendron ponticum*)	Tree	0.6	4.2	8.4	12.4

    (ii) Describe and explain the pattern of succession shown. [4]

    (iii) During the investigation, only plant biomass above the ground surface was measured. Suggest reasons for this. [2]

Question taken from CCEA's Biology Assessment Unit A2 1, Physiology and Ecosystems, January 2012, © CCEA 2013

5. An experiment was set up to investigate the growth of a yeast population.

    A small number of yeast cells was allowed to multiply in a nutrient medium. The number of cells was estimated by removing a sample of the population at regular intervals and counting the yeast cells using a haemocytometer slide (shown below).

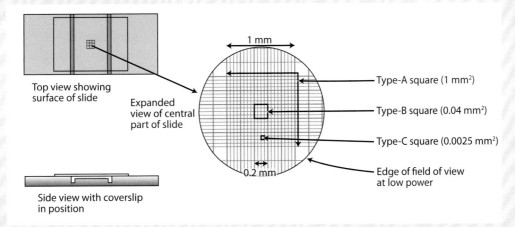

Top view showing surface of slide

Expanded view of central part of slide

Side view with coverslip in position

1 mm

Type-A square (1 mm²)

Type-B square (0.04 mm²)

Type-C square (0.0025 mm²)

Edge of field of view at low power

0.2 mm

Note: For copyright reasons, this image has replaced the one that appeared in the original exam paper.

  (a) The samples removed need to be representative of the yeast population at the time of sampling. Suggest how this is achieved. [1]

The diagram below represents four type-C squares from a haemocytometer slide. The distance between the surface of these type-C squares and the overlying coverslip is 0.1 mm.

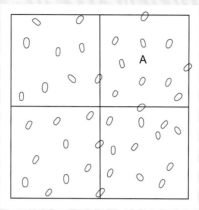

(b) (i) Count the number of yeast cells in the type-C square marked A. [1]

(ii) Using your answer from (b)(i) above, calculate the number of yeast cells per mm³.
(Show your working.) [2]

(c) Towards the end of the experiment there may be too many yeast cells to clearly see the grid lines on the haemocytometer slide.

Suggest how such a dense population might be treated to enable a count to be made, and how this count would subsequently be used to obtain an estimate of the population size. [2]

The population was sampled daily and the results are shown in the graph below.

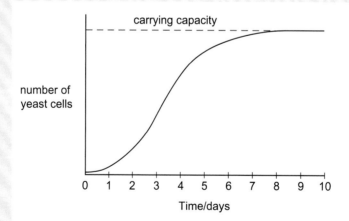

(d) Make a copy of the graph shown above.

(i) Suggest an appropriate title for the graph. [1]

(ii) Indicate on the graph with the letter X, the point at which the growth rate of the population was greatest. [1]

(iii) Explain what is meant by the term 'carrying capacity' shown on the graph. [1]

Question taken from CCEA's Biology Assessment Unit A2 1, Physiology and Ecosystems, May 2010, © CCEA 2013

6. Graph A below illustrates how the application of insecticides may protect an orchard by reducing the numbers of the potentially crop-damaging leaf roller moth, *Acleris rhombana*. Graph B shows how a break in the application of the insecticide protects other orchard-dwelling animals such as the mites, *Tetranychus uriticae* and *Stethorus punctum*.

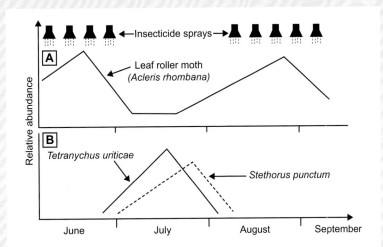

An orchard is an example of a "monoculture". Explain why monocultures are particularly susceptible to pest infestations. [1]

The insecticide used in the orchard is biodegradable.

    (i) Identify one piece of evidence that suggests this insecticide is biodegradable. [1]

    (ii) Explain why the use of a biodegradable insecticide is safer for the environment. [1]

Spraying of the insecticide does not take place during the month of July so as not to affect other orchard species such as the mites, *Tetranychus uriticae* and *Stethorus punctum*. One of these species of mite is an important pest of the fruit trees which can cause blemishing of the orchard fruit. The other species is its predator.

(c) Use the information in Graph B to help you to determine which mite species is the predator. Explain your answer. [2]

By not spraying insecticide in July, the population of predatory mites remains high and so reduces blemishing of the orchard fruit by keeping the pest population low.

(d) (i) Name the type of pest control illustrated by this example. [1]
    (ii) Suggest one advantage of such a pest control system. [1]

    (iii) Suggest one possible disadvantage of this form of pest control. [1]

Biologists interested in the efficiency of such a pest control system may need to estimate the population of the leaf roller moths in the orchard using the mark/recapture technique.

(e) (i) Describe how the biologists would carry out the mark/recapture technique to allow them to estimate the size of the population of moths. [3]

    (ii) Suggest one assumption which must be fulfilled in order to obtain a valid estimate of the population size. [1]

Question taken from CCEA's Biology Assessment Unit A2 1, Physiology and Ecosystems, January 2010, © CCEA 2013

7. Scientists discovered a new species of grasshopper in a meadow habitat.

The grasshoppers were difficult to spot, being well camouflaged in the leaves of the tall grass and herbs typical of the habitat. The grasshoppers of this species appeared to be particularly mobile. Although poor fliers, they frequently 'hop' between the leaves and stalks of the meadow plants, often moving considerable distances. When not feeding on plant leaves, or moving between plants, they often rest on the leaves and use the heat from the sun to raise their body temperature.

The scientists wanted to estimate the population size of the grasshoppers belonging to the new species in the meadow by using a mark/recapture technique. This involved taking an initial sample, marking the grasshoppers and releasing them back into the population; followed by taking a subsequent sample to determine the number of those recaptured.

(a) Suggest how the scientists could capture and mark the initial sample of grasshoppers. Your answer should describe the sampling procedure used, the technique used to capture the insects and the marking procedure. [4]

(b) Having released the marked grasshoppers, the scientists collected a subsequent sample for analysis the following day.

(i) Explain why the subsequent sample should not be taken immediately after the initial sample. [1]

(ii) Suggest two distinct reasons for obtaining a subsequent sample for analysis so quickly (one day later) after the initial sample was taken. [2]

(c) The table below shows the results obtained from the survey.

Sample	Total number of grasshoppers	Number of marked grasshoppers
Initial sample (caught and marked)	64	64
Subsequent sample (caught for analysis)	42	8

Calculate the estimated population rise of grasshoppers in the meadow. (Show your working.) [2]

(d) It was proposed that the meadow be designated as a nature reserve since it contained a new species of grasshopper.

Suggest what further work should be carried out by the scientists before recommending special protection for the grasshoppers. [1]

(e) It was noted that the grasshoppers "use the heat from the sun to raise their body temperature". Suggest reasons for this behaviour. [3]

Question taken from CCEA's Biology Assessment Unit A2 1, Physiology and Ecosystems, May 2012, © CCEA 2013

Chapter 7 – Ecological Energetics and Nutrient Cycling

The organisms belonging to the populations that make up the community in any ecosystem are usually interrelated at many levels. In the previous chapter we reviewed how the organisms associated with one sere modify the environment making it more suitable for the organisms in the subsequent sere. The feeding relationships that exist within an ecosystem are another very obvious, and important, example of the links between the different individuals, and species, in an ecosystem.

Energy Flow

Feeding involves the **transfer of energy** between living things. Some key terms relating to the feeding relationships and transfer of energy in ecosystems are described and explained in the next section.

Food chains and food webs

Producers are organisms that manufacture **organic substances** from **inorganic substances** using energy. Almost all producers (plants) use light energy to produce organic compounds by photosynthesis.

> **Note:** A very small number of producer species, the **chemoautotrophs**, use chemical energy (rather than light) to produce organic compounds from inorganic materials. Examples include some species of bacteria that live in deep cave systems far from available light (and with no possibility of organic content seeping into the system from above). These bacteria are able to make organic substances using the minerals in the rock as a source of chemical energy. Communities in these ecosystems have only been able to develop and survive as the producers have evolved an energy source other than light. Nitrifying bacteria are also chemoautotrophs – we will meet these later in the chapter.

Consumers are organisms that obtain their energy by feeding on other organisms. Animals are consumers. **Primary consumers** feed on producers (plants). **Secondary consumers** being next in the link feed on primary consumers. **Tertiary consumers** feed on secondary consumers. Primary consumers are also called **herbivores** (plant feeders) and secondary and tertiary consumers are **carnivores** as they feed on other animals.

Decomposers and **detritivores** are groups of organisms involved in **decay** and **decomposition**. While energy flows through an ecosystem as a consequence of photosynthesis by producers and the subsequent feeding relationships involved, the flow through the **detritus pathway** is equally important. **Decomposers**, e.g. bacteria and fungi, and **detritivores** (small animals such as earthworms, millipedes, springtails and woodlice) are important groups of organisms involved in decay and decomposition.

Food chains and **food webs** – A **food chain** shows the link between a producer, a primary consumer, a secondary consumer and possibly a tertiary consumer as shown in the example below. Each stage is referred to as a **trophic level** with producers being at the first trophic level and primary consumers at the second trophic level and so on.

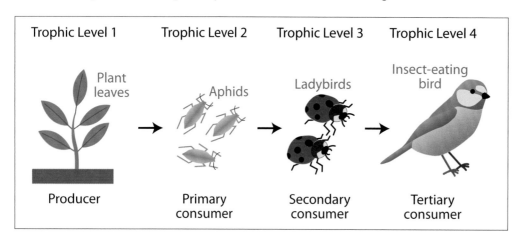

A food chain with four trophic levels

In reality, food chains are usually not a realistic representation of the feeding relationships involved as most animals do not rely on a single food source – this would be far too risky in most ecosystems. A **food web** is the pattern of interrelated 'food chains' that operate in an ecosystem. In complex ecosystems such as the climax community stage, food webs tend to be very complex involving many different species.

The quantitative relationships between trophic levels

Food chains and food webs are useful in that they show the path of energy flow but they do not provide any information concerning the number, or biomass, of organisms at each trophic level, i.e. the **quantitative relationships**. The relative number, biomass, or even energy of the organisms involved can be represented through the display of **ecological pyramids**.

Pyramids of numbers – a pyramid of numbers represents the total **number** of organisms at each trophic level in a food chain or web. The length of the bars in a pyramid of numbers is usually drawn proportional to the number at each level (the depth of bars should be the same for each level). Normally as there will be more organisms at the producer level than there are primary consumers and so on, this gives a pyramid shape, hence the term pyramid of numbers.

Pyramids of numbers are often a very simplified or inaccurate picture of the energy flow between trophic levels. They do not take account of the **size** of the organism. The diagram on the next page shows an example of a 'typical' pyramid of numbers representing a common food chain in grassland (**a**) and an inverted pyramid from woodland (**b**).

A pyramid of numbers

Numbers decrease

Tertiary consumers

Secondary consumers

Primary consumers

Producers

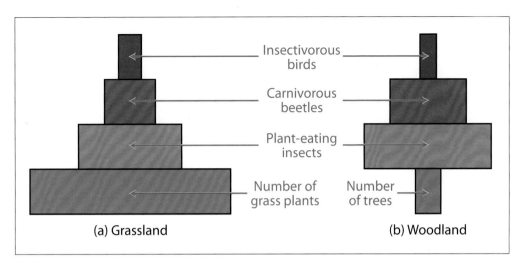

'Typical' and inverted pyramids of number

(a) Grassland — Insectivorous birds, Carnivorous beetles, Plant-eating insects, Number of grass plants

(b) Woodland — Insectivorous birds, Carnivorous beetles, Plant-eating insects, Number of trees

When **very large numbers** are involved at any trophic level it is very difficult, or impossible, to scale the bars accurately. For example one large oak tree may have several million insects operating as primary consumers.

Pyramids of biomass – pyramids of biomass represent the **biomass** of the organisms at a particular trophic level in a food chain or food web. Biomass can be measured as fresh mass or dry mass. Fresh mass is more variable but will still normally give an accurate representation. Dry mass (drying the organism(s) until constant mass is achieved) is more accurate but time consuming and also means that the organisms are killed in the process.

With a pyramid of biomass (as with a pyramid of numbers) only the organisms present at any one time (the **standing crop**) are considered. Consequently, inverted pyramids of biomass can result, but for different reasons than pyramids of numbers. Inverted pyramids of biomass are much less common than inverted pyramids of numbers.

Commonly used examples include some marine or aquatic pyramids of biomass as they do not take into account the biomass over the whole year but only represent an instantaneous value. In early spring the biomass of zooplankton (protoctistans and small animals that feed on phytoplankton) may exceed that of the phytoplankton. The food web is only sustainable because the phytoplankton reproduce at such a rapid rate that their numbers are quickly replenished.

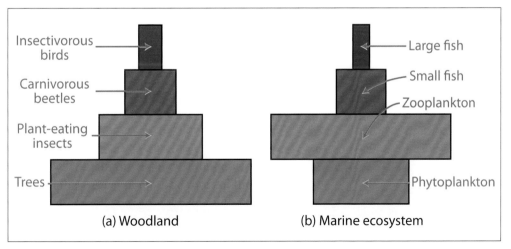

'Typical' and inverted pyramids of biomass

(a) Woodland — Insectivorous birds, Carnivorous beetles, Plant-eating insects, Trees

(b) Marine ecosystem — Large fish, Small fish, Zooplankton, Phytoplankton

Pyramids of biomass are **more representative** than pyramids of number but their disadvantages include problems with obtaining the data required – we have already noted the problems associated with dry mass but how do you obtain even the fresh mass of an oak tree? Additionally, pyramids of biomass can sometimes give a false picture of the amount of energy available to be transferred. A single oak tree can provide food for millions of leaf eating insects as described above, but should the value represented in the pyramid be the mass of the entire tree or just the edible leaves?

Pyramids of energy (productivity) – The term productivity means how much new material is produced. Pyramids of energy reflect the new material produced (productivity) over a period of time. Pyramids of energy give the **most accurate** representation of the energy at a particular level but the values are more **difficult to obtain** as values need to be obtained over a time period to compare the before and after.

The data may be presented as kJ m^{-2} y^{-1} (kilojoules per square metre per year) and this indicates how much new material, represented as the energy it contains, is produced in a square metre of ecosystem over the period of one year. Pyramids of energy are particularly useful in comparing ecosystems (including agricultural ecosystems). Stable ecosystems will always represent energy flow as a pyramid.

The efficiency of energy flow through ecosystems

As the Sun is the ultimate energy source for all ecosystems, photosynthesis is the principal route by which the energy is made available to the communities within the ecosystem.

However, only a very small percentage of the energy reaching the Earth's atmosphere is used by producers to make organic compounds in the process of photosynthesis and even less is available to consumers. The following sections explain why energy flow can be relatively inefficient.

Energy losses between the Sun and the plants - Less that 1% of the Sun's energy reaching the atmosphere is available to plants for a number of reasons as over 90% of the energy is **reflected** back into space by dust particles or clouds or is **absorbed** by the water vapour or dust in the atmosphere and then re-radiated as heat energy.

Of the small percentage of the Sun's energy reaching the surface of the Earth only a small proportion of this is used as most will fall on bare ground and will therefore **miss the leaves of a plant**. As much as 99.9% of the light energy **reaching** the Earth's surface will not be available to plants for this reason.

Of the Sun's energy that actually strikes a **leaf**, most is lost through:

- being **reflected** from the surface of leaves – this process is often exacerbated by the presence of a thick waxy cuticle (a necessary compromise between maximising light harvesting and reducing water loss)

- some energy is used in the **evaporation** of water (on the leaf surface)

- missing the **chloroplasts** within the leaf. Although the chloroplasts are arranged in the cells of the palisade layer to trap as much light as possible, the volume of a palisade cell consisting of chloroplasts is very small

- over half of the light reaching the leaves is of the **wrong wavelength**. Most plants have pigments that absorb the blue and red parts of the visible spectrum with the green part of the spectrum being reflected

- the **photosynthetic (photochemical) reactions** are **inefficient** with much of the energy being lost as heat

Between **0.5 and 1%** of the incident light that **reaches the leaf surface** will be converted into chemical energy (organic compounds) as a result of photosynthesis.

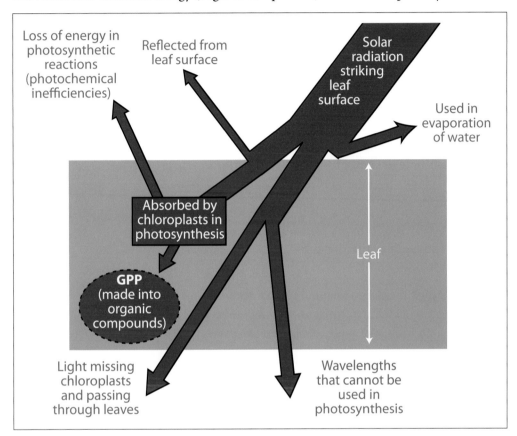

The fate of light energy reaching the leaf surface

Gross Primary Production and Net Primary Production - the energy in the organic compounds produced by plants in photosynthesis is called the **gross primary production (GPP).** However, plants use up to 50% of the GPP in **respiration (R).** The remainder, the **net primary production (NPP),** is available for plant growth, or for the other trophic levels in the ecosystem should the plant die or be eaten.

Therefore NPP = GPP – R

Note 1: GPP or NPP is often represented as kilojoules per square metre per year ($kJ\ m^{-2}\ y^{-1}$) as it is usually taken to represent the energy in the ecosystem as opposed to being a calculation based on individual plants. GPP and NPP are indicators of the **productivity** of an ecosystem.

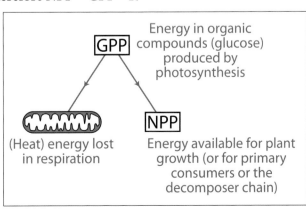

The relationship between gross primary production, net primary production and respiration

Note 2: In terrestrial (land based) ecosystems the GPP (and NPP) is generally limited by temperature and moisture – the most productive natural ecosystems are tropical swamps and tropical forests where both temperature and moisture availability are approaching optimum levels. In aquatic and marine ecosystems, nutrient (mineral) availability is often the limiting resource.

Energy transfer between producers and consumers – the transfer of energy between producers and primary consumers and among consumers is much more efficient than the conversion of solar energy into organic compounds. Nonetheless, it is still relatively inefficient.

The least efficient stage is between **producers and primary consumers** (typically between 5-10%). Much plant material **cannot be accessed**, e.g. plant roots and tree trunks are not grazed to the extent that succulent and accessible leaves are. Much plant material is **very difficult to digest** – very few species have the enzymes necessary to digest cellulose. Therefore, herbivores typically can only assimilate a small percentage of the plant material they eat with considerable quantities of indigested material being egested. **Excretory losses** also contribute to energy losses – metabolic waste, e.g. urea, is excreted and this represents energy that is not available to be transferred to the next trophic level.

Much of the organic content that is eaten by primary consumers is used in **respiration** to generate ATP. The energy 'lost' through respiration is lost as '**heat**' – heat is produced as a byproduct of the respiratory process.

Respiratory losses are particularly high in mammals and birds (**endotherms**). The maintenance of a high and constant body temperature requires high metabolic activity and consequently high levels of respiration and unavoidable heat loss.

Additionally, some plants (or plant parts, e.g. leaves from deciduous trees in autumn) enter the **decomposer food chain** and are not available to primary consumers.

Energy transfer between consumers – energy transfer between animals (consumers) is more efficient (typically between 10 – 20%) than between plants and herbivores. Generally, more of an animal can be eaten and digested. However, again only a small proportion of the energy in any animal will be built up into organic compounds in the next trophic level due to excretory losses, or being used in respiration or through death and entry into the decomposer food chain.

Energy flow through the different trophic levels of a food chain

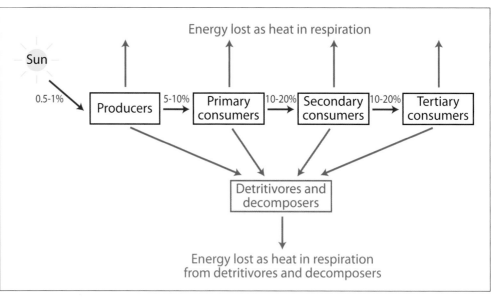

Note 1: The values used in the diagram on page 112 are very approximate. The actual amount of energy that flows (and is lost) in a particular ecosystem depends on the species involved and may vary considerably from the 'typical' values used here.

Note 2: There are typically no more than three steps in a food chain (and very seldom more than four or five) due to the inefficiency of energy transfer and the huge efficiency losses that take place at each step.

Note 3: The transfer of energy through trophic levels is **energy flow**. It is not a cycle – energy needs to continually enter the system from the Sun.

Implications for agriculture

Agricultural ecosystems are particularly important in Northern Ireland. These ecosystems can be crop or animal based. For both crop and livestock systems, key aims are the increased efficiency of energy transfer into the crops (and animals) and the reduction of losses due to respiration, through unwanted consumption by consumers or losses through the decomposer pathway.

There is much investment in increasing agricultural **productivity**.

Increasing primary productivity in plants – plant (crop) growth can be increased by removing or reducing the limiting factors affecting growth. This can be done artificially in, e.g. glasshouses by providing extra light, heat and carbon dioxide. However, most crops are grown outside and the most realistic way of increasing productivity is through the use of **fertiliser** and reducing the effect of **pests**.

Fertilisers typically contain nitrogen, phosphorus and potassium (NPK), elements needed to stimulate plant growth. Both the use of fertilisers and the use of pesticides have ecological implications and will be discussed further in the next chapter.

Productivity can also be enhanced through the **appropriate spacing of crops** in a field. Sowing seeds at the optimum density ensures that competition between adjacent crop plants is reduced yet allows the crop to maximise coverage of the land used – another delicate balancing act.

Even spacing of maize for maximum productivity

Intensive farming of domestic livestock – the general principle is that by making energy conversion more efficient and restricting energy losses, where possible, more energy (meat products) will be available to humans.

Intensive farming of domestic livestock often involves the **confinement** of the animals to very specific areas – this can be cattle in a fenced-off section of a field or pigs in an outhouse ensuring that less energy is used in movement. Keeping cattle in a small section of a field also ensures that less land is utilised at any one time and that manure from the animals is more evenly spread over the land.

Keeping animals indoors in **warm conditions** (much of the warmth, in all but the coldest conditions, is often produced by the animals themselves) reduces the energy required to produce heat and maintain body temperature.

The use of **high energy** foods such a silage and **high protein** foods (e.g. soya meal) are other measures geared to increasing productivity.

Note: What exactly is silage? Silage is cut grass that is chopped into small pieces and stored in anaerobic conditions. The anaerobic conditions can be produced through covering the silage by large sheets of plastic (often held in place by old tyres) or through producing plastic covered bales. Microorganisms respire in the anaerobic conditions created and produce lactic acid. The low pH as a consequence of lactic acid buildup restricts other (decomposing) microbial growth thus preserving the high nutrient status of the grass throughout the winter. The grass can be cut several times during the growing period and preserved as silage at the time when it is most productive and nutritious and therefore provides a highly nutritious winter fodder (at a time when other sources are in short supply).

The intensive farming of domestic livestock raises many **ethical** issues (intensively farmed animals suffer high stress levels and often bone and joint damage; hooves of cattle did not evolve for movement on concrete, especially slats!) but also **management** issues. **Disease** is much more

Baled silage

likely to spread rapidly when animals are confined in close proximity. The overuse of antibiotics to control (and often to prevent) disease has been significant in the spread of **antibiotic resistance** in bacteria. Reduced **genetic diversity** results through the selective breeding of the most productive and profitable varieties. Increased **pollution** from the increased use of fossil fuels or general farmland waste is another consequence.

Energy efficiency and the human diet - The production of animal products is much less efficient than using crops. The inefficiency of energy transfer through food chains means that much more energy is available to humans through eating plant products rather than animal products. In effect, each human who eats meat as a significant part of his / her diet requires much more land to produce the food required than does a vegetarian. For this reason very highly populated countries such as some of those found in parts of Asia have human populations that have a staple diet of plant products, e.g. rice, with meat being an uncommon luxury. In much of Europe and North America, meat products are more commonly used. Due to the inefficiency of eating meat products, this is possible only through the relatively low population densities involved, e.g. France, or through importing meat from other countries, e.g. as happens in Britain.

Productivity in animals (secondary productivity) – the energy used in the production of new tissue in animals is referred to as **secondary productivity**. Crop farmers are concerned with increasing primary productivity (crop growth) but farmers of livestock are concerned with both primary productivity (if producing own animal feeds) and secondary productivity in the animals themselves.

The efficiency of secondary productivity can be worked out using **energy budgets**.

In the worked example below, the net secondary productivity (**P**) is the energy consumed (**C**) minus the energy lost through respiration (**R**), faeces (**F**) and urine (**U**).

$$P = C - (R + U + F)$$

In intensive farming, maximising **P** (by using high energy foods) and reducing any of **R**, **U** and/or **F** (most easily done with **R** by e.g. confinement) can lead to increases in growth and profit.

Nutrient Cycling

In the previous section we reviewed **energy** flow in ecosystems, a process that requires the input of energy from the Sun. However, there is no input of **nutrients** from another source, therefore the finite supply we have on Earth is **recycled** through ecosystems. The recycling of nutrients can be considered in terms of the recycling of the elements they contain, for example, **carbon** and **nitrogen**.

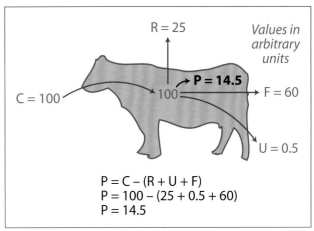

The energy budget of a bullock

R = 25
Values in arbitrary units
C = 100
P = 14.5
F = 60
U = 0.5
P = C – (R + U + F)
P = 100 – (25 + 0.5 + 60)
P = 14.5

There are many similarities between the flow of energy and the recycling of nutrients. The recycling of nutrients also involves transfer from producer to consumer, between consumers, and through the decomposer chain. The key difference is that the nutrient enters the producer from **within** the ecosystem (e.g. plants absorbing carbon dioxide from the atmosphere for photosynthesis). In this section we will consider the carbon and nitrogen cycles.

The carbon cycle

Carbon is an essential component of all the major macromolecules found in living organisms – essentially the 'building block of life'. Carbon is recycled through the processes of photosynthesis and respiration, the two key biochemical processes in the evolution of life. In **photosynthesis**, producers (plants) are able to fix inorganic carbon dioxide and incorporate it into a range of organic products. In **respiration**, organic products such as carbohydrates, fats and proteins (all containing carbon) are broken down to produce ATP, with carbon dioxide being released as a waste product.

Consumers gain carbon through **feeding**. Both plant and animal tissue are rich in carbon and complex organic compounds are broken down and built up in the ongoing cycle of feeding, digestion and the assimilation of food products in animals.

Saprobiotic microorganisms (decomposers) break down the organic molecules 'trapped' in dead organisms during **decay** and **decomposition** and release the carbon as carbon dioxide, again in the process of respiration.

However, at certain stages of the Earth's history some dead organisms have been preserved in environments hostile to decay (**fossilisation**). Fossil fuels such as coal and peat contain 'locked in' carbon that has not been released as the process of decay and decomposition could not take place. This carbon is released (often many millions of years later) by the process of **combustion**.

The following diagram summarises the carbon cycle.

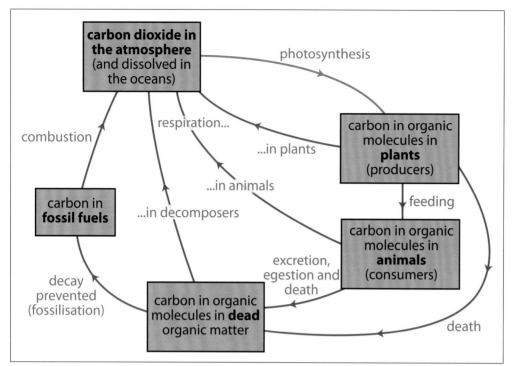

The carbon cycle

Note: The world's oceans contain a vast reserve of carbon dioxide dissolved in water as hydrogencarbonate (HCO_3^-) ions. This acts as a buffer being able to take up (or return) carbon dioxide from or to the atmosphere.

It was the evolution of plants in the Earth's geological history that was largely responsible for producing the oxygen, through photosynthesis, that provided the levels of atmospheric oxygen needed to sustain complex animal life. In recent millenia, the balance between photosynthesis and respiration has remained fairly stable although there are short term fluctuations, e.g. between summer and winter and between night and day.

However, over the last few centuries, there has been an increase in atmospheric carbon dioxide levels. The main reasons for this are an increase in the combustion of fossil fuels and deforestation. The implications of this on the carbon cycle will be discussed in more detail in the next chapter.

The nitrogen cycle

A source of nitrogen is necessary for living organisms to make the nitrogen-containing compounds essential for life. These include proteins, the nitrogenous bases in nucleic acids (DNA and RNA) and ATP.

The nitrogen normally enters the producers (plants) as **nitrate ions** (NO_3^-), absorbed from the soil by the process of active transport. Within the plants the nitrate is then used to build the nitrogen-containing organic compounds such as amino acids and nucleotides and subsequently into compounds such as those listed in the previous paragraph.

The nitrogen-containing compounds in plants enter the consumer pathway when eaten by animals. Eventually the nitrogen-containing compounds are excreted (e.g. as urea), egested in faeces, or end up in non-living organic matter following death.

Decay and decomposition by saprobiotic microorganisms is necessary to recycle the nitrogen contained in dead organisms, excreta and faeces to its usable inorganic form (nitrate), a process called **mineralisation**. The decay / decomposition and mineralisation of nitrogen-containing compounds involves two distinct stages, ammonification and nitrification.

Ammonification – this **decay** stage ends with the production of **ammonium ions** (NH_4^+) or ammonia (NH_3). Decomposing microorganisms (fungi and bacteria) use the nitrogen-rich compounds (e.g. protein, urea, or in faeces) as food and eventually break them down into ammonium ions or ammonia.

> **Note:** The process of decay (ammonification) is aided by the action of detritivores such as earthworms. The detritivores feed on the dead organisms breaking them into small pieces (with larger surface area) and help distribute the dead material through the soil.

Nitrification – nitrification is the conversion of **ammonium ions / ammonia** to **nitrate**. The process is carried out in two stages by **nitrifying bacteria**.

- In the first stage nitrifying bacteria of the genus *Nitrosomonas* oxidise ammonium ions / ammonia to **nitrite ions** (NO_2^-).

- In the second stage nitrifying bacteria of the genus *Nitrobacter* oxidise nitrite ions to **nitrate ions** (NO_3^-).

> **Note:** The nitrifying bacteria are chemoautotrophs. They obtain their energy from the oxidation reactions involved rather than the Sun.

As oxidiation reactions are involved, **nitrifying bacteria need oxygen** (the process is **aerobic**) to carry out the process of nitrification. The nitrates produced by nitrification are available in the soil to be absorbed by plants and the cycle continues.

The processes already reviewed as part of the nitrogen cycle are summarised in the following diagram.

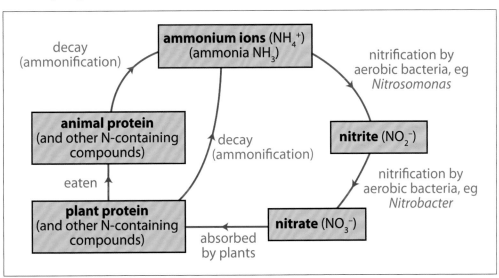

A simplified nitrogen cycle

Superimposed on the basic process involved in the cycle above, two other processes, **nitrogen fixation** and **denitrification** are important in the recycling of nitrogen.

Nitrogen fixation – in nitrogen fixation, **nitrogen-fixing bacteria** convert nitrogen gas into nitrogen-containing compounds. The bacteria are mainly of the genus *Rhizobium* and they contain the enzyme **nitrogenase** responsible for fixing the nitrogen. Some species of nitrogen-fixing bacteria are **aerobic** and some are **anaerobic**.

The nitrogen-fixing bacteria can be **free living** in the soil or may form **mutualistic** relationships with a number of plant species. Legumes (e.g. beans, peas and clover) contain nitrogen-fixing bacteria in **root nodules**. The legumes gain by obtaining nitrogen-containing compounds from the bacteria and the bacteria have a stable environment and a ready supply of carbohydrate.

Clearly nitrogen fixation is a very beneficial process as it enriches the soil. Farmers make use of this fact by growing legumes and allowing them to decay in the soil as part of a crop rotation cycle. The value of nitrogen fixation in crop systems can be very significant - white clover can provide as much as 150 kg ha^{-1} y^{-1} of nitrogen in agricultural grasslands.

> **Note 1:** Nitrogen fixation also takes place as a result of **lightning**. The lightning breaks the bonds holding the two atoms together in atmospheric nitrogen (N_2) and the N-compounds formed then dissolve in rain water. However, the amount of nitrogen fixed by this method is insignificant compared to that fixed by microorganisms.

> **Note 2:** As well as farmers making use of nitrogen-fixing microorganisms, nitrogen fixation is also important **ecologically**. Nitrogen fixers are important colonisers of barren land as they can survive in nitrogen-deficient soils.

Denitrification – denitrification is the process whereby **denitrifying bacteria** convert nitrates into atmospheric nitrogen. This is a harmful process that can significantly reduce soil fertility. Unlike nitrifying and some nitrogen-fixing bacteria, denitrifying bacteria e.g. *Pseudomonas*, are **anaerobic**. Anaerobic conditions are particularly likely to occur if the soil is compacted or waterlogged. Consequently, denitrifying bacteria are more numerous and more active in waterlogged or very compacted soils that are deficient in oxygen.

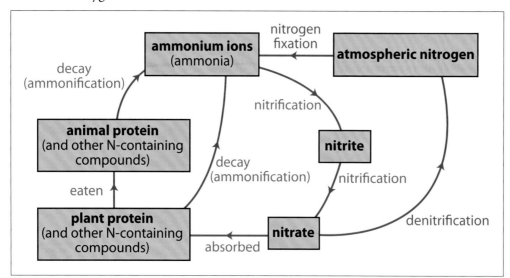

The nitrogen cycle

> **Note:** The role of earthworms (and other detritivores) in decay was noted in an earlier section. Earthworms provide additional benefits in that their burrows aerate the soil (encouraging nitrification and nitrogen fixing activity) and also drain the soil (reducing the activity of denitrifying bacteria).

Exam questions

1. The diagram below shows the productivity at various trophic levels in an ecosystem. All productivity values are in kJ $m^{-2}y^{-1}$.

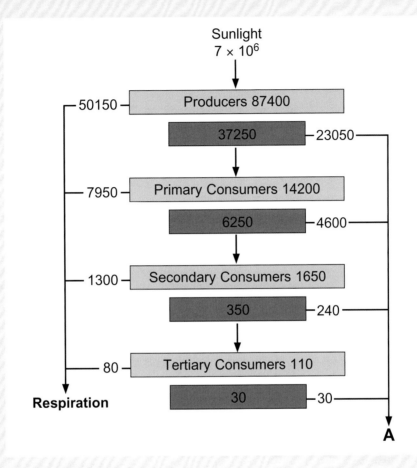

Key

Gross productivity

Productivity minus energy used in respiration

(a) (i) Using the information in the diagram, state the following values.

- NPP (net primary productivity)
- The energy available to carnivores [2]

(ii) State **two** processes which may result in the losses shown by arrow **A**. [2]

(b) The energy transfers shown in the diagram are for a natural meadow ecosystem. Suggest how energy transfer would differ in a field of grass cut, on several occasions during the year, and removed for the production of silage. [3]

Question taken from CCEA's Biology Assessment Unit A2 1, Physiology and Ecosystems, May 2010, © CCEA 2013

2. The diagram below shows the transfer of energy in an agricultural ecosystem prior to harvesting. The figures are in kJ m^{-2} year^{-1}.

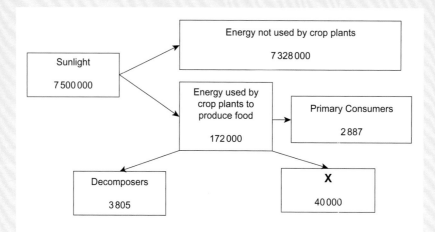

(a) (i) Calculate the percentage of sunlight trapped as GPP. (Show your working.) [2]

   (ii) State **two** reasons why the energy transfer from sunlight to the producers (crop plants) is so low. [2]

   (iii) Suggest what process X represents. [1]

(b) The data in the diagram was obtained from a crop-based agricultural ecosystem. Using the information in the diagram, identify one piece of evidence for this and explain your reasoning. [2]

Question taken from CCEA's Biology Assessment Unit A2 1, Physiology and Ecosystems, May 2012, © CCEA 2013

3. During photosynthesis by green plants, light energy is converted into chemical energy, some of which is subsequently used in respiration.

(a) The diagram below shows the fate of incident light energy on 1 m^2 of grass. (Units kJ m^{-2} y^{-1}.)

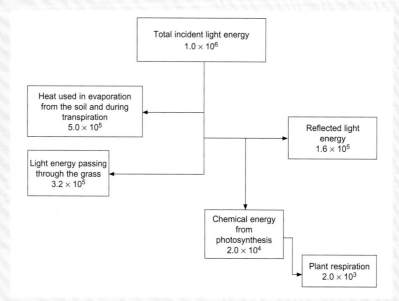

(i) Calculate the percentage of the total incident light energy which is converted into chemical energy. Show your working. [2]

(ii) Define the term Net Primary Production (NPP). [1]

(iii) Calculate NPP for the grass. [1]

(b) The processes of photosynthesis and respiration are both influenced by temperature. The graph below shows NPP of grass at different temperatures.

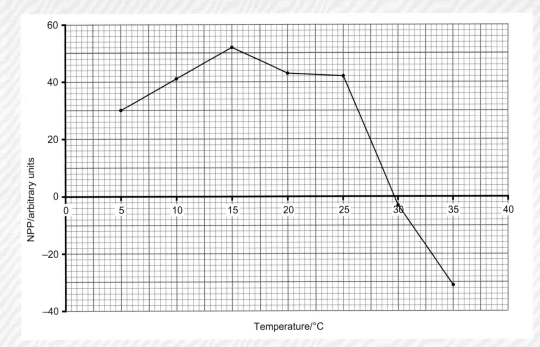

(i) Explain the negative NPP values above 30 °C. [2]

(ii) Early summer temperatures are in the range 5 to 20 °C. Explain why grass is a suitable species for cropping as silage in early summer. [1]

(c) Explain **two** advantages of using silage to feed cattle over allowing the cattle to graze the field. [2]

Question taken from CCEA's Biology Assessment Unit A2 1, Physiology and Ecosystems, January 2011, © CCEA 2013

4. The photograph below shows part of a lake surrounded by forest which is the climax community in this environment. An imaginary transect line has been drawn from the lake, at point **A,** to the edge of forest at point **C.** Along this transect line there is evidence of succession.

Source: Principal Examiner

(a) Explain what is meant by the terms 'succession' and 'climax community'. [2]

(b) Some of the plants have been labelled. Using the information in the photograph, describe and explain the process of succession that is suggested along the transect line from point **A** to point **C.** [4]

(c) In the photograph both vetch and alder have been identified. Both these plants have the ability to fix nitrogen.

(i) Explain the meaning of the term 'nitrogen fixation'. [1]

(ii) Explain how the subsequent decay of vetch and alder leaves may help to increase the level of nitrate available to other plants. [3]

Question taken from CCEA's Biology Assessment Unit A2 1, Physiology and Ecosystems, May 2011, © CCEA 2013

Chapter 8 – The Effect of Human Activity on the Environment

Students should be able to:

4.4.15	State the source / cause of specific pollutants and understand the effects of these pollutants on food chains / the environment and human health
4.4.16	Appreciate traditional farming methods
4.4.17	Appreciate the adverse impact of intensive farming methods
4.4.18	Understand the particular problems of agricultural pollution in NI
4.4.19	Appreciate strategies to reduce the risk of eutrophication in water bodies due to leaching of artificial fertilisers
4.4.20	Understand that sustainable farming depends on the effective management of the conflict between increased food production and the need for environmental conservation
4.4.21	Understand the concept of managed timber production as a sustainable resource

All organisms interact with their environment but it is the human species that interacts to the extent that we are modifying the environment in a way that affects all life on Earth. The large, and increasing, impact we are having can be traced to two main factors – our rapidly expanding population and our increasing use of technology. Human activity has its significant effects on land, water and air ecosystems.

Atmospheric pollution

Air pollution involves the introduction of substances into the atmosphere that harms living organisms or changes the environment in a non-beneficial way. In some situations the substance is only harmful because it is present in unnaturally high concentrations, e.g. carbon dioxide and global warming. Global warming, ozone depletion and acid rain are all consequences of air pollution.

Global warming

In the last chapter we reviewed the carbon cycle. For millions of years the carbon cycle has remained relatively balanced with the carbon dioxide removed from the atmosphere in photosynthesis being approximately the same as the carbon dioxide added in respiration (and relatively small scale combustion). However, in the last few centuries two major changes have taken place.

- Increased **combustion** of fossil fuels for domestic, but more significantly industrial, use pumps much more carbon dioxide into the atmosphere.

- **Deforestation** on a major scale to create land for farming, industry or urban development has reduced the amount of photosynthesis taking place and consequently the removal of carbon dioxide from the atmosphere. Additionally, trees that have been removed to clear space are often burned, further adding to atmospheric levels of carbon dioxide.

These changes have resulted in the carbon cycle becoming **unbalanced** and the concentrations of carbon dioxide in the atmosphere have increased as a result.

The link between increasing carbon dioxide and global warming – there is clear evidence that atmospheric carbon dioxide levels are increasing. Carbon dioxide levels in the atmosphere are approximately 390 parts per million (ppm) today compared with a level of under 300 ppm two hundred years ago, an increase of around 30%. In some parts of the world the increase in average temperature has exceeded 2 °C over the last 100 years. Furthermore the rate of increase is increasing and is now almost 0.2 °C per decade.

There is clear evidence that there is a close **positive correlation** between increasing carbon dioxide and global temperature. Where the debate lies is whether the increase in carbon dioxide level is the only, or major, cause of increasing atmospheric temperatures. There is no doubt that carbon dioxide is a 'greenhouse' gas. Consequently, most of the scientific community believes that increasing carbon dioxide levels is the main cause of global warming.

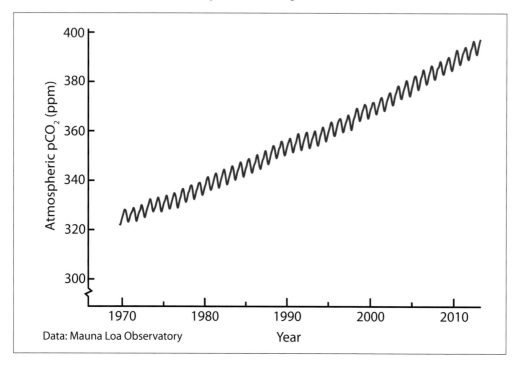

Changing atmospheric levels of carbon dioxide over the last 40 years

Note: The diagram above shows how atmospheric carbon dioxide levels are rising. The annual fluctuations reflect the higher winter (compared to summer) levels due to reduced photosynthesis and increased combustion of fossil fuels for heating.

The 'greenhouse effect': the cause of global warming - carbon dioxide and other 'greenhouse' gases form a layer (the 'greenhouse' layer) in the atmosphere that traps heat. Relatively short(er) wave solar radiation (mainly visible light and ultraviolet (UV) radiation) reaches the Earth's surface; however the radiation emitted from the Earth into the atmosphere is long(er) wave (infrared) radiation (heat). Some of this longer wave radiation escapes the Earth's atmosphere and enters Space but some is trapped by the greenhouse layer, reflected back and retained in the Earth's atmosphere as shown in the diagram below. This reflected and retained heat results in the atmospheric temperatures rising.

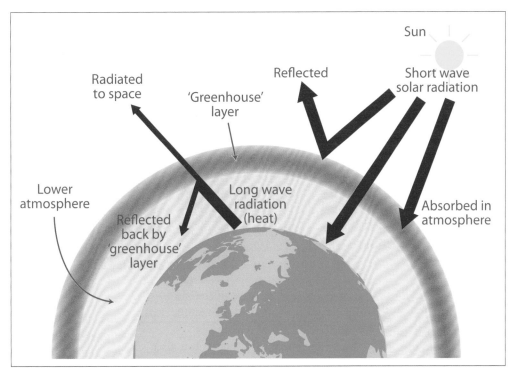

The greenhouse effect

Note: The greenhouse effect is a natural process that is necessary to sustain life as we know it. Without a greenhouse effect the average temperature at the Earth's surface would fall to −18°C. The problem is that the ability of the greenhouse layer to trap heat energy has increased.

Carbon dioxide (thought to be responsible for 60 – 70 % of global warming) is not the only greenhouse gas – a gas that traps / reflects long wave radiation as it moves up through the Earth's atmosphere. **Methane** (CH_4) is an even more potent greenhouse gas (nearly thirty times more powerful than carbon dioxide) but as its concentration is much lower, and it is shorter lasting in the atmosphere than CO_2, its effect is less. Nonetheless, it is still a very significant contributor to the greenhouse effect. Methane comes from a number of sources including:

- anaerobic activity by microorganisms in natural wetlands and crops cultivated in waterlogged or very wet conditions such as rice (the main source)

- the fermentation of waste in landfill sites – the methane is produced as a byproduct when the waste is broken down in anaerobic conditions

- as waste gas expelled from cows and other ruminants – produced as a byproduct of the metabolism of the mutualistic microorganisms

- escaping from oil, gas or coal fields

Other greenhouse gases include **chlorofluorocarbons** (CFCs) and **nitrous oxide** (N_2O).

We will come to CFCs later. Denitrifying bacteria can convert a small proportion of the nitrogen (nitrate and ammonia) in artificial fertilisers into nitrous oxide.

The effects of global warming – The **melting of the ice caps** in polar regions is an obvious consequence that is being monitored in detail. This has the effect of **raising sea levels** with the risk of the flooding of many lowland areas such as Holland, Bangladesh and even parts of Britain including East Anglia. In the summer of 2012 the extent of the Arctic icecap had shrunk to its smallest ever size (the previous smallest extent was in 2007). The shrinkage is exacerbated by the fact that the ice is also getting thinner. The average thickness of the polar ice was only about 1.5 m in summer 2012 whereas 20 years earlier it was closer to 4 m in thickness – a reduction in volume of around 70%. The extra fresh water in the oceans is likely to disrupt ocean currents. Britain would be adversely affected if the Gulf Stream current bringing warmer water across the Atlantic was pushed further north.

Note: The higher global temperatures will also make the water in the oceans expand. Some scientists believe that this might have as much an effect on sea levels as melting ice caps.

Changing climates are another consequence of global warming. The meteorological data for the British Isles shows that in recent years, summers are getting warmer and wetter.

Ecosystems are affected in many ways by changing climates. The distribution of both plant and animal species change as the temperatures change. In the British Isles this could mean the loss of some of our more northerly species but also the introduction of some species that currently do not extend as far north as the British Isles. Global warming could lead to the introduction into Britain of the heat-requiring mosquito (and its malarial parasite), a change that would have potentially deadly consequences.

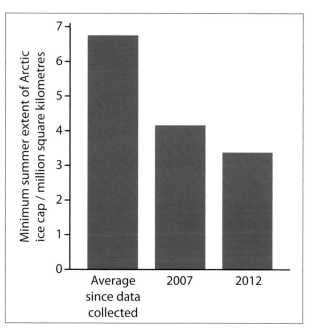

Minimum summer extent of Arctic ice – average values and values for the two years that recorded lowest values (data from the National Snow and Ice Data Center, Colorado)

There is still an element of scientific debate as to how much of the change in our climate is part of a natural cycle and how much is due to human activity, particularly the increase in the combustion of fossil fuels. It is a complex area but the consensus is that global warming is largely attributable to human activity. Furthermore, an increasing number of scientists are suggesting that we are rapidly reaching the 'tipping point', the point where the change to the climate becomes irreversible.

Can we reduce global warming? - Many scientists suggest that the initial priority is to slow down the **rate of increase** in global temperatures. International conferences involving the main industrial nations of the world attempt to reduce the use of fossil fuels and devise other strategies that will slow down (and hopefully eventually reverse) the warming of the atmosphere. However, in an attempt to get agreement among as many countries as possible, the targets are often less ambitious than they need to be. At a local level much is being done – often as a consequence of European legislation - e.g. the mushrooming of recycling bins in recent years, the 'paperless' office and levying costs on supermarket plastic bags.

However, a **major reduction in the use of fossil fuels** and a switch to alternative power sources such as wind and nuclear power, allied to increased energy saving schemes, is necessary in the short term to avoid major environmental change in the lifetime of the students reading this book.

Ozone depletion

The ozone layer is the zone in the stratosphere that lies between 15 - 40 km above the Earth's surface. Ozone (O_3) layer acts as a screen and prevents too much harmful UV radiation penetrating through to reach the surface of the Earth. Ozone is a highly reactive molecule and is continually being built up and broken down.

However, this protective layer has been reduced by up to 70 % of its original thickness in some areas with the most obvious 'gaps' appearing over the Antarctica polar region in the Southern Hemisphere; elsewhere the depletion is between 5 – 20 %. As with global warming, man appears to be responsible for this harmful change. Man-made **chlorofluorocarbons (CFCs)** break down ozone. For many decades CFCs were used as **coolants in refrigerators**, as propellants in **aerosol spray cans** and in **air conditioning** units. It is almost certain that it is the use of CFCs that has reduced the ozone layer.

The CFCs released pass up into the stratosphere and react with the UV rays, reactions which result in the release of chlorine. The chlorine reacts with the oxygen in the ozone consequently breaking the ozone molecule down.

Increased levels of UV radiation reaching the Earth's surface is of course harmful, particularly when taken in the context of increasing global warming as well. The increased UV penetration leads to an increase in the incidence of **skin cancer** and **cataracts** (the clouding of the transparent lens in the eye). There is also some evidence that that the reproductive cycles of phytoplankton species can be affected.

In most countries the use of CFCs is banned with replacement products used in refrigerators and aerosol cans. Sensible precautions such as using high factor sun block creams, remaining in shelter or covering up in the hottest parts of the day and wearing a hat will also help reduce the incidence of skin cancer and cataracts.

Acid Rain

Acid rain is not new; rain under normal circumstances is slightly acidic with a pH around 5.7. This is a consequence of the carbon dioxide in the air combining with rain water to form the weakly acidic carbonic acid. Acid rain is a term commonly used to describe precipitation (rain or snow) with a pH of less than 5.

Acid rain began making the news about fifty years ago when it became apparent that the rain was becoming more acidic and that it was corroding and damaging buildings, causing the defoliation of trees and damaging other wildlife, in particular life in lakes. Rain with a pH 3 – 4 was typical in geographical regions most affected by acid rain.

What causes acid rain? – Acid rain is yet another consequence of industrialisation and the pollution that comes with it. In particular, the burning of vast quantities of fossil fuels in power stations is the prime cause. The burning of fossil fuels releases **sulfur dioxide** (SO_2), **nitric oxide** (NO) and **nitrogen dioxide** (NO_2). The nitrogen oxides – represented as NO_x - are also given out as waste products in vehicle exhaust emissions. These pollutants react with water in the clouds to produce **sulfuric** and **nitric acid**.

Acid rain

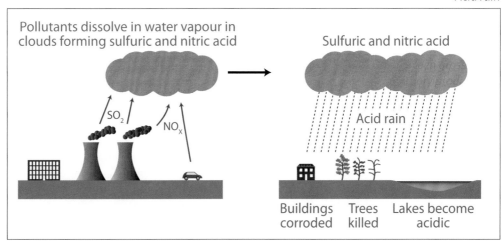

Pollutants dissolve in water vapour in clouds forming sulfuric and nitric acid

Sulfuric and nitric acid

SO_2

NO_x

Acid rain

Buildings corroded

Trees killed

Lakes become acidic

A particular problem with acid rain is that it can affect countries well away from where the pollution originates (the power stations) – one country's pollution can destroy another country's forests and lakes. Acid rain has caused a lot of harm to the forests and lakes in Scandinavia but the acidic clouds have blown from the much more industrialised countries in the British Isles and Germany to cause the harm.

The effect on forest and aquatic ecosystems – research has shown that acid rain is particularly harmful to forest and aquatic ecosystems.

Trees (and plants) in **forest ecosystems** are directly affected as the acidic rain damages the leaves when it falls on them. The acid rain can break down the protective cuticle and harm the delicate tissue beneath. Many of the coniferous forests in northern Europe have been damaged with many of the trees becoming defoliated and subsequently dying.

The acid rain prevents the soil from acting as an effective **buffer**. As a consequence the solubility of minerals such as **calcium**, **magnesium** and **potassium** are much **reduced** and therefore they become less available to plant roots. As the beneficial calcium, magnesium and potassium become less available, the harmful **aluminium** becomes more soluble and is released into the soil water where it has a toxic effect on roots. The alteration of soil chemistry is a more indirect effect, but nonetheless has a very important effect on trees in affected regions. Additionally, many species of **decomposer** are less active, or are harmed, in acidic soils. Consequently the processes of decay and decomposition are reduced leading to a decrease in soil fertility.

In **aquatic ecosystems** acid rain has resulted in the pH of the water becoming much lower than it otherwise would have been. Some lakes have been recorded as having a pH of 3 or lower; a level of acidity that is fatal to much of the aquatic life. The effect of increasing **solubility** of the **aluminium** in the soils surrounding waterways results in increased levels of aluminium entering the water.

This has a number of effects on the aquatic organisms including causing the **gills of fish** to become covered with thick **mucus** which prevents **oxygen uptake**. Consequently they die by asphyxiation. Many species of invertebrates are affected in a similar way. **Fish eggs** can fail to hatch if exposed to pH levels below 5.5 therefore putting further pressure on fish populations in affected waterways.

What can be done to reduce the effects of acid rain? – there are a number of actions that can reduce the effects of acid rain. These measures all focus on making the rain less acid. They include:

- using **low-sulfur fuels**. The technology is in place to remove much of the sulfur from fuels though it obviously makes their use more expensive.

- removing the sulfur dioxide in the waste gases produced when burning coal in power stations and industrial plants. 'Scrubbers' or **filters** in the chimneys have been successful in significantly reducing pollutants at this stage.

- Catalytic converters in car engines remove nitrogen dioxide and other pollutants from the waste gases.

The catalytic converters in modern cars reduces their contribution to global warming

- The use of alternative (renewable) fuels. Although alternative fuels have and are being promoted as a means of reducing the rate of increase of global warming, the use of e.g. wind, tidal and nuclear energy is very effective in reducing the emissions that contribute to acid rain. Even using natural gas instead of coal helps as it has lower sulfur content.

The acidic lakes and dead forests common in many northern European and American areas in the 1970 – 80s as a result of acid rain is a much less common phenomenon now. Most forests have recovered as have most of the lakes. The measures taken to reduce the acid levels in the rain can be regarded as a successful example of environmental conservation, certainly when compared with the global warming story.

Note: Acid rain is typically used as an example of air pollution. However, its effects impact mainly on the ground and in waterways. Consequently, if you are answering an exam question on the pollution of land or water, it may be appropriate to include reference to acid rain in your answer, depending on the context of the question.

The pollution of waterways

Waterways (the oceans, seas, lakes and rivers) have been subject to pollution for centuries due to human activity. Increased urbanisation, particularly in the developing world often results in poor sanitation levels. This, combined with increasing amounts of industrial waste has resulted in many of the world's rivers being polluted to the extent that very little life more complex than prokaryotes and protoctistans can survive.

In Northern Ireland, sanitation standards are high and industrial pollution has been much reduced in recent decades. Consequently, much of the pollution affecting our waterways at the start of the twenty first century is agricultural-related.

Organic pollution and eutrophication

Many students are confused between organic pollution and eutrophication – two related but subtly different causes of water pollution and both largely attributable to farming activity.

Organic pollution – organic pollution involves the pollution of water by **organic material**. Organic pollutants include sewage, slurry, silage effluent and spilled milk from dairy farms and from milk and dairy products processing units.

If organic pollutants enter waterways they provide a rich source of nutrients for **bacteria** involved in the decay process. The rich organic food supply results in a **population explosion** of saprobiotic bacteria that subsequently use up much of the **oxygen** in the water due to **aerobic respiration**.

The **Biological Oxygen Demand (BOD)** is an indication of water quality, measured as the usage of oxygen in the water. High organic levels in the water will lead to more bacteria, therefore more aerobic respiration and therefore higher BODs and vice versa.

Note: Silage effluent has a very high BOD (about 65, 000 mg/l). Milk has an even higher value (about 140, 000 mg/l). The very high milk value is not surprising as it is a high-energy organic food for mammals, animals that have high metabolic needs.

Often organic pollution occurs as isolated and specific events. An example is sewage entering waterways as a result of flooding affecting the sewage system or from a slurry tank leak. The typical consequence of such a pollution incident is seen in the graphs on the right.

Indicator species – high BOD levels kill fish and many of the invertebrates that live in waterways. Stonefly and mayfly insect larvae can only survive in unpolluted water where the oxygen levels are high – typically occurring in fast flowing rivers where the turbulent water contains high oxygen levels. However, some species are adapted to live in the reduced oxygen levels of polluted waterways. Species such as the sludge worm (*Tubifex*) are adapted to survive in water that has very low levels of oxygen.

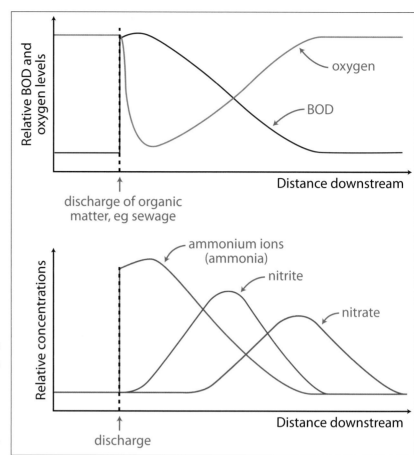

Changes in BOD, oxygen and some water chemical levels as a consequence of organic pollution

Note: *Tubifex* worms are rich in haemoglobin throughout their body (this is why they are red in colour) which acts as an excellent oxygen store. They have a low metabolic rate, therefore have reduced oxygen needs.

Midge larvae (bloodworms) are adapted to survive in the intermediate oxygen levels associated with more moderate levels of pollution compared to the pollution levels associated with *Tubifex*.

Species that are adapted to particular levels of pollution (or BOD) are referred to as **indicator species** in that their presence in a particular stretch of water will give information about the water quality.

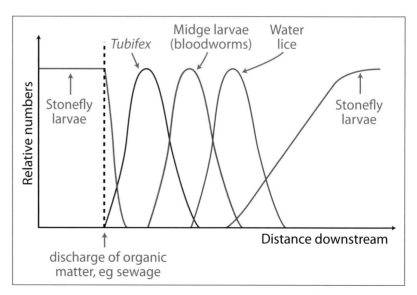

Changes in species composition in a waterway following a pollution discharge

Eutrophication – The (gradual and long term) **nutrient** enrichment of waterways, in particular **nitrates** and **phosphates** (as opposed to an organic pollution incident), is referred to as **eutrophication**. Under natural conditions, eutrophication is not a problem as the amount of nutrient naturally entering waterways is very low and has little effect on aquatic ecosystems.

Nutrient enrichment, as a consequence of farming activities, is a significant problem in Northern Ireland and other intensively farmed countries. Much of the nutrient enrichment comes from the nitrate and phosphate in **artificial fertilisers**. If too much fertiliser is applied, or it is applied on sloping ground too close to waterways or applied in wet conditions, the nitrate and phosphate can **leach** through the soil into the water. When this happens in large enough quantities the following sequence typically results.

- The increased nitrate and phosphate causes a very large increase in algal growth – known as **algal blooms**. (Under 'normal' non-enriched conditions the levels of nitrate and phosphate in lakes and rivers limit algal growth).

- The rapid and extensive growth of the algae (found in highest amounts on the surface of the water) **prevents light penetrating** through the water to the plants at lower levels. The algae also deplete the water of nutrients.

- These **plants die** due to a shortage of light (or nutrients) and are decomposed by saprobiotic bacteria.

- The **bacteria** use up the **oxygen** in **aerobic respiration**.

- The shortage of oxygen results in the **death** of many species of **invertebrates** and **fish** and a loss of **biodiversity**.

Extensive algal growth in a highly eutrophic lake

Note 1: Before phosphate-free detergents and the development of more efficient filtering systems in sewage works, phosphate pollution from washing powder was a significant cause of eutrophication. This was a factor in the original development of Lough Neagh as a highly eutrophic lake (the leaching of phosphate and nitrate from agricultural land has been a more important factor in recent years).

Note 2: Many students mix up organic pollution and eutrophication to their costs in exams. If a question is about an outfall of sewage pollution into a river, the question is about organic pollution – your answer is unlikely to require reference to algal blooms!

Reducing eutrophication of waterways – the main objective has been to reduce the leaching of nitrate and phosphate into waterways and many of the measures taken are linked to European legislation (e.g. the **European Nitrates Directive**). These strategies include:

- testing the **ion content** of soil before the application of fertiliser. This will ensure that only the correct **amount** of fertiliser is used and that the **balance** of nutrients (e.g. nitrate and phosphate) is appropriate for the crop's needs.

- only applying the fertiliser immediately prior to or during periods of **crop growth**, i.e. the need for **'closed periods'** at certain times of the year when it is not beneficial or appropriate to apply fertiliser. This ensures that the nutrients are not in excess and do not get a chance to build up in the soil with the subsequent risk of leaching into surrounding waterways.

- not applying fertiliser when **heavy rain** is forecast.

- not applying fertiliser on land that is **close to waterways** (this can be a particular issue if the land is sloping).

- many isolated farms (and houses) in Northern Ireland are served by septic tanks as they have no mains sewage. Often the septic tanks do not function particularly effectively as they have poor soakaway arrangements. The use of constructed **reed beds** can reduce the level of nutrients escaping into surrounding waterways from septic tanks. Furthermore, the reed beds can be used to treat lightly contaminated farm waste that would normally just leach into surrounding fields. Reed beds typically consist of the common reed (*Phragmites australis*) and other plants that help break down organic compounds and then use the breakdown products for growth. As well as reducing organic pollution, the reed beds require little management once constructed, are aesthetically easy on the eye and provide a range of habitats thus promoting biodiversity.

Large modern slurry tank for secure storage

- the requirement to have **adequate storage facilities** for slurry and other farm wastes that can cause water enrichment.

- **Government guidelines** at both European (e.g. Nitrates Directive) and local levels (DARD NI Code of Good Agricultural Practice) provide both legislation and guidelines aimed at reducing eutrophication and the encouragement of conservation in agricultural settings in general.

Case Study

The Northern Ireland Department of Agriculture and Rural Development (DARD) Nitrates Action Programme and Phosphorus Regulations (2011-14) Guidance Booklet builds on earlier regulations relating to nitrate and phosphorus use. Its requirements / recommendations include specific dates by which the application of fertiliser must be completed. For example, chemical fertiliser must not be applied between 15 September – 31 January and farmyard manure must not be applied between 31 October and 31 January.

Trailing shoe used for spreading slurry

The guidance document specifies that fertiliser must not be applied on waterlogged or frozen soils or land liable to flood, if heavy rain is forecast in the next 48 hours or on sloping ground. To reduce the risk of slurry being accidently spread into waterways (or too close to waterways) it has to be applied using inverted splashplate, bandspreaders, trailing shoe, trailing hose or soil injection technologies. Specific maximum limits are also set

for nitrogen (nitrate) application to farms (272 kg N/ha on dairy farms and 222 kg N/ha on other farms) and the maximum slurry application is 50 m³/ha.

Water pollution – other consequences

Organic pollution or eutrophication of water, if it is severe enough or occurs for a long enough time period, can have the following consequences:

- A **loss of fisheries**. Many lakes and rivers in Northern Ireland are important for both commercial and recreational fishing. Fish stocks can be lost or reduced through periodic 'fish kills' caused by discrete pollution incidents or through the general deterioration of water quality by organic pollution or eutrophication.

- High nitrate levels in **drinking water** can be harmful to young babies and gives the water a poor taste.

- Slurry and sewage run off into rivers will lead to organic pollution and subsequent increase in BOD. However, slurry will also **smother aquatic vegetation** due to the density of suspended solids – the slurry may also contain the toxic residues of **veterinary medicines**.

- Drinking water contaminated by species of **toxic algae** (that reach high densities due to eutrophication) creates environmental health issues and the cost of their removal can be expensive.

Note: Slurry is animal (pig and cattle) manure that has been mixed with urine and water to produce an easily-spread, nutrient-rich organic fertiliser.

Agriculture

Apart from the link between agriculture and pollution discussed in the previous sections, agriculture impacts in many other ways on the environment. Most of the ecological harm is linked to **intensive farming**. Intensive farming serves to maximise food production but there is often an associated ecological cost.

Intensive farming methods

Intensive farming is often associated with the following:

Barley grown as a monoculture – this becomes a particular problem if barley is grown in this field year after year

- Monoculture – monoculture is the growing of only one species of crop in a particular area. This is particularly harmful when the same crop, e.g. maize, is grown in the same field year after year. Each species of crop has **different mineral ion requirements** and in monoculture these minerals rapidly become depleted in the soil. The problem with the depletion of a specific mineral is further exacerbated by the fact that the crop is invariably **harvested** before the processes of decay and mineralisation can take place and return the minerals to the soil. Monoculture also encourages the establishment of **pests** specific to the crop – the pests have ongoing unlimited food supplies, therefore have the potential to become established in large numbers. Monocultures clearly **reduce biodiversity** and encourage the establishment of **weeds**.

- **Overuse of artificial fertiliser** – intensive crop farming usually requires the use of high levels of artificial fertiliser. Many farms do not produce enough organic fertiliser (farmyard manure or slurry) to fertilise all the land that is being used for crop production. The use of artificial fertiliser has increased agricultural food production in the UK by over 100% in the last fifty years but at a cost. The artificial (inorganic) fertiliser leads to **loss of soil crumb structure** and increased risk of **eutrophication** and **reduced biodiversity** as outlined earlier.

This canal is surrounded by intensively farmed land – extreme eutrophication caused by fertiliser run off

- Problems with **disposal of large quantities of slurry** – although slurry can be used as a fertiliser, many farmers do end up with excessive quantities that cannot be stored effectively. This is most likely to happen on farms that have many livestock, e.g. cattle, producing vast quantities of slurry. The excess slurry can contribute to water pollution through causing **organic pollution** or containing the **toxic residues of veterinary medicines** as discussed in the section on water pollution.

- **The removal of hedgerows** – hedgerows and their contribution to **biodiversity** were discussed in detail as part of the AS course. A consequence of intensive farming has been that many hedgerows have been removed, typically to produce larger fields more suitable for the efficient planting and harvesting of crops using modern machinery. The presence of hedgerows helps reduce **soil erosion**. They protect the land (and the livestock and crops), particularly in the environs of the hedgerow from wind and rain. Additionally, the roots from hedgerow trees extend across neighbouring fields and help bind the soil together.

- **Dependency on pesticides** – pests have been discussed in detail in Chapter 6. However, it is worth reminding ourselves that the overuse of pesticides is associated with the intensification of farming. **Herbicides** (kill weeds), **insecticides** (kill insecticides) and **fungicides** (kill fungal parasites affecting crop plants, e.g. potato blight that affects potatoes and mildews that affect cereal crops) are types of pesticides commonly used to reduce the effects of pests. Pests, if allowed to accumulate, can cause considerable damage to crops. Therefore, maximising crop productivity invariably involves attempts to reduce pest incidence. Many pesticides are **broad spectrum** and therefore harm non-pest species, e.g. the predators of insect pests or insect pollinators of plants. Their harmful chemicals may be **non-biodegradable** and therefore build up in the food chain in a process known as **bioaccumulation**.

The benefits of traditional and sustainable farming methods

Traditional farming methods are sustainable and can more effectively address the conflict between increasing food production to meet the needs of an expanding population and the need for environmental conservation.

Traditional and sustainable farming methods include the following examples.

- The planting of a variety of crops (**polyculture**) on the same land. Intercropping is the growing of a range of crop types at the same time and crop rotation is rotating the species of crop grown in a particular field over a number of years. **Intercropping** supports greater **species diversity** as it provides a wider range of habitats for species. **Crop rotation** is more beneficial for the **soil** – it is less likely to lead to mineral depletion, particularly if nitrogen-fixing legumes are included as part of the cycle. It also makes it harder for pest populations to become established. Changing the crop each year will often prevent the completion of **pest life cycles**.

- The use of **mixed livestock** rather than the concentration on one species. Again this benefits the land as different fodder crops can be used and different livestock make different grazing demands. Additionally, waste accumulation (and the possible contamination of waterways) is very different for different livestock.

- The use of **organic fertiliser** (especially farmyard manure) has many advantages. Farmyard manure improves **soil crumb structure**. The manure helps bind the soil particles together creating the larger spaces necessary for **aeration** and **drainage**. The aeration of soil is necessary for soil microorganisms involved in decomposition. It is also needed for the **oxygen-requiring nitrifying bacteria** and for respiration in plants roots thus releasing the energy necessary for the **active uptake** of nitrate and other minerals. Good drainage prevents the anaerobic conditions necessary for the **harmful denitrifying bacteria**. Organic fertiliser releases its nutrients much more slowly than artificial fertilisers and therefore reduces the risk of **leaching** into waterways and **eutrophication**. In general, an appropriate balance of artificial and organic fertiliser is often the best strategy for maximising productivity over the long term as both have advantages and disadvantages as highlighted in the following table.

Feature	Organic fertiliser	Artificial fertiliser
Soil quality	Improves soil crumb structure and reduces the risk of soil erosion as the organic content (humus) helps bind the soil particles together into crumbs	Does not contribute to soil crumb structure
Solubility	Less soluble and more slowly broken down so minerals are less likely to leach into waterways	Very soluble and readily leaches into waterways if applied in excess or in wet conditions
Application	Difficult to calculate the mineral composition	Can be applied in a controlled manner with knowledge of exact mineral composition
Cost	'Free' waste on farm	Has to be purchased
Storage	Can be difficult to store if in large quantities	Easily stored or purchased as required

- The **replanting of hedgerows** and/or the **maintenance** of existing ones decreases the risk of **soil erosion** and improves **biodiversity**. The risk of soil erosion can also be reduced by **ploughing across slopes** as opposed to up and down hills. This traps water and allows it to sink into the soil both ensuring that the soil has sufficient moisture and also reducing the soil erosion aided by fast flowing rainwater running down the troughs or furrows on sloping ground.

Crop stubble left following harvesting

- Leaving **cereal crop stubble** over the winter as opposed to immediately ploughing the land after a crop is harvested – this has major advantages in providing winter feed (e.g. barley or wheat seed) for many species of birds but also reduces soil erosion as there is less bare soil and although most of the crop has been harvested, the roots remain and help bind the soil together.

- The use of **integrated pest management (IPM) systems**. Integrated pest management is the development of a long term strategy involving a range of methods to reduce the damage caused by pests to an economically acceptable level. Integrated pest management will typically involve both the use of pesticides and the use of biological control. IPM will usually include:

1. many of the **traditional**, less intensive, strategies already discussed, e.g. crop rotation.

2. the use of **varieties** that have a degree of pest resistance – these can be developed through traditional breeding methods or by genetically modified (GM) technologies. For example, some varieties of GM maize are able to produce a protein toxic to insects that feed directly on the maize.

3. the use of **narrow spectrum, biodegradable pesticides** will target only the pest species and will not lead to bioaccumulation of harmful chemicals.

Beetle bank

4. **biological control** – encouraging the natural predators of the main pests by the use of predator strips around the edge of fields or 'beetle banks' extending into the crop.

5. the **sterilisation of males** of pest species. The sterilisation of large numbers of males of pest species and their subsequent release into the wild is an effective method of reducing pest numbers. The males mate with the females but no offspring are produced.

There are two very obvious benefits to this method. It is very **specific** with only the pest species targeted and the sterilised males actually **seek out** the females – many applications of conventional pesticides miss the pests as they are shaded by the crops or the pesticide may extend beyond the target area, e.g. field margins.

Note: The sterilisation of male mosquitoes has been used to reduce mosquito numbers in areas where malaria is prevalent. The mosquito is a vector for *Plasmodium*, the protoctistan that causes malaria. Although not used in a crop protection context, this example shows the benefits of the sterilisation of male pests.

Remember that the word 'pest' is also a term that can be applied to weeds – the photographs below show the effect of treating a field of maize with herbicide compared to a field that had no herbicide applied.

Fields of maize treated with herbicide (A) and with no herbicide (B)

A   B

The planting of crops, e.g. maize, under **biodegradable plastic** is a particular example of a method used to maximise productivity in a way that will not harm the environment. The biodegradable plastic allows light through but leads to a significant increase in soil temperature promoting both earlier crop emergence and faster earlier growth. There are other benefits including the retention of moisture under the plastic thus preventing the surface layers of the soil drying out and protection against strong winds. In due course the maize penetrates and emerges through the plastic and the plastic degrades in a manner not harmful to the environment.

Managed timber production as a sustainable resource

Northern Ireland, compared to other European countries, has a very small percentage of its land as woods or forests. This is largely due to the removal of large tracts of woodland to create land for agriculture. Timber is also a valuable renewable resource.

Softwood and hardwood forests

In Northern Ireland commercial forests, producing wood for domestic use and industry, tend to be **coniferous (softwood)** comprising species such as pine, spruce and larch. Coniferous forests are commercially important as they **grow very quickly** compared to deciduous (hardwood) species. They are typically grown in similar aged stands at high densities. The following graph shows the light penetrating to ground level in coniferous (softwood) and deciduous (hardwood) forests.

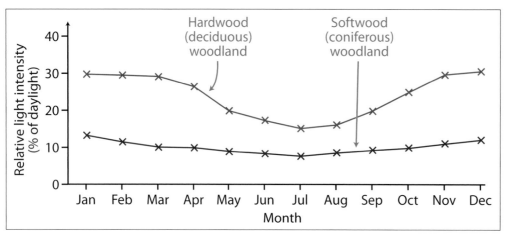

Relative light intensities reaching the woodland floor in hardwood and softwood woodland

The graph shows that indigenous hardwood forests such as ash and oak have relatively high light levels in early spring before the tree leaf canopy forms. This encourages the growth of species such as wild garlic, wood anemone and bluebell. The overall higher light levels and the greater range in light intensity throughout the year ensures that our native woodlands have a **greater variety of habitats** and **increased biodiversity** compared to introduced commercial coniferous forests. Additionally, commercial forests are harvested not allowing habitats to be fully developed and restricting the availability of biomass that can be decomposed.

A commercial coniferous forest in spring – note the lack of vegetation on the woodland floor and the thick layer of needles, twigs and branches that is very slow to decompose

A mixed deciduous woodland in spring – note the dense ground layer of bluebells

Additionally, pine and other coniferous tree needles decompose more slowly than the leaves of deciduous trees and the soils are usually less fertile and more acidic - the ability of coniferous trees to grow well in poorer soils than deciduous trees enables the commercial woodland to be sited in areas not particularly suitable for intensive agriculture. The annual leaf fall in deciduous forests provides significant decomposable matter resulting in the rich soils associated with hardwood forests.

Managing hardwood forests

Nonetheless, native woodland is a renewable resource that can be managed to provide sustainable yields. Timber from oak, ash, beech and other hardwood trees is much sought after for a range of purposes including furniture making, kitchen cabinets and worktops.

Coppicing woodland is an ancient strategy that maximises the production of new growth. In **coppicing**, many of the trees in the woodland are cut down close to ground level when they reach a particular age (at intervals a number of mature trees, called standards, are left uncut). Coppicing causes a number of shoots to regenerate from the cut stumps, producing very dense foliage that can be harvested after a number of years.

Note 1: The high light levels produced in the years immediately following coppicing create conditions conducive to increasing biodiversity as more plant species will grow.

Coppiced hazel – note the large number of shoots formed at the base of each coppiced tree

Note 2: The coppicing and subsequent harvesting of **willow** as a biofuel has been increasing in popularity in recent years. Growth rates of willow following coppicing are so high that harvesting can take place in a three year cycle. This has many advantages – the willow is **renewable** and sustainable, **saving fossil fuels** reserves. **Native forests** are also protected conserving long established **habitats** and **biodiversity**. Additionally, as the willow grows it **photosynthesises** using carbon dioxide which offsets the **carbon dioxide** produced when the willow is burned as a fuel. Therefore it can be considered a **carbon neutral** fuel.

A willow plantation

'Set-aside' land schemes are designed to encourage landowners to allow areas of land, e.g. at field margins or small areas of isolated land, to return to nature. This has aesthetic benefits and also creates a range of habitats that further encourage biodiversity.

Exam questions

1. The diagram (right) represents the carbon cycle.

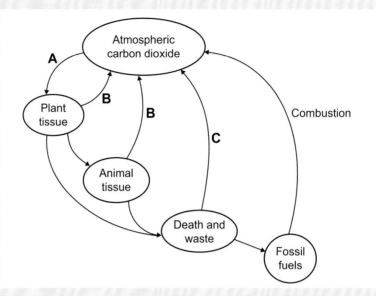

(a) Identify the processes labelled **A** to **C**. [3]

(b) The combustion of fossil fuels illustrated in the diagram adds extra carbon dioxide to the atmosphere. Describe the consequences of a build up of carbon dioxide in the atmosphere. [5]

(c) (i) Other gases are liberated into the atmosphere during the combustion of fossil fuels. Name **one** of these other gases which can cause acid rain. [1]

   (ii) Describe and explain **one biological** problem caused by acid rain. [2]

Question taken from CCEA's Biology Assessment Unit A2 1, Physiology and Ecosystems, January 2010, © CCEA 2013

2. A river, otherwise unpolluted, was sampled from the source of a sewage outflow. Oxygen content of the river was measured at the point of outflow and at intervals downriver. The results are shown in the graph (right).

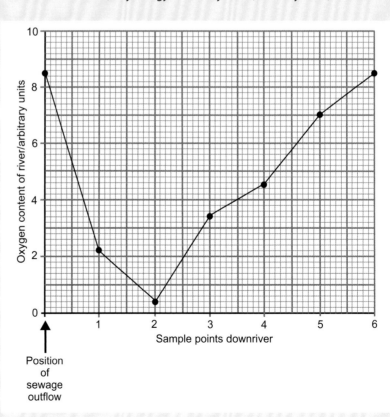

(a) (i) Calculate the percentage decrease in the oxygen content between the sewage outflow and sample point 2. (Show your working.) [2]

(ii) Explain this decrease in oxygen content. [3]

(b) Suggest **two** reasons for the increase in oxygen content from sample points **2** to **6**. [2]

(c) Identify the sample point from the graph where you would expect to find the lowest biodiversity in the river. Explain your answer. [2]

(d) Aquatic invertebrates can act as 'indicator species' in monitoring river pollution. Suggest why these species are a better indicator of pollution than chemical tests for oxygen levels. [2]

Question taken from CCEA's Biology Assessment Unit A2 1, Physiology and Ecosystems, May 2011, © CCEA 2013

3. Rivers in Northern Ireland have a wide biodiversity of over 1500 invertebrate aquatic species. However pollution reduces biodiversity.

    The diagram below illustrates a river in which an organic discharge entered at point **A** and its subsequent effect on the BOD (Biological Oxygen Demand) downstream. Some of the aquatic animals (Indicator species) sampled along the river are also illustrated.

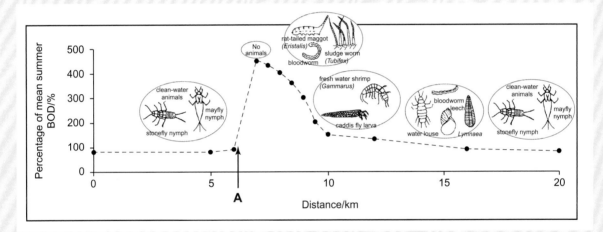

(a) Organic discharges, such as slurry, contain many bacteria and fungi as well as dead organic matter.

(i) Explain the huge increase in the BOD immediately after the organic discharge at **A**. [1]

(ii) Describe what happens to cause a decrease in the BOD downstream. [2]

(b) The first animals sampled after the discharge include the rat-tailed maggot *(Eristalis)* and the sludge worm *(Tubifex)*. These animals have adaptations: the rat-tailed maggot can extend its tail to the surface of the water and the sludge worm possesses haemoglobin within its tail.

(i) Suggest how these adaptations increase their tolerance of the organic pollution. [3]

(ii) Explain the change in the aquatic communities with distance from the organic discharge. [2]

(c) (i) Explain why eutrophication may occur downstream from the source of this organic pollution. [1]

(ii) Explain the consequences of eutrophication. [3]

Question taken from CCEA's Biology Assessment Unit A2 1, Physiology and Ecosystems, May 2010, © CCEA 2013

4. It is important that fertiliser is applied to farmland in appropriate concentrations to maximise productivity and profit, and also at levels that are not harmful to the environment.

The graph below shows the relationship between levels of application of artificial fertiliser and crop yield for maize.

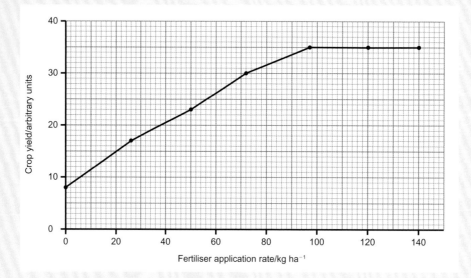

(a) (i)   Using the graph, state the optimum fertiliser application rate for this crop. Explain your answer. [2]

(ii) Suggest **one** reason why the crop yield would decrease if the fertiliser application was significantly increased above 140 kg ha^{-1}. [1]

(iii) The use of organic fertiliser (farmyard manure), as opposed to artificial fertiliser, helps improve soil crumb structure. Explain, as fully as possible, **two** distinct ways in which an improved soil crumb structure can improve crop yield. [2]

(b) Maize and other crops are subject to attack by pests.

(i) Describe and explain **two** ways in which pests can reduce crop yield. [2]

Many pesticides kill a wide range of insects. The graph below shows the effect of a series of pesticide applications on the numbers of a common pest of maize plants.

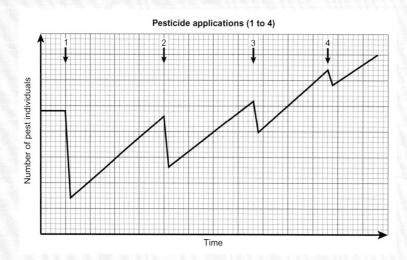

(ii) Describe and explain the trends evident in the graph. [4]

Integrated Pest Management Systems involve the use of a range of strategies to combat pests.

(c) Explain how the use of crop rotation and the sterilisation of the males of pest species can reduce the damage caused by pests. [2]

Question taken from CCEA's Biology Assessment Unit A2 1, Physiology and Ecosystems, May 2012, © CCEA 2013

5. Crop rotation is used by farmers to maintain the fertility of the soil.

Often crop rotation includes the planting of a grass–clover mixture. Clover is a legume with root nodules rich in amino acids and protein. In the autumn the grass–clover crop is ploughed into the soil as 'green manure' before the planting of winter wheat.

(a) (i) Explain why clover root nodules are rich in amino acids and protein. [2]

(ii) Following the ploughing of the grass–clover crop into the soil, the plants die and the soil subsequently becomes rich in nitrates. Describe the processes involved in the soil becoming rich in nitrates. [3]

(b) The graph below shows the influence of different mixtures of grass–clover on the yield of wheat grain following the ploughing-in of the grass–clover crop.

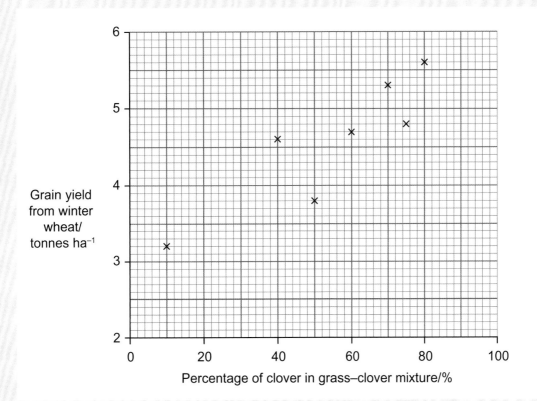

(i) Explain the trend evident in the graph. [2]

(ii) Describe and explain one additional benefit of crop rotation. [2]

Question taken from CCEA's Biology Assessment Unit A2 1, Physiology and Ecosystems, May 2010, © CCEA 2013

6. The famous environmental scientist, James Lovelock proposed the Gaia hypothesis. In this he referred to the Earth and its atmosphere as a self-regulating system that has allowed life to thrive through biological processes maintaining an atmosphere that supports life.

Lovelock and other scientists have since suggested that the Earth is at serious risk due to global warming. In his book, The Revenge of Gaia (2006), Lovelock concludes that the only hope for the planet lies in dramatic reductions in both habitat destruction and the use of fossil fuels.

(a) (i) State **two** biological processes that contribute to the "self-regulating system" of the Earth and its atmosphere. [1]

(ii) Explain the link between increasing atmospheric carbon dioxide levels and global warming. [2]

(iii) Suggest how an increased reliance on farming has contributed to global warming. [2]

(b) Willow is a fast-growing biofuel that can be harvested after as little as three years' growth.

Explain why the growing of willow plants and its use as a biofuel is advantageous to the environment. [4]

Question taken from CCEA's Biology Assessment Unit A2 1, Physiology and Ecosystems, May 2012, © CCEA 2013

7. Native hardwood (oak) forest and softwood (spruce) commercial plantations are very different ecosystems.

A comparison was made of the light intensity at ground level in an oak forest and a spruce plantation. In this investigation, light intensity on the woodland floor was calculated as a percentage of the light intensity outside the woodland (where there is no shade).

(a) Explain why the percentage daylight data for each month would have been an average of a number of measurements made at different regions of the woodland floor. [2]

The results of the investigation are shown in the graph below.

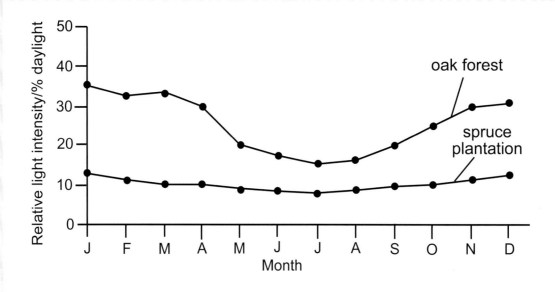

(b) (i)   Using the information in the graph, suggest which woodland would show greater diversity. Explain your choice. [4]

    (ii) Scientists estimated the biodiversity in each type of woodland by counting the number of species and the number of each species present in 30 quadrats within each type of woodland. They carried out this survey in mid-June.

       Suggest **one** reason why their survey probably underestimated the biodiversity in the woodlands. [1]

(c)   The scientists wanted to monitor the numbers of a species of beetle that lived on the floor of the spruce plantation over a three year period.

    Describe how they could use a mark/recapture technique to obtain a reliable estimate of the number of beetles. [5]

Question taken from CCEA's Biology Assessment Unit A2 1, Physiology and Ecosystems, May 2011, © CCEA 2013

8. Quality of written communication is awarded a maximum of [2] marks in this section.

  (a) Describe and explain the link between human activity and water pollution. [10]

  (b) Discuss the strategies used to minimise the effects of human activity on water pollution. [6]

Question taken from CCEA's Biology Assessment Unit A2 1, Physiology and Ecosystems, January 2012, © CCEA 2013

Unit A2 2: Biochemistry, Genetics and Evolutionary Trends

Chapter 9 – Respiration

ATP

Throughout the AS course and in earlier sections of the A2 course there have been many references to ATP. This has often been in the context of the mitochondrion being the organelle that makes ATP in respiration or that ATP is the molecule that allows work, e.g. active transport to take place. But what exactly is ATP?

ATP is **adenosine triphosphate** and as the name suggests has **three phosphate groups** combined with the nucleotide base **adenine** and a **ribose** sugar. It is the presence of the phosphate groups that provides ATP with its energy-releasing properties.

ATP is the **immediate source of energy** in a cell, a (very) short-term store. It is the ATP that drives metabolism. Glucose can be used to make ATP but it cannot release energy directly.

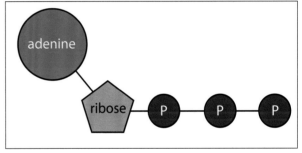

ATP

ATP is synthesised from **ADP** (**adenosine diphosphate**), a molecule with two phosphate groups and **inorganic phosphate (P$_i$)** as shown in the following diagram.

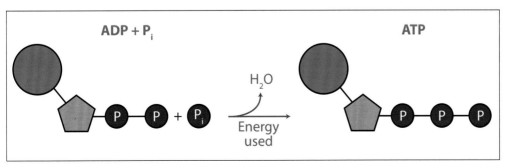

The synthesis of ATP

This process is known as **phosphorylation** (the addition of phosphate to a molecule) and the effect is to make the molecule with the extra phosphate (ATP) more energy rich. The synthesis of ATP involves condensation with the removal of a water molecule.

When the terminal (third) phosphate is subsequently removed from ATP, **energy is released** as shown in the next diagram.

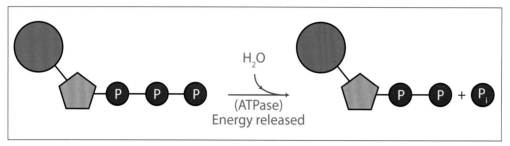

The release of energy from ATP

The breakdown of ATP (to ADP and inorganic phosphate with the release of energy) involves **hydrolysis** – the splitting of a molecule using water. The reaction is catalysed by the enzyme **ATPase**.

Note 1: ATP **releases energy** – energy cannot be created or destroyed; it can only be changed from one form to another.

Note 2: Many students incorrectly use the terms **ATP** and **energy** synonymously. ATP is an energy-rich molecule that releases/provides energy when hydrolysed.

Note 3: Cells do not store large amounts of ATP - there may be as little as 5 g of ATP in the body at any one time. However, it can be rapidly built up from ADP and P_i. In cells there is a continuous cycle between ADP and P_i, and ATP.

What makes ATP so suitable as an immediate energy store?

- The hydrolysis of an ATP molecule releases a relatively **small amount of energy** (compared to glucose). This allows energy to be released in small, manageable steps during energy-requiring reactions.

- The hydrolysis of ATP is a **single reaction** – involving the breaking of one bond - releasing immediate energy, again providing the cell with fine control over its immediate energy budget. Compare this with the number of steps required to break down a molecule of glucose (see following sections).

- As a small, soluble molecule, ATP can be **transported** around the cell easily. This enables it to be easily transported from mitochondria (the main site of synthesis) to any part of the cell.

Using ATP in the cell

We have already reviewed in detail the role of ATP in **active transport** and **muscle contraction**. However, anywhere 'work' is required, ATP is used. It provides the energy for many **metabolic processes** including anabolic reactions involving the building up of macromolecules. The role of ATP in the **activation of molecules** (through phosphorylation) will be discussed in detail in the next sections.

Note: Most ATP is made in respiration. However, ATP is also made in the light-dependent stage of photosynthesis (see Chapter 10).

The biochemistry of respiration

The conversion of glucose into ATP takes place during respiration. In mammals, and most living organisms, the principal respiratory substrate is **glucose**. Although the cellular respiration of glucose is a complex integrated process, it is convenient to divide the process into four stages:

1. **Glycolysis** – the splitting of glucose (a hexose sugar) into two 3-carbon pyruvate molecules

2. **Link reaction** – the conversion of the pyruvate into 2-carbon acetyl coenzyme A (acetyl CoA)

3. **Krebs cycle** – the feeding of acetyl CoA into a cycle of oxidation-reduction reactions

4. The **electron transport chain** – the use of electrons (and hydrogens) produced (mainly) in the Krebs cycle to synthesise ATP

Glycolysis

Glycolysis, the first step in cellular respiration, is a series of reactions that take place in the **cytoplasm**. Glycolysis can be simplified into the following stages.

The initial stage is the **activation** of glucose by **phosphorylation**. This makes the glucose more reactive. The two phosphates required come from the hydrolysis of **two ATP molecules**. This happens in two stages with initially glucose phosphate being formed following the first phosphorylation and eventually **fructose bisphosphate** following the second phosphorylation.

Following phosphorylation, the 6C fructose bisphosphate splits into two 3-carbon molecules of **triose phosphate**. The triose phosphate is **oxidised** through the loss of two hydrogen atoms to form **glycerate bisphosphate**. The hydrogen atoms are collected by the **hydrogen carrier** molecule **NAD** (nicotinamide adenine dinucleotide) which becomes reduced to form **reduced NAD (NADH)**. The removal of hydrogen involves **dehydrogenase** enzymes in a process called **dehydrogenation**.

Note: To be strictly correct it is the NAD ion, NAD^+ that is the hydrogen carrier and when accepting hydrogen it picks up one hydrogen ion plus the electron of another with a proton remaining in solution. This is represented as **$NAD^+ + 2H \rightarrow NADH (+ H^+)$**. However, representing the NADH + H^+ as **reduced NAD** or **NADH** is appropriate and easier to learn for students bar those with a specific interest in biochemistry.

In converting **each** glycerate bisphosphate molecule into a pyruvate molecule in a series of small steps two ATP molecules are produced.

However, as each glucose molecule **splits** to form 2 triose phosphate molecules (and therefore two glycerate bisphosphate molecules) this produces 2 ATP molecules for **each** of the glycerate bisphosphate molecules, a gain of 4 ATP. This gives a net gain of **2 ATP** for glycolysis (as 2 ATP were initially used to activate the glucose).

Glycolysis can be summarised as:

- The initial stage of the cellular respiration of glucose that **does not require oxygen** and takes place in the **cytoplasm**

- the reduction of NAD between the triose phosphate and glycerate bisphosphate stages to give **2 reduced NAD (NADH)**

- a net gain of **2 ATP**

Note 1: Glycolysis involves the oxidation of triose phosphate and the reduction of NAD. **Reduction** involves the gain of hydrogen or electrons or the loss of oxygen. Conversely, **oxidation** involves the gain of oxygen or the loss of hydrogen or electrons. Reduction involves the gain of energy and oxidation the release of energy.

Note 2: The hydrogen carrier NAD is a **coenzyme**. It is needed for the dehydrogenases to pass on the hydrogen they remove. The hydrogen cannot simply build up in the cell as a waste product! In effect, NAD carries hydrogen from one molecule to another. We will find out very soon the contribution the reduced NAD makes to the process of respiration.

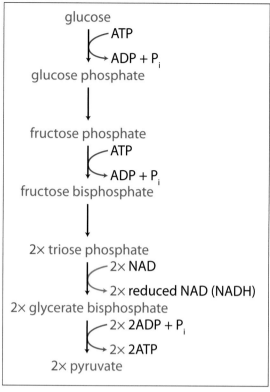

Glycolysis

The link reaction

The pyruvate produced in glycolysis is transported into the **matrix** of a **mitochondrion**. During the link reaction the pyruvate is converted to **acetyl coenzyme A (acetyl CoA)**.

The pyruvate is **decarboxylated** with the removal of one molecule of CO_2. **Dehydrogenation** also takes place with the removal of hydrogen leading to the formation of **reduced NAD (NADH)**. Following decarboxylation and dehydrogenation, the resulting 2-carbon acetate combines with coenzyme A (CoA) to form the 2-carbon acetyl CoA.

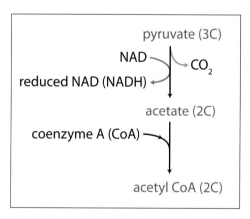

The link reaction

The Krebs cycle

The Krebs cycle also takes place in the **matrix of the mitochondrion**. It involves a cyclical series of reactions.

The key stages in Krebs cycle include:

- The **2-carbon** acetyl CoA from the link reaction combines with the **4-carbon** acid (oxaloacetate) to produce a **6-carbon** acid (citrate).

- **Decarboxylation** of the 6-carbon acid (citrate) results in the formation of the 5-carbon acid (oxoglutarate) with the loss of a molecule of CO_2.

- **Decarboxylation** of the 5-carbon acid (oxoglutarate) results in the formation of the 4-carbon acid oxaloacetate with the loss of a molecule of CO_2 and the cycle continues.

- The reactions in the cycle also involve **dehydrogenation** (and dehydrogenase enzymes). At three points in the cycle hydrogen is released that subsequently reduces NAD to form **reduced NAD (NADH)**. At one point the hydrogen is picked up not by NAD but by another hydrogen carrier FAD (flavin adenine dinucleotide) to form **reduced FAD ($FADH_2$)**.

- One molecule of **ATP** is produced by the transfer of a phosphate group from an intermediate compound to ADP. ATP produced in this way is referred to as **substrate-level phosphorylation**.

The Krebs cycle

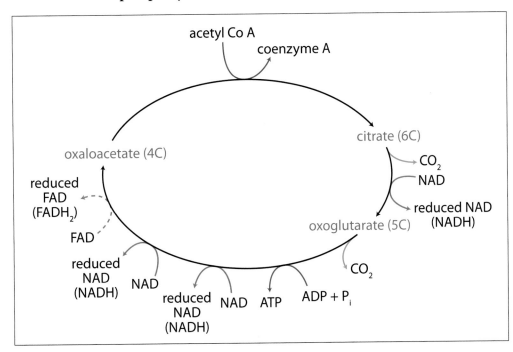

Note: As there are two molecules of acetyl CoA formed for every molecule of glucose there will be two turns of the cycle for each glucose. Consequently, when working out the energy produced from each molecule of glucose it is important to double the values referred to above and in the diagram.

So far we have not discussed what happens to the reduced coenzymes (**reduced NAD** and **reduced FAD**) – their very important role in the respiration process will be discussed in the next section, the **electron transport chain**.

Note: The description of the Krebs cycle given here is a much simplified version. In reality, it is much more complex with many more intermediate steps.

The electron transport chain

The electron transport chain is based in and on the **inner mitochondrial membrane (cristae)**. The hydrogen atoms collected by **NAD** from the process of dehydrogenation in glycolysis, the link reaction and Krebs cycle (and by **FAD** in the Krebs cycle) are carried into the next stage of the process (as NADH and $FADH_2$ respectively). In the **electron transport chain** the energy in the hydrogen (and more particularly their electrons) is converted into **ATP**, the form of energy that cells can use.

Revisiting the mitochondrion – you will remember from AS that the inner mitochondrial membrane is highly folded. The coenzymes and many of the enzymes involved in the electron transport chain are attached to the inner mitochondrial membrane. The more deeply infolded the cristae, and the more infoldings there are, the more extensive the ultrastructure that exists for ATP production in the mitochondrion.

The NAD, FAD and other coenzymes and carriers in the electron transport chain are highly organised and arranged in a sequence of decreasing potential energy. Each carrier downstream has slightly stronger reducing power than the one immediately before it. Therefore, the hydrogens (and electrons) are able to move along the chain with carriers being successively reduced and oxidised as hydrogen / electrons pass along the chain in a series of oxidation-reduction (**redox**) reactions.

The carriers of the electron transport chain - The **NAD / FAD** operate as hydrogen carriers – although the next diagram shows NAD at the start of the electron transport chain it (and FAD) also functions by bringing the hydrogen to the chain.

Note: In the inner mitochondrial membrane the NAD can be arranged in such a position that it is 'physically' situated at the 'start' of the electron transport chain. This is clearly not the case for the NAD that becomes reduced in the cytoplasm as a consequence of the reactions that take place during glycolysis. The reduced NAD from glycolysis has to be transported into the mitochondrion from the cytoplasm to deliver these hydrogen atoms to the electron transport chain.

Initially **hydrogen** passes along the carriers **NAD**, **flavoprotein**, and **coenzyme Q** as seen in the following diagram. Following the coenzyme Q stage, the hydrogen dissociates into **electrons** (and protons) and the electron transport chain subsequently acts as an **electron carrier**. The electrons pass along the **cytochromes** in a series of redox reactions.

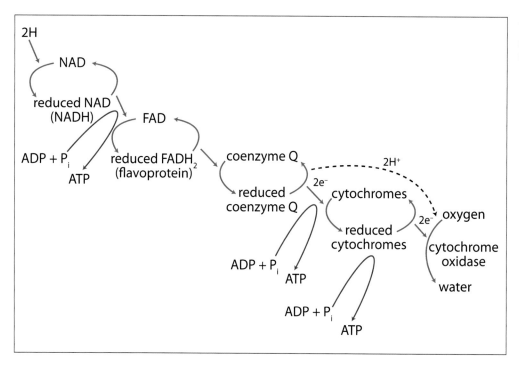

Oxidative phosphorylation and the electron transport chain

The **final hydrogen (electron) acceptor** is **oxygen**; it is at this stage that oxygen is used in respiration. The oxygen combines with hydrogen (at this stage the electrons and protons from the original dissociation of hydrogen rejoin) to form **water**, a waste product of respiration. This final stage in the electron transport chain is catalysed by the enzyme **cytochrome oxidase**.

As the carriers lie at progressively lower energy levels along the chain, energy becomes available as the redox reaction take place. At certain points there is enough energy to produce **ATP** by **oxidative phosphorylation**.

Note: Oxidative phosphorylation is the coupling of electron transport and ATP production in the presence of oxygen.

How much energy is produced in respiration?

It is generally assumed that for each reduced **NAD** sufficient energy is released to produce **3 ATP** molecules in the electron transport chain. Reduced **FAD** enters the chain further along than reduced NAD and there is only sufficient energy available to produce **2 ATP**.

The overall energy budget for aerobic respiration of one glucose molecule can be summarised in the following table.

Stage of respiration	Site	Reduced NAD	Reduced FAD	ATP by substrate-level phosphorylation	ATP by oxidative phosphorylation
Glycolysis	cytoplasm	2		2	
Link reaction	mitochondrial matrix	2			
Krebs cycle	mitochondrial matrix	6	2	2	
Electron transport chain	inner mitochondrial membrane				34 (10 x 3) + (2 x 2)
Totals				4	34

Theoretically each molecule produces up to **38 ATP** as shown in the table.

Note: The 38 ATP produced from a molecule of glucose is a theoretical maximum. In reality for each molecule of glucose the value is likely to be closer to 30 as explained below. On average, reduced NAD is likely to produce closer to 2.5 ATP molecules and reduced FAD 1.5 rather than the idealistic 3 and 2 respectively. This can be for a number of reasons, e.g. the NAD can be used as a reducing agent for other metabolic compounds, not just those involved in respiration. Energy is also used in transporting the reduced NAD (and other molecules, e.g. pyruvate) from the cytoplasm into the mitochondrion, energy which should be incorporated into the respiration budget.

Summary of the biochemistry of respiration

The following diagram summarises the four stages of respiration.

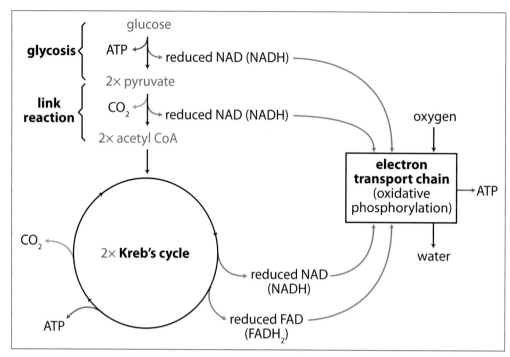

Summary of the biochemistry of respiration of glucose

As we have worked through the biochemistry of respiration we have referred to the mitochondrion on many occasions. The mitochondrion is the organelle of respiration – although you should not forget that a small amount of ATP can be produced by glycolysis in the cytoplasm. The following diagram summarises the role of the mitochondrion in respiration.

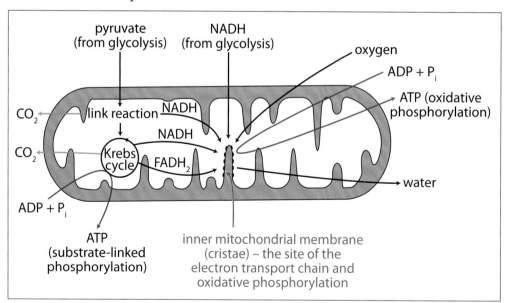

The role of the mitochondrion in the respiration of glucose

The process of the respiration of glucose can be summarised by the following equation.

$$C_6H_{12}O_6 + 6O_2 \rightarrow 6CO_2 + 6 H_2O + \text{energy (38 ATP)}$$

In the previous section we reviewed where the (theoretical) 38 ATP are produced. The oxygen is necessary for the electron transport process to be completed and it is used as the final electron acceptor – without oxygen the carriers would remain reduced. The water is produced as a waste product at the same point where the oxygen is used. The origin of the six molecules of carbon dioxide produced for each molecule of glucose respired can be identified from the previous sections – the decarboxylation reaction in the link reaction and the two decarboxylations in the Krebs cycle (each × 2 for reasons discussed before).

Other respiratory substrates

While glucose is the primary respiratory substrate in many living organisms, it is not the only one. If glucose supplies are low, **fat** (and eventually **protein** in near-starvation conditions) can be utilised.

When triglycerides are hydrolysed into glycerol and fatty acids, the **glycerol** enters the glycolysis pathway with the **fatty acids** entering at the acetyl CoA stage. Triglycerides are very energy rich (39 kJ g^{-1}) compared to carbohydrate (16 kJ g^{-1}). Proteins are hydrolysed to **amino acids**. Following the removal of the amino group by deamination, the residue enters the cycle as acetyl CoA (main point), pyruvate, or as one of the intermediate compounds in the Krebs cycle. Other carbohydrates can be used; fructose enters glycolysis and other more complex carbohydrates can be broken down to glucose or a similar sugar before entering glycolysis. The various pathways for the different respiratory substrates are summarised in the next diagram.

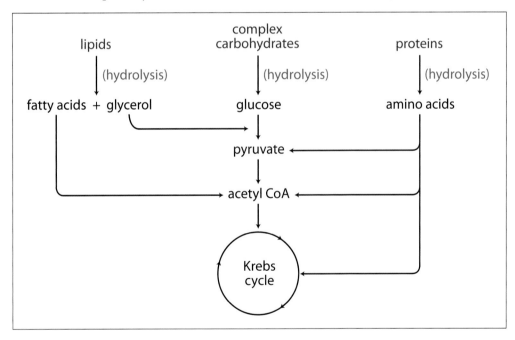

The metabolism of different respiratory substrates

The diagram highlights that other respiratory substrates originating from fat or protein are eventually channelled through the Krebs cycle with many entering at the acetyl CoA stage. For this reason **acetyl CoA** is often referred to as the 'hub' of the various respiratory pathways.

Aerobic and anaerobic respiration

The processes discussed in the earlier sections describe what happens when oxygen is available, i.e. **aerobic respiration**. When oxygen is not available, **anaerobic respiration** can take place.

Although oxygen is only used in the electron transport chain, without it the link reaction, Krebs cycle or the electron transport chain (the processes that take place in the mitochondrion) cannot take place.

In anaerobic respiration, glycolysis will only continue if its products are removed and not allowed to accumulate. The pyruvate is converted to lactate in animals and ethanol in plants and yeast. However, it is also necessary that the reduced NAD formed during glycolysis is oxidised again so that (oxidised) NAD will be available to take up further hydrogen atoms from glycolysis. If this did not happen all the NAD would be reduced and glycolysis would stop as there would be no hydrogen acceptors available. The 'mopping up' of these hydrogen atoms is achieved by the hydrogen being used in the reactions between the pyruvate and the lactate / ethanol.

Glycolysis is the only energy producing stage of anaerobic respiration. There is a net gain of only **2 ATP**, clearly very inefficient when compared to aerobic respiration. However, it is a relatively **fast process** – it takes place throughout the **cytoplasm** and substances do not have to diffuse in and out of the mitochondrion in addition to it being only a very short part of the normal aerobic pathway.

Not surprisingly, aerobic respiration is the main respiratory pathway in active and complex living organisms. However, most living organisms can carry out anaerobic respiration in some of their tissues for a short period of time.

Anaerobic respiration in animals

Anaerobic respiration in animals is summarised by the diagram below.

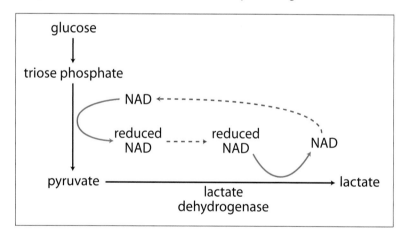

In animals the ability to respire anaerobically can be very advantageous. In healthy mammals including humans, anaerobic respiration is most likely to take place in the skeletal muscles as a consequence of strenuous exercise. It is important to note that during strenuous exercise the muscles will be respiring **both** aerobically and anaerobically, but that the additional anaerobic respiration provides **extra energy** above and beyond what the aerobic respiration can provide. This extra energy may not be much compared with that produced in aerobic respiration, but it may be enough to make the crucial difference between escaping from a predator or not, or if human, winning that race.

Note: Before the anaerobic pathway is used the animal will physiologically maximise ATP production from aerobic respiration. This will involve increased breathing and heart rates to ensure that as much oxygen (and glucose) reaches the muscles and the operation of the Bohr shift to maximise the release of oxygen by haemoglobin. Anaerobic respiration is very much the last resort.

The lactate produced by anaerobic respiration accumulates in the muscles and can cause muscle fatigue and cramp. It is eventually removed when sufficient oxygen becomes available again and anaerobic respiration is no longer necessary. The lactate is oxidised back to pyruvate and at that stage can enter the link reaction or be converted into glycogen for storage. The conversion of the lactate back to pyruvate involves oxidation so oxygen is used in the process. The extra oxygen used (above and beyond other metabolic requirements) to convert the lactate back to pyruvate and / or used to resynthesise depleted ATP is called the **oxygen debt**.

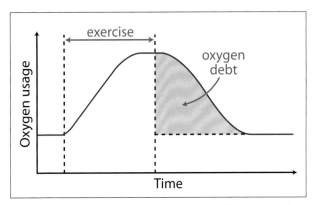

The oxygen debt

Anaerobic respiration in plants and fungi

In plants and fungi the end product of anaerobic respiration is **ethanol**, not lactate. Additionally, anaerobic respiration in plants and fungi produces **carbon dioxide** as a waste product. Anaerobic respiration in plants and fungi is summarised by the diagram on the right.

The ethanol is not reconverted back to pyruvate but is eliminated as a waste product. The value of anaerobic respiration to plants and fungi is different to that in animals. A significant part of most plants (e.g. roots) or fungi penetrates through soil or other substrata. Oxygen levels can often be low in these environments and the ability to respire anaerobically allows the production of ATP to be maintained. The much lower metabolic rate in plants / fungi, compared to the more complex animals, means that the lower ATP yield from anaerobic respiration is not as significant an issue.

Anaerobic respiration in plants and fungi

Note: Anaerobic respiration can only use glucose (or other carbohydrate) as a respiratory substrate. As the breakdown products of fat and protein enter the pathway well through glycolysis, or beyond, they cannot be used for anaerobic respiration.

The respiratory quotient

Analysis of the volume of carbon dioxide released during respiration relative to the amount of oxygen consumed provides information about the type of respiratory substrate used and the type of respiration (aerobic or anaerobic) taking place.

The respiratory quotient (RQ) is the volume (or number of molecules) of carbon dioxide released divided by the volume (or number of molecules) of oxygen consumed and can be represented by the following equation.

$$RQ = \frac{\text{Volume (molecules) of } CO_2 \text{ released}}{\text{Volume (molecules) of } O_2 \text{ consumed}}$$

In the following examples the RQ can be worked out by using the number of molecules equating to carbon dioxide and oxygen in the equations.

Glucose

$$C_6H_{12}O_6 + 6O_2 \longrightarrow 6CO_2 + 6H_2O + \text{energy}$$
(glucose)

$$RQ = \frac{6}{6} = 1 \quad \text{(typical carbohydrate RQ)}$$

Palmitic acid (a fatty acid)

$$C_{16}H_{32}O_2 + 23O_2 \longrightarrow 16CO_2 + 16H_2O + \text{energy}$$
(palmitic acid)

$$RQ = \frac{16}{23} = 0.7 \quad \text{(typical lipid RQ)}$$

The RQ values obtained for glucose (carbohydrate) and palmitic acid (a fatty acid) represent the overall values for carbohydrates and lipids.

The table below shows the RQ values for the main groups of substances used as respiratory substrates.

Respiratory substrate	RQ
carbohydrates	1
lipids (triglycerides)	0.7
proteins	0.9

The values in the table represent RQ values when only the substance in question is being respired. In many organisms, a mixture of respiratory substrates is used. Therefore the actual RQ value obtained is likely to fall somewhere between 1 – 0.7. In humans, a value around 0.85 is normal; this is because humans typically use a combination of carbohydrates and lipids as respiratory substrates.

What else can RQ values tell us?

A RQ value of **more than 1** suggests that **anaerobic respiration** is taking place. Remember that when anaerobic respiration is taking place, normally both aerobic and anaerobic respiration is taking place. The aerobic component will give a RQ value between 0.7 – 1 but anaerobic respiration will involve the production of carbon dioxide (in plants and fungi) without the input of oxygen. If enough anaerobic respiration is taking place this will push the RQ value above 1 – the higher the value is above 1 the higher the proportion of anaerobic respiration.

Note 1: If data shows a RQ value of more than 1, it will almost certainly be for plant or fungal tissue – remember anaerobic respiration in animals does not produce carbon dioxide.

Note 2: If the RQ value exceeds 1 **both** aerobic **and** anaerobic respiration are taking place. The RQ value for anaerobic respiration only is infinity.

Under normal conditions the RQ value can vary considerably. In humans, following a meal rich in carbohydrate the RQ can approach 1, but after a number of hours without eating it is likely to drop as lipids will be used. Variation is also very likely when measuring plant RQ values during the daytime. Photosynthesis also involves gas exchange and will almost certainly cloud the RQ values.

Practical work

Calculating RQ values

RQ values can be calculated using the simple respirometer we came across at AS level. To calculate the RQ value, it is necessary to calculate both the oxygen uptake and carbon dioxide production.

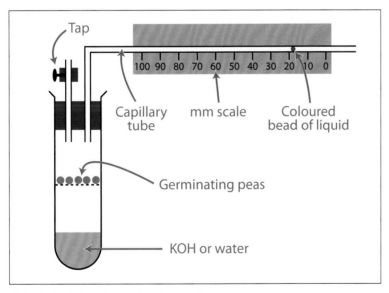

Calculating RQ values using the respirometer

Calculating oxygen uptake - The carbon dioxide produced in respiration by the germinating peas is absorbed by the **potassium hydroxide (KOH)** in the respirometer. Oxygen taken in leads to a reduction in volume of air in the closed system and therefore the pressure falls. The coloured bead of liquid (or bubble within liquid) is drawn along the capillary tube towards the respirometer due to the reduction in pressure. The distance moved by the coloured bead represents the oxygen used in respiration.

The actual quantity of oxygen used can be obtained by calculating the volume of the lumen of the capillary tube travelled by the coloured bead.

Calculating carbon dioxide production – Repeat the process with the KOH replaced by **water**. Carbon dioxide produced in respiration is not absorbed as there is no KOH present. If over time the bead does **not** move, this means there is no pressure change – therefore the carbon dioxide produced in respiration must be **exactly the same** as the oxygen taken in, e.g. if the respiring tissue originally used 20 mm^3 of oxygen (calculated with potassium hydroxide present) in 10 minutes, then if the same tissue (organism(s)) is used for 10 minutes with water replacing the KOH, and the bead does not move, it can be assumed that 20 mm^3 of carbon dioxide is produced. In this example the RQ value = 1.

In practice, there may be more or less carbon dioxide produced than oxygen used therefore the coloured bead may move a small distance in either direction from its starting position. If the coloured bead moves **away** from the respirometer there is **more carbon dioxide produced than oxygen taken in** but if it moves **closer** to the respirometer there is **less carbon dioxide produced than oxygen taken in** (i.e. the carbon dioxide produced does not compensate for the pressure reduction caused by the oxygen uptake). If, in our example in the previous paragraph, the coloured bead moved 3 mm^3 away from the respirometer, when the water is used, the amount of carbon dioxide produced is 20 + 3 = 23 mm^3. Therefore the RQ = 23/20 = 1.15 suggesting that **anaerobic respiration** is taking place.

As well as being able to identify that anaerobic respiration is occurring, the apparatus can be used to identify the respiratory substrate(s) being used. Germinating peas can have a RQ value of between 0.7 – 0.8, a consequence of respiring stored lipid.

In this type of experiment, it is critical that all possible **variables are controlled**. Where possible it is often best to use the same apparatus for calculating the oxygen uptake (with KOH) and for calculating carbon dioxide production (with water) with the **same living organisms** (this ensures factors such as age and metabolic rate of the organisms are controlled as far as possible). Other variables such as **temperature** can be controlled by placing the apparatus in a **water bath** at the same temperature for both parts of the experiment – the control of temperature is important as changes in temperature can affect both rate of respiration and gas volume in the system. It is also important to calculate oxygen uptake and carbon dioxide production over the same **time** period. In the particular experiment described above, it would be important to cover the test tube containing the germinating peas with **foil** to prevent photosynthesis taking place.

Using redox indicators to demonstrate dehydrogenation in respiration

At several stages in respiration, hydrogen atoms are removed from molecules in reactions.

Dehydrogenase enzymes catalyse these reactions and the process is described as dehydrogenation The hydrogen atoms are taken up by NAD (or FAD) forming reduced NAD (or reduced FAD).

It is possible to use **redox indicators**, chemicals which are a different colour when reduced compared to their oxidised state to demonstrate dehydrogenation taking place. The indicators (as opposed to NAD / FAD) take up the hydrogen and become reduced.

The colour changes for three redox indicators are shown in the following table.

Redox indicator	Colour when oxidised	Colour when reduced
Methylene blue	blue	colourless
DCPIP	blue	colourless
Triphenyltetrazolium (TTC)	colourless	pink

By adding the redox indicator to suspensions containing the living material, e.g. yeast, it is possible to demonstrate dehydrogenase activity or to compare activity in different conditions.

Exam questions

1. The diagram below summarises the various stages involved in the respiration of a glucose molecule.

   (a) (i) Name the missing compound in the empty box. [1]

   (ii) State where in the cell process **A** occurs. [1]

   (iii) Name each of the processes which take place at locations **B** and **C**. [2]

   (b) The diagram summarises the respiration of glucose. Describe how fatty acids are respired. [2]

   Question taken from CCEA's Biology Assessment Unit A2 2, Biochemistry, Genetics and Evolutionary Trends, June 2010, © CCEA 2013

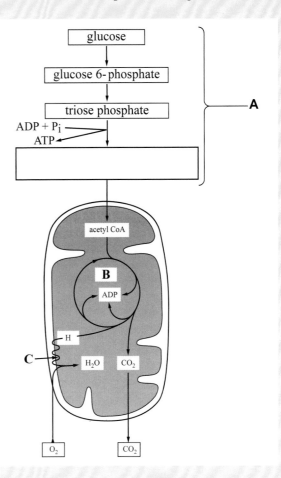

Exam questions

2. (a) The diagram on the right shows part of the
process of aerobic respiration.

   (i) Name the respiratory process that
   produces pyruvate. [1]

   (ii) Name molecule A. [1]

   (iii) State the precise location of the
   electron transport chain. [1]

   (iv) Explain how ATP is produced in the
   electron transport chain. [4]

   (b) An investigation into the respiratory
   quotient (RQ) of yeast cells under
   different conditions was undertaken. The
   resulting RQ values are shown in the
   table below. Identify the missing
   'respiratory substrate(s)' and 'type(s) of
   respiration'.

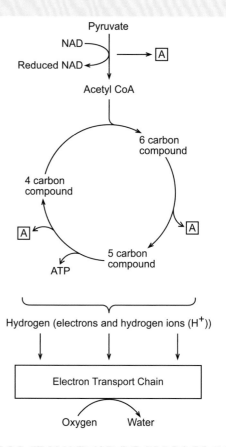

RQ value	Respiratory substrate(s)	Type(s) of respiration
0.68		aerobic
0.84	mixed	aerobic
1.24	carbohydrate	

Question taken from CCEA's Biology Assessment Unit A2 2, Biochemistry,
Genetics and Evolutionary Trends, May 2011, © CCEA 2013

Chapter 10 – Photosynthesis

In photosynthesis energy in sunlight is used to make complex organic compounds from inorganic compounds. Chlorophyll is the major light-trapping pigment involved in harnessing the Sun's energy. Water and carbon dioxide are the raw materials used and glucose is an initial end product. The process of photosynthesis can be summarised by the equation:

$$6CO_2 + 6H_2O \rightarrow C_6H_{12}O_6 + 6O_2$$

The site of photosynthesis

In most plants the **leaf** is the organ specialised for photosynthesis. In the leaf, the cells in the layer immediately under the upper epidermis, the **palisade layer**, are highly adapted for this role. The palisade cells are therefore close to the leaf upper surface (where most light enters the leaf), are tightly packed together and have numerous chloroplasts in their cytoplasm. The spongy mesophyll layer below the palisade cells is less tightly packed and has numerous large air spaces that form a continuous pathway with the stomata in the lower epidermis. This facilitates gas exchange between the palisade cells and the outside environment.

Leaves tend to orientate themselves in such a way that they maximise incident light reaching their upper surfaces (as with these nettle plants)

The chloroplast

In green plants photosynthesis takes place in the **chloroplast**. The chloroplast is a large organelle (up to 20 μm in length and 5 μm wide) highly adapted for photosynthesis. The chlorophyll is arranged in a system of flattened membranes called **thylakoids**. The thylakoids contain the **chlorophyll** (and other plant pigments) that absorb the light energy. They also contain systems of **electron carriers** and associated enzymes involved in the photosynthesis reactions. Thylakoids are typically arranged in clumps or 'stacks' of membranes called **grana** (singular **granum**). As the grana contain concentrated areas of light-absorbing photopigments, much of the light harvesting takes place at these points in the chloroplast. The thylakoids are linked together by **intergranal lamellae**.

Although light harvesting takes place in the thylakoids, the carbon dioxide is used ('fixed') and sugars and other compounds are made in a cyclical series of reactions that take place in the **stroma**. In effect, photosynthesis involves two distinct, but interlinked phases, which take place in the thylakoids and the stroma. The reactions that take place in the stroma are dependent on a steady supply of products from the reactions associated with the absorption of light energy.

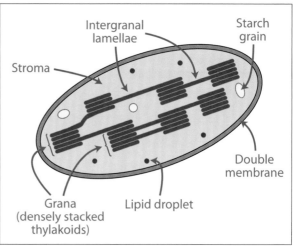

The chloroplast

Absorption and action spectra

Not surprisingly, there is a close association between light absorption and the rate of photosynthesis in the chloroplast.

The absorption spectrum – the absorption spectrum can be represented by a graph that shows the relative **absorption of light** at particular wavelengths. The absorption can be represented as a graph that shows the overall absorption of light by all the pigments that absorb light in photosynthesis and / or can show the light absorbed by individual pigments, for example chlorophyll *a*, chlorophyll *b* and carotene. Absorption spectra of individual pigments show that the pigments complement each other by absorbing light over a different range of wavelengths – this ensures that by absorbing light over as great a range of wavelengths as possible more light energy can be harvested. The relationship between the different pigments and their roles in harvesting light energy will be discussed in the following sections.

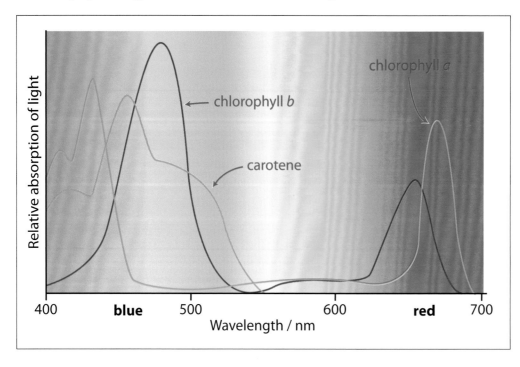

Absorption spectra of the main photosynthetic pigments

Note: Absorption spectra show the relative proportions of light that can be absorbed at different **wavelengths**. It is not necessarily linked to light **intensity**.

The action spectrum – The action spectrum is the **rate of photosynthesis** that takes place at different wavelengths. Comparison of the graphs of the absorption spectra of the main pigments (see diagram on page 164) or the overall absorption spectrum (showing the light absorbed by all pigments) and the action spectrum show a very close correlation as seen in the diagram below – the rate of photosynthesis is high for those wavelengths over which most light is absorbed (and converse).

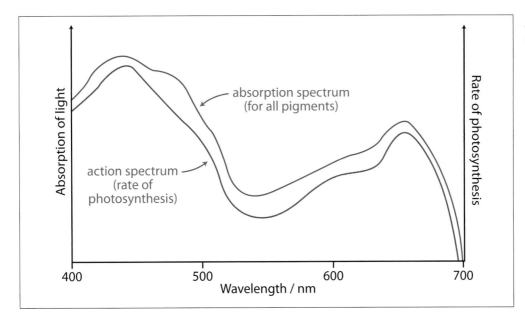

Absorption and action spectra

The biochemistry of photosynthesis

The process of photosynthesis can be conveniently separated into three main stages:

- **light harvesting** - the absorption of light in the thylakoids; a consequence of which is to raise the energy level of the electrons in chlorophyll.

- the **light-dependent stage** – energised electrons are used to make the energy-rich compounds ATP and reduced NADP. These reactions take place in or on the thylakoid membranes of the grana.

- The **light-independent stage** – the products of the light reaction are used to make simple carbohydrate. Carbon dioxide is fixed as part of the cyclical series of reactions that take place in the stroma.

Light harvesting

The chlorophyll and other pigments (**accessory pigments**) are located in the **thylakoid membranes**. They are arranged in clusters, with each cluster containing several hundred molecules. Each cluster is called an **antenna complex**. A molecule of **chlorophyll *a***, called the **primary pigment**, is situated at the base of the antenna complex in a region called the **reaction centre**.

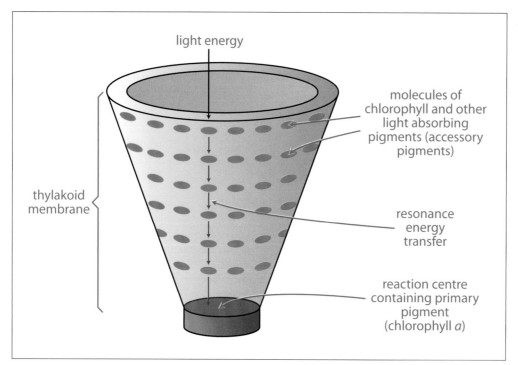

An antenna complex

The whole antenna complex harvests light over a range of wavelengths, due to the presence of different pigments with different absorption maxima. As light energy is absorbed throughout the complex, special proteins help pass the absorbed energy from one molecule to its adjacent molecule by the process of **resonance transfer**. The energy is funnelled in the direction of the reaction centre. The nature of resonance transfer requires the molecules in the antenna complex to be part of a regularly arranged structure.

Note: A key feature of resonance transfer is that it is energy that is transferred, not electrons – compare this with the reactions of the light-dependent stage in the next section.

Each antenna complex forms a **photosystem**. In the light-dependent stage of photosynthesis, there are two different types of photosystem as we shall see in the next section.

The light-dependent stage

The reactions of the light-dependent stage also take place in the **thylakoid membranes** and are very tightly linked to the process of light harvesting.

The arrangement of many accessory pigments in an antenna complex ensures that if sufficient light is available, enough energy can pass to the reaction centre allowing electrons in **chlorophyll *a*** (the **primary pigment**) to move to higher energy levels – they become **excited** in the process of **photoactivation**. If enough energy is available the electrons are **emitted** and taken up by an **electron acceptor** – in effect, the chlorophyll becomes an **electron donor**. The electron acceptor that accepts the emitted electrons is arranged at the start of an **electron carrier chain**, with **cytochromes** forming the carriers in the chain itself.

Note 1: Carriers are progressively reduced and oxidised in a series of redox reactions as they take up and pass on electrons.

Note 2: Each new carrier is at a slightly lower energy level than the previous one, so the electrons lose energy as they pass along the chain.

Note 3: At certain stages in the electron transport chain there is sufficient energy available to make ATP from ADP and P_i.

Note 4: Note the similarities in the previous three points to the process of electron (hydrogen) transfer in respiration.

In photosynthesis (as with the electron transport chain in respiration), the formation of ATP is tightly coupled with electron transport. However, in photosynthesis the energy comes from light so it is called **photophosphorylation**.

Of course, it is necessary that the electrons that are excited and subsequently emitted from the antenna complex are replaced in the reaction centre. These come from the **splitting of water** (**photolysis**). When the water is split the hydrogen dissociates into hydrogen ions (protons) and electrons. The electrons are used to replace the electrons lost during photoactivation and the hydrogen ions are used later in the light-dependent reaction (see next diagram) with **oxygen** being given off as a waste product.

The photosystem that emits the electrons that leads to the electron transfer as described above is **photosystem II** (**PSII**). Photosystem II is also referred to as P680 as the absorption peak of the chlorophyll *a* molecule is **680 nm**.

As the diagram on page 168 shows, the electron carrier chain is linked to another photosystem – **photosystem I** (**PS I**) or P700 as it has a chlorophyll *a* primary pigment molecule with an absorption peak of **700 nm**.

The chlorophyll *a* molecule in photosystem I emits electrons, as happens in photosystem II described earlier, if enough light energy reaches the antenna complex. These electrons are trapped by another electron acceptor and subsequently passed on to **NADP** to form **reduced NADP** or **NADPH**. To provide the hydrogen necessary to reduce NADP the electrons combine with the hydrogen ions (protons) provided by the splitting of water in photolysis.

Note 1: NADP is nicotinamide adenine dinucleotide phosphate – a very similar but subtly different coenzyme to the NAD hydrogen acceptor involved in respiration.

Note 2: The NADP is really $NADP^+$ and it is $NADPH + H^+$ that are formed. But again, as with the biochemistry of respiration, it is acceptable (and easier for most students) to use NADP and reduced NADP or NADPH.

In photosystem I electrons lost from the chlorophyll *a* are replaced by electrons passing down the electron chain, electrons that originated in photosystem II.

The electron pathway and reactions of the light-dependent stage, as summarised in the diagram on the right, is described as the **Z-scheme**.

Note 1: NADP is the **final electron acceptor** in photosynthesis (it is oxygen in respiration).

Note 2: The production of ATP as described in this chapter (also applies to oxidative phosphorylation in respiration) is non-cyclic with the electrons passing through the electron transport chain needing to be continually supplied from earlier reactions. Consequently the production of ATP in photosynthesis is referred to as **non-cyclic photophosphorylation**.

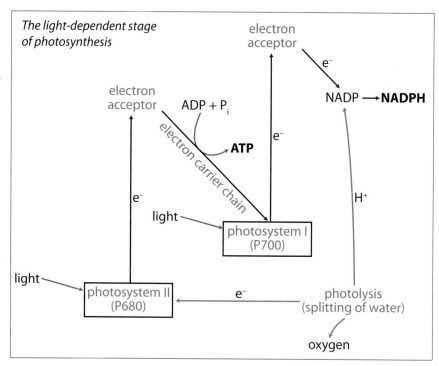

The light-dependent stage of photosynthesis

The end products of the light-dependent reaction are **ATP** and **NADPH (reduced NADP)**, both of which are used in the light-independent reaction.

The light-independent stage

The light-independent stage takes place in the **stroma** of the chloroplast and it is dependent on products (ATP and NADPH) of the light-dependent stage. It is during this light-independent stage that the inorganic carbon dioxide is 'fixed' (incorporated) into organic compounds.

Carbon dioxide that has diffused into the chloroplast combines with the **5-carbon** compound **ribulose bisphosphate (RuBP)**, a reaction catalysed by the enzyme ribulose bisphosphate carboxylase (**rubisco**). This forms two molecules of the **3-carbon glycerate phosphate (GP)**. **ATP** and **NADPH (reduced NADP)** are used to reduce the glycerate phosphate to **triose phosphate (TP)**. The NADPH provides the reducing power required and the ATP provides the energy.

Five out of every six molecules of triose phosphate produced are used in the recycling of ribulose bisphosphate. ATP (also from the

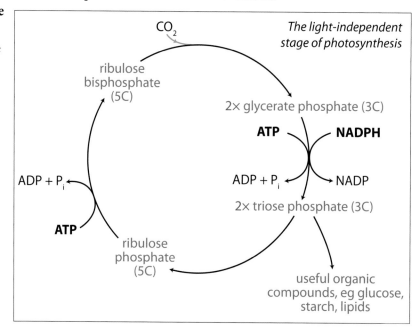

The light-independent stage of photosynthesis

light-dependent reaction) is used to provide energy and also to provide the phosphate to make the RuBP. The regeneration of the RuBP is a cyclical process as seen in the last diagram. One sixth (approx 17%) of the triose phosphate made in the light-independent reaction (the net 'gain') is used to produce other organic molecules such as glucose, sucrose, starch, glycerol, fatty acids and amino acids (the latter using absorbed nitrate).

Note: Although called the light-independent stage as direct light is **not** required, the light-independent stage will usually only take place when light is present (as it requires products from the light-dependent stage). When the biochemistry of photosynthesis was first worked out, the two stages were referred to as the 'light reaction' and the 'dark reaction' – terms not used now as they do not identify the requirement for light in the light-dependent stage, nor the fact that the light-independent stage takes place almost always in the light (and not in the dark).

The following two diagrams help demonstrate and explain the link between the light-dependent stage and the light-independent stage.

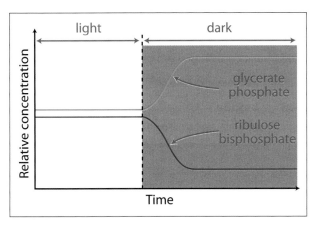

The effect of light and darkness on the concentrations of glycerate phosphate and ribulose bisphosphate

Explanation: When the light is removed (the plant is in darkness) the light-dependent reaction stops. Consequently ATP and NADPH will no longer be made and be available for the light-independent reaction. This means that glycerate phosphate cannot be converted into triose phosphate, leading to a buildup of glycerate phosphate and a reduction in ribulose bisphosphate (as the ribulose bisphosphate present in the stroma fixes CO_2 to form glycerate phosphate and no more can be regenerated from triose phosphate). The concentrations of each level off as the cycle grinds to a halt.

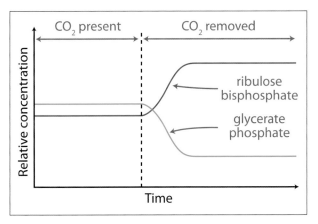

The effect of the presence and absence of carbon dioxide on the concentrations of glycerate phosphate and ribulose bisphosphate

Explanation: When CO_2 is no longer available it cannot be 'fixed' and combine with ribulose bisphosphate therefore glycerate phosphate cannot be formed. The ribulose bisphosphate therefore builds up and the glycerate phosphate already in the system gets converted to triose phosphate leading to its rapid fall. As before the concentrations of each level off as the cycle stops.

Summary of the role of the chloroplast

The previous sections have described the reactions that take place in the different regions of the chloroplast. The following diagram outlines the role of the chloroplast in photosynthesis.

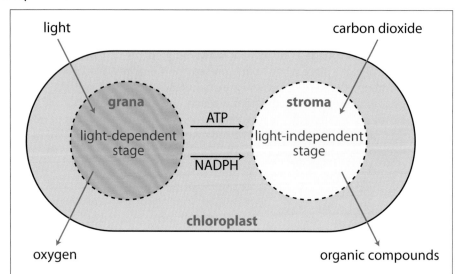

The chloroplast and photosynthesis

Case studies (two famous historical photosynthesis experiments)

1 Engelmann (1880s) was able to show that photosynthesis mainly used light from the blue and red parts of the spectrum. He used the filamentous alga *Spirogyra*, a genus that typically has its chloroplasts arranged in a spiral pattern that 'spiral' just inside the cell wall of each cell, analogous to the appearance of the spiral thickening of lignin in xylem. Engelmann also used motile, aerobic bacteria in his investigation, reasoning that the bacteria are likely to cluster in oxygen-rich regions. By passing light through a prism (and thus separating light into its spectral components) and then onto the *Spirogyra* in the presence of the bacteria, Engelmann observed that the motile bacteria clustered close to the algal chloroplasts in the cells that received blue and red light as shown in the diagram below.

Engelmann's conclusion was that the bacteria (being aerobic) accumulated in greater numbers around the parts of the chloroplasts that photosynthesised at the fastest rates and therefore produced most oxygen. The cells, and chloroplasts, in the red and blue light (but not the green) were photosynthesising at the fastest rates showing that the alga could utilise the red and blue part of the spectrum but that green light was less readily absorbed.

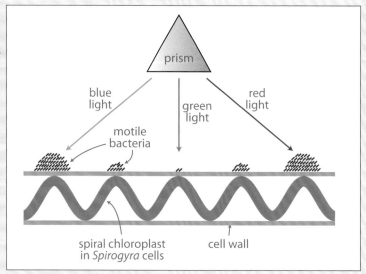

Engelmann's experiment showing that blue and red light was used in photosynthesis

2 Calvin The light-independent reaction is also called the Calvin Cycle as it was worked out by Melvin Calvin and his co-workers just over sixty years ago. Calvin's experiment is referred to as the 'lollipop' experiment as the apparatus he used resembled a lollipop, flattened from front to back.

In the experiment, Calvin added radioactive carbon dioxide ($^{14}CO_2$) to a suspension of the autotrophic protoctistan *Chlorella* in the 'lollipop' as shown in the diagram below.

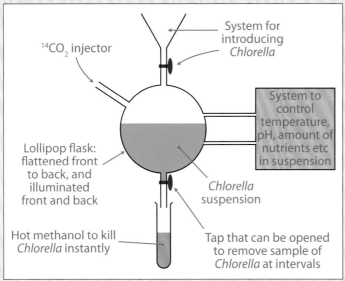

Calvin's lollipop apparatus used in working out the light-independent stage of photosynthesis

After a **very short interval of time** the tap was opened and the *Chlorella* was released into the hot methanol, killing it **immediately** and preventing any further reactions taking place. Following this, the *Chlorella* was homogenised and the compounds present identified by chromatography. Calvin deduced that any compounds present containing radioactive carbon must have been produced following the 'fixing' of the radioactive carbon dioxide in the light-independent stage of photosynthesis. Using this logic, he was able to identify **glycerate phosphate** as the first compound produced.

By very gradually increasing the time interval between adding the radioactive carbon dioxide and killing the *Chlorella*, he was able to identify the compounds produced at successive stages of the cycle. The graph on the right shows that the number of radioactive compounds identified increased as the time interval the *Chlorella* was exposed to the radioactive carbon dioxide increased. This is consistent with successive compounds in the light-independent stage being labelled with increasing time. Eventually the number of different radioactively labelled compounds identified levelled off as all the compounds in the light-independent stage (and other compounds subsequently formed) were identified.

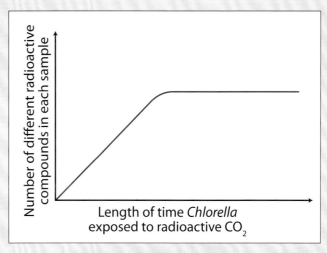

The relationship between the number of different radioactively labelled compounds formed and the length of time Chlorella was exposed to radioactive CO_2.

External factors affecting the rate of photosynthesis

Limiting factors in photosynthesis

Light intensity, **carbon dioxide** concentration and **temperature** are the main factors that affect the rate of photosynthesis. The actual photosynthetic rate at any one time is determined by whichever of these factors is least favourable – the least favourable factor being the **limiting factor**.

Two key features of limiting factors.

- If a factor is limiting, increasing its amount will increase the rate of photosynthesis.

- Increasing the rate of the other (non-limiting) factors will not increase the rate of photosynthesis, if the rate of the limiting factor is left unchanged.

The following graph illustrates the effects of light intensity, carbon dioxide level and temperature on photosynthesis, demonstrating the principle of limiting factors.

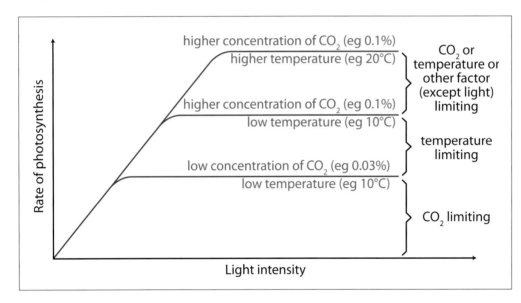

The effects of light intensity, carbon dioxide concentration and temperature on rates of photosynthesis

Light intensity and photosynthesis – The graph above shows that at low light intensities, light is the limiting factor, irrespective of the levels of carbon dioxide and temperature.

In most natural ecosystems, light tends to become limiting as dusk (nightfall) approaches, with photosynthesis unable to take place during the darkness of the night. In early morning (dawn) light usually ceases to be the limiting factor. However, light intensity can also become limiting for periods during very dark, cloudy days when temperature and carbon dioxide levels are high (or adequate).

If light intensity is limiting, it exerts its effect through there being not enough **ATP** and **NADPH** produced in the **light-dependent** stage of photosynthesis.

Carbon dioxide concentration and photosynthesis – The atmospheric level of carbon dioxide is around 390 ppm (approx. 0.04%); 0.04% is a sub-optimal level for most plants, so increasing atmospheric levels of carbon dioxide leads to higher rates of photosynthesis (the optimum level for many plant species is around 0.1% carbon dioxide). On a bright summer day, when light intensity and temperature levels are not limiting, carbon dioxide can be the limiting factor. Growers of glasshouse crops often artificially raise carbon dioxide levels to increase growth rates.

If carbon dioxide levels are increased, there is more available for the **carboxylation of RuBP** in the **light-independent** stage, allowing more glycerate phosphate to be formed.

Temperature and photosynthesis – Temperature can limit the rate of photosynthesis if light intensity and carbon dioxide levels are not limiting. In Britain, it is often the temperature that limits grass and other plant growth during the winter. Glasshouse growers can produce optimum growing conditions by increasing temperature (and light intensity and carbon dioxide levels) as necessary.

If temperature is increased (up to an optimum) the **enzyme-catalysed reactions** of the **light-independent** stage of photosynthesis occur at a faster rate.

Note 1: The optimum temperature for growth in many plants is around 25 °C (not 37 °C).

Note 2: Temperature is a limiting factor at low levels, but will also reduce photosynthesis rate if too high, due to enzymes being denatured.

A shortage of **water** can also affect photosynthesis. Unlike light intensity, carbon dioxide levels and temperature, shortage of water will not affect photosynthesis directly. However, if water is in short supply stomata will close as part of the plant's response in reducing water loss. Additionally, the plant will wilt and the orientation of the leaves will change reducing incident solar radiation and many reactions will slow down. A dehydrated plant is likely to be dead long before there is not enough water available for the light-dependent stage.

Gross photosynthesis, net photosynthesis and the compensation point

We have come across the terms Gross Primary Productivity (GPP) and Net Primary Productivity (NPP) in Chapter 7.

The terms gross photosynthesis and net photosynthesis are very similar to GPP and NPP respectively and are also an indication of the organic material (carbohydrate) produced and the carbohydrate gain when respiratory losses are taken into consideration.

Gross photosynthesis = net photosynthesis + respiration

Note: The terms gross (and net) primary productivity can be regarded as more ecological concepts, providing information on carbohydrate produced in a unit area of the ecosystem. Gross or net photosynthesis is often used to provide information on the carbohydrate produced by a single plant, or even part of a plant.

Gross and net photosynthesis can be considered in terms of **carbon dioxide** or **oxygen exchange** or even change in organic (carbohydrate) content in a plant.

The following graph shows the typical pattern of carbon dioxide exchange in plants in different light intensities.

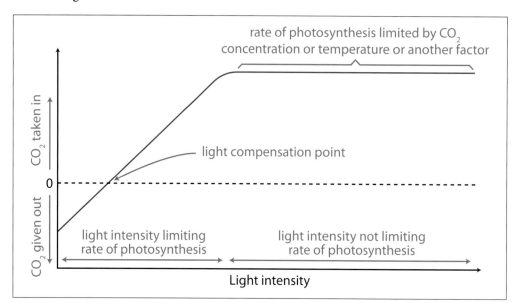

The effect of light intensity on the rate of photosynthesis with reference to rate of carbon dioxide exchange

At low light intensities carbon dioxide is given out (evolved) as the rate of respiration exceeds the rate of photosynthesis. The light **compensation point** is the point where there is no net intake or output of carbon dioxide (i.e. respiration and photosynthesis are taking place at the same rate).

The next diagram shows how carbon dioxide exchange takes place over a 24 hour period. For the plant to grow the area **X** (which represents net photosynthesis) must exceed the combined areas of **Y** (which represent respiratory losses).

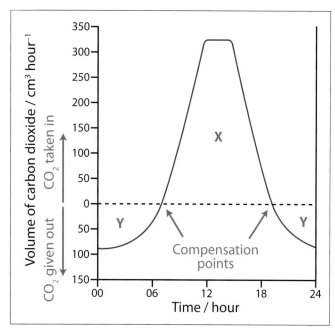

The net volume of carbon dioxide produced (and used) by a plant over a 24 hour period

Note 1: It is important to remember that respiration takes place throughout the 24 hour period – it is not restricted to the times where the line drops below 0. The line above the 0 shows the net intake of carbon dioxide, i.e. the carbon dioxide taken in by the plant above and beyond that produced in respiration (representing **net photosynthesis**).

Note 2: The same information can be easily demonstrated by measuring the relative levels of oxygen taken in and given out. The equivalent graph for oxygen demonstrating gas exchange in a typical plant over a 24 hour period will be an upside down mirror image of the carbon dioxide graph.

Practical work

The Audus apparatus

The Audus apparatus can be used to measure the rate of photosynthesis in different environmental conditions (e.g. different light intensities or different concentrations of carbon dioxide).

The gas produced (mainly oxygen) from photosynthesising pondweed is collected at the flared end of the capillary tube after a **set period of time** (e.g. 5 – 10 minutes). After this time, the gas collected is drawn into the capillary tube by pulling the plunger on the syringe until the **volume** (or length) of the bubble of oxygen produced can be measured on the scale. The experiment can be repeated with the independent variable changed as required.

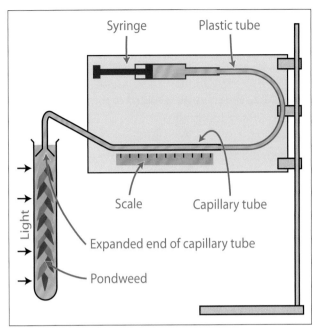

The Audus apparatus

As with many biology experiments, it is important to **control all variables** not being investigated. For example if the effect of light intensity on the rate of photosynthesis is being investigated, it is important to ensure that temperature is controlled by the use of a water bath and that carbon dioxide levels are not limiting by using hydrogencarbonate solution to produce carbon dioxide. The experiment should be **repeated** at least three times for each value of the independent variable to increase **reliability**.

Paper chromatography of plant pigments

The principle of paper chromatography is that some solutes are more soluble than others in the same solution. The more soluble substances will 'travel' further in a solvent that is moving through chromatography paper. Due to the separation of the different solutes by this process the different solutes present can be identified. The method is particularly useful in identifying the plant pigments present in a leaf. Unlike chromatography involving amino acids (see Chapter 1 in AS book) the plant pigments do not need developing using chemicals such as ninhydrin.

Paper chromatography of plant pigments does involve the following stages.

- Preparing the chromatogram
- Running the chromatogram
- Calculating R_f values

Preparing the chromatogram – the chromatography paper is cut to fit the tank / vessel used to hold it in a vertical position. The paper (chromatogram) should be long enough to allow attachment to the lid of the apparatus and to drop to just above the base of the tank. In due course solvent will be placed into the bottom of the tank – it is important that the chromatogram is long enough to extend into the volume of solvent being used.

A horiziontal line should be drawn in pencil a few centimetres above the base of the chromatogram. The key thing is that the line should be drawn in a position that will lie above the level of the solvent when the chromatogram is placed in the solvent.

The solution containing the plant pigments to be tested needs to be 'spotted' on the pencil line. The solution is added to a pre-determined position (origin) by a micro-pipette. After adding a drop of the solution it is then dried before the process is repeated. This allows the solution to be concentrated. At this stage the chromatogram has been prepared and it is now ready to 'run'.

It is important to ensure that the concentrated spot forms as small an area as possible – this is aided by ensuring that the spot is dry before adding an additional drop of solution. In addition, it is important to avoid contamination of the chromatogram – only hold the chromatogram at the edges and avoid setting it on laboratory benches that could be contaminated with a range of chemicals. Before placing the prepared chromatogram in the tank the solvent should be added to allow the atmosphere to become saturated.

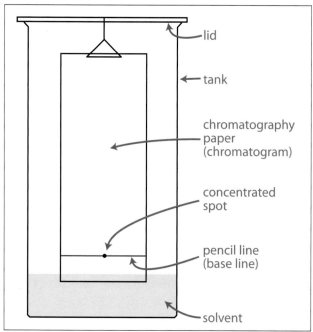

Preparing and running the chromatogram

Running the chromatogram – the chromatogram is carefully suspended into the solvent and attached to the lid of the tank. This is an important and risky stage. It is important to ensure that:

- the line (and concentrated spot(s)) do not make contact with the solvent

- the chromatogram is securely attached

- the chromatogram is not suspended at an angle – if it is at an angle, the solvent cannot 'run' the length of the chromatogram.

As the solvent 'runs' up the chromatogram it carries the plant pigments that begin to become separated as the process continues. The 'run' of the solvent should be stopped when it is well up the chromatogram but **before** it reaches the top.

Developing the chromatogram – the chromatogram should then be dried – before the solvent is dry it is important to mark the 'solvent front' on the chromatogram with a pencil.

Calculating R_f values – A R_f value is the distance moved by a solute (in this case one of the pigments) divided by the distance moved by the solvent front.

It is calculated by measuring the distance from the origin (initial position of concentrated spot) to the position of the solvent front and measuring the distance from the origin to the position of the plant pigment being investigated. As each plant pigment will extend over an area of the chromatogram, it is essential that a consistent approach is taken to measuring the length from the origin. Either the distance from the origin to the leading edge of the spot is measured or from the origin to the centre of the spot.

The R_f value is then calculated (e.g. X/Y in diagram for the plant pigment xanthophyll).

Note: A R_f value is always less than 1. So if you calculate a value greater than 1, you have probably got your two values the wrong way round.

As the leaves of most plants have the same pigments for trapping light energy, chromatograms of leaf tissue from most plants will be similar in that they will show the pigments chlorophyll b, chlorophyll a, xanthophyll and carotene in the order shown in the following diagram.

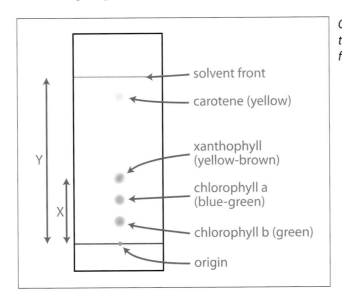

Chromatogram of the plant pigments from a typical plant

Demonstrating the role of hydrogen (electron) acceptors using a redox indicator (e.g. DCPIP)

In the light-dependent stage of photosynthesis, NADP is reduced by the electrons that have passed along the electron transport chain to form NADPH. A redox indicator such as DCPIP can also pick up electrons, but serves as an indicator as it changes colour as it does so. Using the example of DCPIP, the colour changes from blue to colourless as the indicator becomes reduced.

This investigation is normally carried out using **isolated chloroplasts**. The chloroplasts are obtained by homogenising leaves and centrifuging the homogenate to precipitate out the chloroplasts. If DCPIP is added to a chloroplast suspension and the experimental tube strongly illuminated, the DCPIP will turn from blue to colourless. Comparison can be made with the chloroplasts placed in darkness and with the DCPIP added to water (rather than chloroplasts) as a control.

Note: It is important to use isolated chloroplasts for a number of reasons including maximising electron production but also to avoid contamination with mitochondria. Reactions in mitochondria are also capable of reducing the DCPIP.

Exam questions

1. The enzyme ribulose bisphosphate carboxylase (Rubisco) catalyses the reaction between ribulose bisphosphate (RuBP) and carbon dioxide.

Genetically transformed plants can be produced using antisense RNA which results in the synthesis of less Rubisco enzyme. These are called 'reduced Rubisco plants'. They grow slowly and are stunted.

(a) (i) State the product of the reaction between ribulose bisphosphate and carbon dioxide. [1]

(ii) In the Calvin cycle, ribulose bisphosphate is regenerated from triose phosphate. State what else is required for the regeneration of ribulose bisphosphate. [1]

(iii) Explain why the 'reduced Rubisco plants' are slow growing and stunted. [2]

(b) Leaves from a 'reduced Rubisco plant' and an untreated (control) plant were used in a series of experiments. The graph below shows the rate of carbon dioxide assimilation by both plants at different light intensities. A temperature of 25°C and a high concentration of carbon dioxide were maintained at all light intensities.

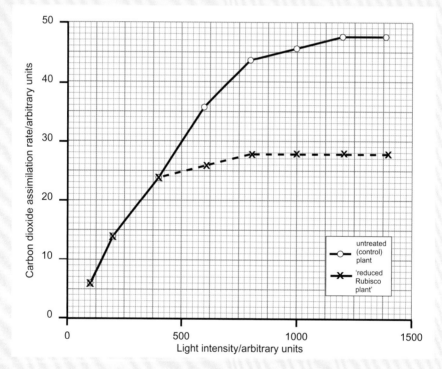

(i) Explain the similar assimilation rates of both plants in low light intensities. [2]

(ii) Explain the different assimilation rates of the plants in high light intensities. [2]

(c) A second experiment was designed to measure the rate of carbon dioxide assimilation for both plants at varying carbon dioxide concentrations.

In this experiment it would be necessary to maintain a temperature of 25°C and a high light intensity.

(i) Explain why a relatively high temperature of 25°C should be maintained in the experiment [2]

(ii) Predict the result of this second experiment for both the 'reduced Rubisco plant' and the untreated (control) plant. [2]

(iii) Explain the result for the 'reduced Rubisco plant'. [1]

Question taken from CCEA's Biology Assessment Unit A2 2, Biochemistry, Genetics and Evolutionary Trends, June 2010, © CCEA 2013

2. (a) Glycerate phosphate and triose phosphate are produced during the light-independent stage of photosynthesis.

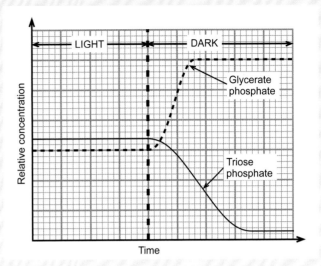

(i) The light-independent stage is sometimes referred to as the 'dark stage'. Explain why light-independent is a more appropriate term. [1]

(ii) State the precise location of the light-independent stage. [1]

(iii) The graph on the right shows the concentrations of glycerate phosphate and triose phosphate during periods of light and dark.

Explain the change in the concentration of triose phosphate, when light is no longer available, as shown in the graph above. [3]

(b) The diagram below shows the absorption spectrum for the photosynthetic pigments in a typical terrestrial plant.

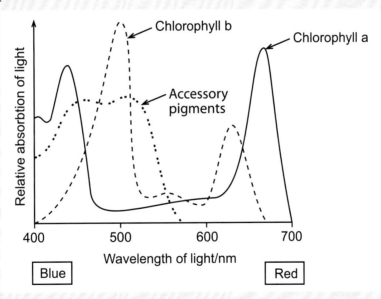

The action spectrum is distinct from the absorption spectrum.

Explain what is meant by the term 'action spectrum'. [1]

(c) White light is composed of different wavelengths. Light filters can be used to control the wavelengths of light reaching a plant.

Devise a plan for an experiment to compare the rates of photosynthesis of a water plant in red and blue light. Your plan should refer to the control of variables, the collection of data and the determination of photosynthetic rate. [4]

Question taken from CCEA's Biology Assessment Unit A2 2, Biochemistry, Genetics and Evolutionary Trends, May 2011, © CCEA 2013

3. (a) The diagram below shows the apparatus used by Melvin Calvin to identify the steps in the light-independent stage of photosynthesis.

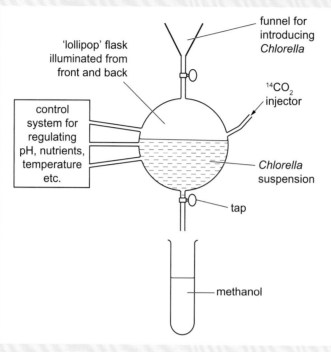

Calvin added radioactive carbon dioxide ($^{14}CO_2$) to the apparatus and, after a very short period of time, he opened the tap to release the *Chlorella* (an autotrophic protoctistan) into the methanol. This killed the *Chlorella* immediately and stopped any further reactions. The *Chlorella* was homogenised and the compounds present were identified by chromatography.

By gradually increasing the time interval between adding the radioactive carbon dioxide and killing the *Chlorella*, Calvin observed that the number of different compounds containing radioactive carbon in each successive sample increased up to a limit and then levelled off.

The bar chart below summarises the results for thirteen consecutive samples.

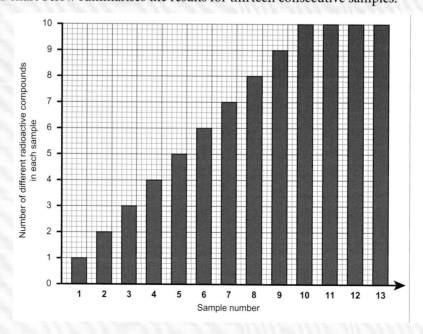

(i) Using your understanding of the light-independent stage, identify the first compound (in sample 1) that contained radioactive carbon. [1]

(ii) The number of radioactive compounds increases with time up to a point and subsequently levels off. Explain why. [2]

(iii) The time that the *Chlorella* was exposed to radioactive carbon dioxide was increased by only a few seconds for consecutive samples. Suggest why. [1]

(iv) Suggest why Calvin used a specially flattened ('lollipop') flask in this investigation. [1]

(b) The graph below shows the rates of carbon dioxide intake by a commercial crop plant in a glasshouse over a 24-hour period.

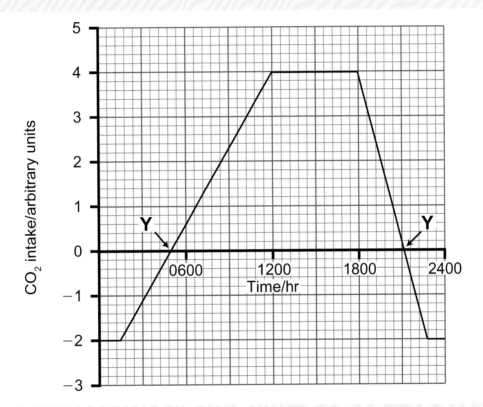

(i) State the term which is used to describe the situation indicated by the positions labelled Y. [1]

(ii) The graph provides information on changes in the rate of net photosynthesis in the plant as opposed to gross photosynthesis. State the evidence for this. [2]

(iii) The glasshouse does not have artificial lighting. Explain why it would be economically undesirable to artificially increase the temperature throughout the 24-hour period but potentially beneficial to increase the temperature between 12 noon and 6 pm. [4]

Question taken from CCEA's Biology Assessment Unit A2 2, Biochemistry, Genetics and Evolutionary Trends, May 2012, © CCEA 2013

4. Quality of written communication is awarded a maximum of [2] marks in this section.

   There are similarities and differences in the way ATP is synthesised in respiration and photosynthesis.

   (a) Give an account of the synthesis of ATP in both respiration and photosynthesis. [11]

   (b) Discuss the similarities and differences between the two processes. [5]

Question taken from CCEA's Biology Assessment Unit A2 2, Biochemistry, Genetics and Evolutionary Trends, May 2012, © CCEA 2013

Chapter 11 – DNA as the Genetic Code (Protein Synthesis)

The nature of the genetic code

Deoxyribonucleic acid (DNA) is the molecule of inheritance. DNA is the 'blueprint' that allows the characteristics of a species, or even a population or family, to pass through generations with limited change. An understanding of DNA also allows us to understand the genetic variation that exists among individuals. DNA carries out its role within cells by determining the polypeptides (and proteins), in particular the enzymes, that are produced by the cell. The enzymes in turn then control cell metabolism.

The nature of the genetic code

We already know that DNA contains repeating units of deoxyribose sugar and phosphate with the two strands linked together by the nitrogenous bases adenine, guanine, cytosine and thymine, with adenine always linking with thymine and cytosine always linking with guanine through hydrogen bonding. It is the **linear order** of the nitrogenous bases along one of the two backbone strands, the **template strand**, which forms the **DNA code**.

Polypeptides and proteins are made up from 20 different types of amino acids. The **sequence of amino acids** (the primary structure) determines the overall polypeptide structure as the primary sequence influences the secondary and tertiary structures. Consequently, DNA works by controlling the **primary structure** of the polypeptides it codes for. The way in which the DNA codes for specific amino acids in specific positions in a polypeptide (protein) is described as the **genetic code**. In general, the length of DNA coding for a particular polypeptide is referred to as a **gene**.

The genetic code

As the DNA contains four different types of base then one base cannot simply code for one type of amino acid (as there are 20 different types of amino acids). Two consecutive bases operating as a code is not enough either – there are only 16 possible different combinations involving any two of the four bases ($4 \times 4 = 16$). The 16 possible combinations are:

AA, AC, AG, AT, CC, CA, CG, CT, GG, GA, GC, GT, TT, TA, TC, TG

However, if three consecutive bases are used then there are 64 possible combinations ($4 \times 4 \times 4 = 64$). Around fifty years ago it was confirmed that the genetic code did indeed involve three consecutive bases coding for a particular amino acid – the **triplet code** with each group of three bases coding for an amino acid called a **base triplet**.

The genetic code for each amino acid was subsequently worked out and the 3-base DNA code (base triplet) for each of the twenty amino acids is now known. For example the DNA sequence of AAT codes for the amino acid leucine and GCG codes for the amino acid arginine.

Some key features of the genetic code include:

- The code is **non-overlapping**. This means that each base in the DNA sequence is read (counted) only once. Using the two examples in the previous paragraph, a DNA sequence of AATGCG codes for leucine and arginine in consecutive positions in the protein primary structure. The diagram below demonstrates the linear, but non-overlapping nature of the genetic code.

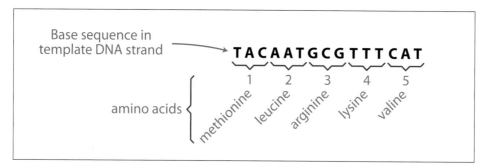

The non-overlapping nature of the genetic code

- The code is **degenerate**. This means that most amino acids have more than one possible code. With 64 possible sequences of three bases coding for 20 amino acids this allows a degree of duplication. For many amino acids it is the first two DNA bases in a triplet that are crucial in determining the amino acid produced. For example, **GG**A, **GG**C, **GG**G and **GG**T all code for the amino acid proline.

- Some base triplets do not code for an amino acid but terminate the coding sequence, much in the way a full stop ends a sentence. They are called **stop** base triplets. Similarly, the sequence **TAC** codes for methionine but also acts as a **start** triplet, starting a coding sequence.

- The DNA code is a **universal code**. With very few exceptions, and occasional modifications, the DNA code described above is present in all living organisms.

The chromosomes in the nucleus contain the genetic code. However, the process of protein synthesis takes place in the cytoplasm. Consequently, the 'code' has to pass from the nucleus to the cytoplasm. This is where **messenger RNA (mRNA)** comes into play. The copying of the code from the DNA in the nucleus to the mRNA is described as transcription and will be discussed in the next section. Once the code is transcribed it is then 'translated' into polypeptide (protein). Consequently protein synthesis consists of the two distinct, but closely related, stages of **transcription** followed by **translation**.

Transcription

Transcription is the process of forming complementary copies of mRNA from sequences of DNA that code for a particular polypeptide or protein.

Messenger RNA

Why use mRNA? - The use of mRNA, as opposed to the DNA in the chromosomes, leaving the nucleus to the sites of protein synthesis, has many advantages. The DNA is copied producing many complementary copies of RNA that can each form the template for the production of many polypeptides or proteins. By remaining in the nucleus, the DNA is always available for 'copying' and is less likely to be damaged in the nucleus than in the metabolically more volatile cytoplasm.

Structure of mRNA – mRNA is a long strand organised as a **single** strand, unlike DNA which has a double helix arrangement. Other differences with DNA include the presence of a **ribose** pentose sugar in the backbone (as opposed to deoxyribose) and the presence of **uracil** as a nitrogenous base (which replaces the thymine of DNA).

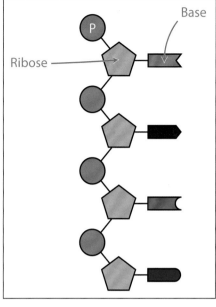

Short section of a mRNA molecule

As a mRNA strand is a complementary copy of the template DNA strand there are as many different arrangements of coding bases in the mRNA as there are in the DNA. As the mRNA is a facility for transporting the DNA code from the nucleus to the cytoplasm, the same principles concerning the nature of the code apply. This means that each sequence of three bases along the mRNA strand code for an amino acid as a **base triplet**.

As a mRNA molecule codes for a polypeptide (or protein) it will only be complementary to a relatively short section of DNA (as DNA runs the length of the chromosome it can code for many polypeptides). Therefore mRNA is usually a much **shorter** molecule than DNA. The main differences between mRNA and DNA are summarised in the following table.

Feature	DNA	mRNA
Relative size	Much longer than mRNA (millions of nucleotides – in humans range from 50 million – 250 million base pairs)	Much shorter than DNA (75 – 3000 nucleotides)
Polynucleotide arrangement	Double stranded (double helix)	Single stranded (single helix – not twisted)
Pentose sugar	Deoxyribose	Ribose
Nitrogenous bases	Adenine (A), guanine (G), cytosine (C) and thymine (T)	Adenine, guanine, cytosine and uracil (U)
Location	Found mostly in nucleus (some found in mitochondria and chloroplasts)	Produced in nucleus but found throughout cell (in particular in association with rough ER and ribosomes)

The process of transcription

The enzyme **DNA helicase** separates the two DNA strands of the relevant section of DNA to be copied. It does this by breaking the **hydrogen bonds** between the bases linking the two strands of the double helix causing the DNA double helix to **unzip** (separate).

The enzyme **RNA polymerase** moves along the **template (coding) strand** linking the (now exposed) nucleotides in that strand with free complementary nucleotides from the nucleotide pool that is found within the nucleus. The building up of the mRNA strand alongside its complementary DNA template strand follows the rules of **complementary base pairing** ensuring that the mRNA bases are aligned in a sequence complementary to the template DNA strand.

> **Note:** During transcription normal C-G, G-C, T-A base pairing arrangements apply. The one exception is that an A base on the DNA template strand will be matched by a U (uracil) base on the mRNA strand.

As the mRNA strand is assembled, increasing in length one nucleotide at a time, the unzipped DNA rejoins behind the assembly area. As a result only around 20 base pairs of the DNA are exposed at the one time. When the RNA polymerase reaches a 'stop' triplet code on the DNA, it detaches and the copying of this particular section of DNA is completed. The process of transcription is summarised in the following diagram.

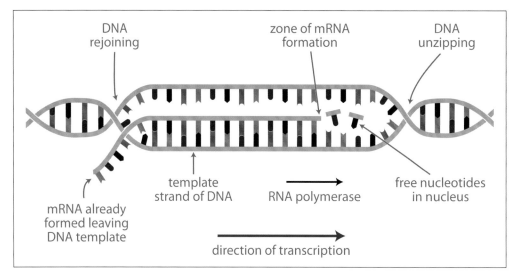

Transcription

Modification of the mRNA

DNA is made up of sections that code for polypeptide / protein (**exons**) and other sections (**introns**) that have a number of functions but do not code for polypeptide or protein directly. The introns are often referred to as 'junk' DNA, but it has long been known that at least some of this has a regulatory role controlling the activity of the coding genes themselves. Research published in 2012 indicates that much of the non-coding DNA (introns) may have a function as genetic 'switches' that can turn on or off the coding genes in particular circumstances, thus regulating their function.

Note 1: Only around 2% of our DNA is in the form of exons – enough to code for around 21 000 different genes. The remaining 98% forms intron sections that exist both between and within genes. Some very large genes can have well over one hundred introns.

Note 2: Prokaryotic DNA does not have introns – prokaryotic DNA is all coding.

Irrespective of the exact function of the introns, it is clear that they do not directly code for specific polypeptides or protein. However, intron sections of DNA are often sited within the coding exon sections of DNA. How does transcription deal with this particular problem? There are two possibilities – either the transcription process is able to bypass introns as the mRNA is formed or the template DNA is copied as it is and the intron sections are subsequently removed.

In practice, it is the subsequent removal of introns following transcription that actually takes place. Adjacent exons and introns are copied in the formation of the mRNA from the DNA template strand. Following transcription, the introns are removed from the **pre-mRNA** and the exons are **spliced** back together again to produce the coding sequence that actually codes for the required polypeptide or protein.

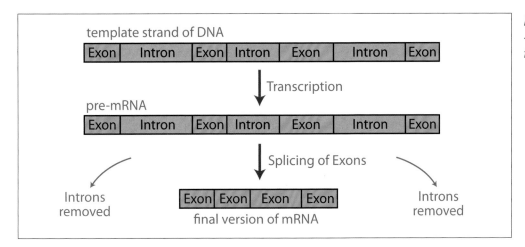

Exons and introns – the making of functional mRNA

Note: Following the removal of introns, the exons can be spliced back together in a range of different combinations. This flexibility allows a gene to code for a number of different polypeptides or proteins depending on the order in which the exons are recombined. It is likely that some of the non-coding DNA (part of the 98%) is involved in the regulation of this. This explains the fact that the 21 000 genes in humans can code for the 100 000 different proteins that occur in the body.

Following the removal of introns, the final version of the mRNA (**the functional mRNA**) moves out of the nucleus through a nuclear pore and into the cytoplasm where the actual formation of new proteins takes place, a process known as **translation**.

Translation

Translation involves the 'translation' of the mRNA code into the polypeptide **primary structure** (sequence of amino acids). Each sequence of three bases on the mRNA (the base triplet) that codes for a particular amino acid is referred to as a **codon**.

As well as the coding mRNA, very important components of the translation process are **transfer RNA (tRNA)** and **ribosomes**. These two structures will be discussed in more detail in the next section.

Transfer RNA and ribosomes

tRNA – tRNA is a small molecule consisting of around **70 – 80 nucleotides**. It is a single stranded molecule twisted into a clover leaf shape. The two key 'functional' parts of the tRNA molecule are a sequence of three bases (**anticodon**) at one end that form complementary base pairs with a mRNA codon and the 'exposed' nucleotide section (at the opposite end of the molecule) to which an amino acid can attach. Enzymes help attach amino acids in the cytoplasm to the appropriate tRNA molecule.

There is a different tRNA molecule for each of the twenty different types of amino acid, with each type being able to attach to only one type of amino acid. Similarly, each of the different types of tRNA has a particular anticodon code, e.g. AAA, that is unique to that type of tRNA, and also which matches with a particular codon (in this case UUU) on the mRNA.

Consequently the role of the tRNA is to:

1. **transport** amino acids within the cytoplasm to the site of protein synthesis

tRNA

2. and ensure that each **mRNA codon codes for a particular amino acid**. In effect, this means that as the protein is being built up, each amino acid will be aligned in sequence adjacent to its matching codon on the mRNA.

Ribosomes – ribosomes are small organelles (up to about 30 nm in diameter) that are found free in the cytoplasm or attached to endoplasmic reticulum. Each ribosome contains a **large** and a **small sub-unit** and is made of **protein** and **ribosomal RNA**.

The sub-units are assembled in the **nucleolus** within the nucleus and subsequently transported into the cytoplasm. At the start of translation the two sub-units link together as they lock on to the start of the mRNA strand to be copied.

The ribosome contains two sites, each of which can cover a codon (analogous to a zip fastener covering six 'teeth' in a zip with the six 'teeth' representing the bases in two adjacent codons). The first codon-linking site is the **aminoacyl (A)** site and the second is the **peptidyl (P)** site. The **A** site, sometimes called the acceptor site, is where the tRNA molecules link together in the correct position on the mRNA strand through the linking of complementary anticodons and codons. The P site is where adjacent amino acids are linked together by peptide bonds.

> **Note:** In summary, the role of the ribosome is to hold the mRNA, the tRNA and the enzymes involved in protein synthesis in place.

The process of translation

The process of translation can be summarised as:

- A ribosome attaches to the initial or **start codon** (AUG) on the mRNA by its A (acceptor) site.

- The tRNA molecule with the complementary anticodon (UAC) moves to the ribosome and pairs up with its complementary codon (AUG) following complementary base pairing rules. This tRNA carries the amino acid methionine to the ribosome. Polypeptide chains usually begin with methionine.

- As the ribosome moves along the mRNA to cover two codons a tRNA molecule with a complementary anticodon pairs up with the next (second) codon on the mRNA strand. Again this tRNA carries its particular amino acid. By this stage the AUG (methionine) will now be in the P site, leaving the A site free for the second amino acid (serine in the diagram).

- A **peptide bond** links the first two amino acids together to form a dipeptide.

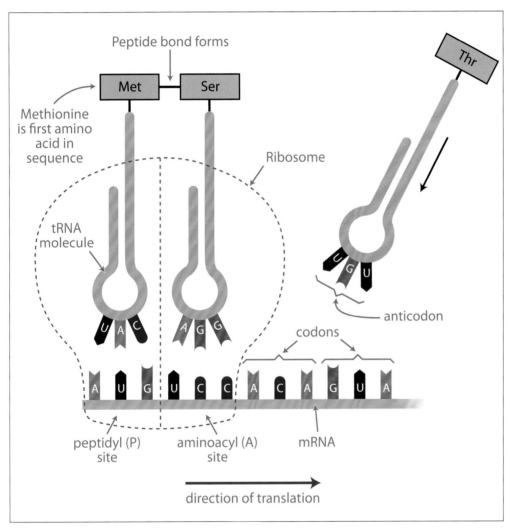

The start of the translation process

- As the ribosome notches along another codon, the tRNA for the methionine is set free and the tRNA for the second amino acid (serine) now occupies the P site. Again this leaves the A site free and the third amino acid (threonine) is brought into place by its tRNA molecule, again following base pairing rules.

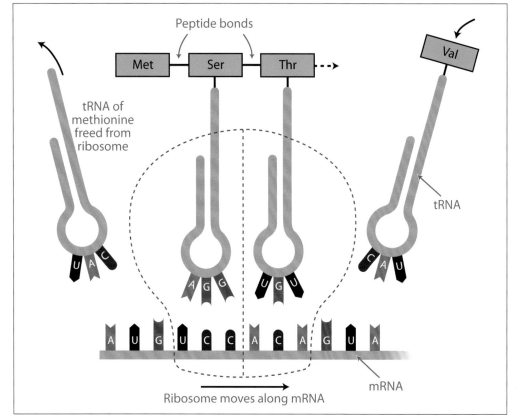

Translation – the next stage

- The process continues and a polypeptide sequence of many amino acids is built up as shown in the next diagram.

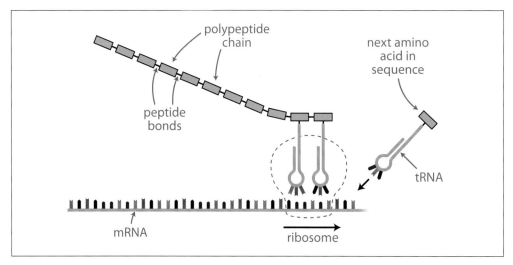

The building of a polypeptide

- The process continues until a stop codon is reached.

Note 1: Although AUG is the **start** codon necessary to start the translation process, not all polypeptides or proteins contain the amino acid methionine at the start. In many proteins the methionine is subsequently removed following translation.

Note 2: Many ribosomes can operate in concert, one immediately after the other along the same strand of mRNA. This is obviously a more efficient process meaning that many polypeptides or proteins can be assembled in a very short time from the same section of mRNA. The complex of ribosomes involved is called a **polyribosome**.

The following diagram shows a **genetic dictionary** – the mRNA codes involved in translation and the amino acids or actions they code for. The degenerate nature of the genetic code can be clearly seen in the diagram.

The genetic dictionary (the mRNA codons)

second base in codon

first base in codon		U	C	A	G		third base in codon
U		phenylalanine	serine	tryosine	cysteine	**U**	
		phenylalanine	serine	tyrosine	cysteine	**C**	
		leucine	serine	stop	stop	**A**	
		leucine	serine	stop	tryptophan	**G**	
C		leucine	proline	histidine	arginine	**U**	
		leucine	proline	histidine	arginine	**C**	
		leucine	proline	glutamine	arginine	**A**	
		leucine	proline	glutamine	arginine	**G**	
A		isoleucine	threonine	asparagine	serine	**U**	
		isoleucine	threonine	asparagine	serine	**C**	
		isoleucine	threonine	lysine	arginine	**A**	
		methionine and start	threonine	lysine	arginine	**G**	
G		valine	alanine	aspartate	glycine	**U**	
		valine	alanine	aspartate	glycine	**C**	
		valine	alanine	glutamate	glycine	**A**	
		valine	alanine	glutamate	glycine	**G**	

Note: In an examination question you will not be expected to have memorised the opposite table in detail. However, you will be expected to understand it. You could be given either the genetic dictionary represented as the mRNA codons (as opposite) or as the original DNA base triplets. In either case, you need to be clear which you are working with.

In this section on the translation phase of protein synthesis, the two nucleic acids most involved are mRNA and tRNA (although ribosomal RNA has a role in the formation of ribosomes). The main similarities and differences between mRNA and tRNA are summarised in the following table.

Feature	mRNA	tRNA
Relative size	Larger molecule (75 – 3000 nucleotides)	Smaller molecule (70 – 80 nucleotides)
Polynucleotide arrangement	Single stranded (not twisted)	Clover shaped molecule
Pentose sugar	Ribose	Ribose
Nitrogenous bases	A, G, C, U	A, G, C, U
Location	Produced in nucleus but found throughout cell (in particular in association with rough ER and ribosomes)	Produced in nucleus but found throughout cell

Once the newly synthesised polypeptides are formed by translation they are normally transported to the Golgi apparatus in vesicles. Here they fuse with the convex (formative or forming) face. In the Golgi apparatus the polypeptides are processed to produce the final functional proteins before being pinched off from the concave (maturing) face and transported by vesicles for use either within the cell or to be secreted.

The one gene one polypeptide theory

Francis Crick and James Watson worked out the structure of DNA around sixty years ago following earlier work by Chargaff and then by Franklin and Wilkins.

Crick produced what he described as the 'central dogma of molecular biology' in which he and others built up the key link between DNA, RNA and protein as described in this chapter. Crick's 'central dogma' can be summarised as:

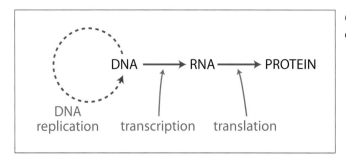

Crick's 'central dogma'

Current understanding shows that the above diagram is somewhat simplified. Retroviruses such as HIV have **reverse transcriptase** enzymes which can use a mRNA template to make complementary DNA (normal transcription in reverse). Taking account of current understanding, Crick's original summary would now be written as:

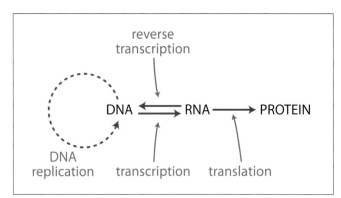

Current understanding of the link between DNA and protein synthesis

Throughout this chapter we have usually described the DNA as coding for a **polypeptide**, (an exception being the short section above relating to Crick's work). This is accurate as a coding sequence of DNA (the gene) codes for a particular polypeptide. The polypeptide is formed as the amino acids are linked together during translation in a particular sequence (the primary structure).

However, before the term **'one gene one polypeptide'** was widely used, the terms 'one gene one protein' or 'one gene one enzyme' were used to describe the essential role of DNA.

The term **'one gene one protein'** is appropriate when the protein concerned has only **one** polypeptide. However, it is a less suitable term for those proteins that are formed of more than one polypeptide, e.g. haemoglobin and insulin, proteins that both have quaternary structures. For proteins formed of more than one polypeptide, there is often a different gene that codes for each polypeptide (and the genes involved may not even be on the same chromosome).

Similarly, the term **'one gene one enzyme'** may be regarded as a simplification for the reason noted above (enzymes may be formed of more than one polypeptide) but also because not all proteins are enzymes. The two examples already used (haemoglobin and the hormone insulin) are not enzymes and proteins can also be channel proteins in membranes, antibodies and have many other roles, including structural roles such as collagen.

However, although the term 'one gene one polypeptide' may be the most accurate in terms of the link between the DNA and its products, the DNA is able to control overall development in organisms through its control of enzyme activity. As enzymes control all metabolic pathways in cells, DNA through controlling enzyme synthesis, ultimately controls the cell (and the organism's) development.

Exam questions

1. (a) The diagram below represents the process of transcription.

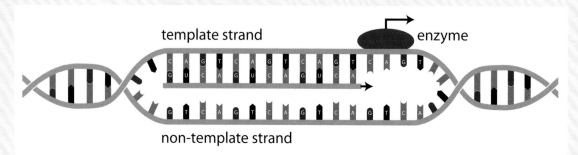

template strand

enzyme

non-template strand

Note: For copyright reasons, this diagram has replaced the one included in the original CCEA paper.

 (i) Using the information provided, describe the process of transcription. [4]

 (ii) Using **only** the information in the diagram, state **two** structural differences between DNA and RNA. [2]

 (b) It has long been known that genes are sections of chromosomes which control specific aspects of an organism's characteristics. Early research suggested that each gene coded for a protein or even for an enzyme: hence the *'one gene one protein'* and the *'one gene one enzyme'* hypotheses that were promoted several decades ago.

 Current understanding of gene action suggests that the *'one gene one polypeptide'* hypothesis is a more accurate description.

 (i) Using your understanding of protein structure, suggest why the *'one gene one polypeptide'* hypothesis is a more accurate description than each of the two earlier hypotheses. [2]

 (ii) Explain precisely what is meant by the term *'one gene one polypeptide'*. [1]

 (c) DNA length is measured in base pairs. Analysis of a particular polypeptide shows that the gene involved in its synthesis is 330 base pairs long yet the polypeptide itself has only 84 amino acids in its primary sequence.

 (i) How many base pairs would be required to code for 84 amino acids? [1]

 (ii) Suggest why the gene contains 330 base pairs. [1]

Question taken from CCEA's Biology Assessment Unit A2 2, Biochemistry, Genetics and Evolutionary Trends, May 2012, © CCEA 2013

2. The diagram below shows a step in the synthesis of a polypeptide during translation.

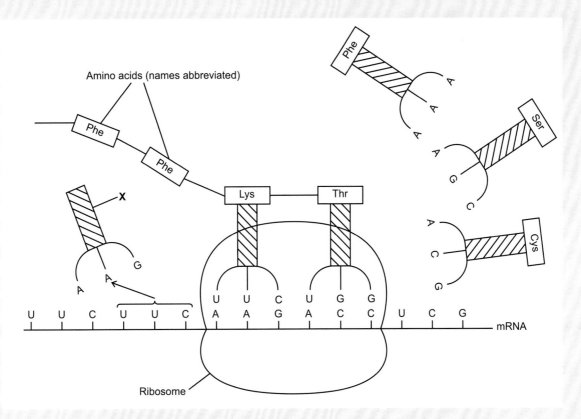

(a) Name molecule **X**. [1]

(b) Using the information in the diagram describe precisely what happens in the next step of polypeptide synthesis. [4]

(c) The genetic code is described as degenerate. Explain what is meant by the term 'degenerate' and identify where in the diagram a degenerate code is illustrated. [2]

Note: Part (d) of the original question has been omitted.

Question taken from CCEA's Biology Assessment Unit A2 2, Biochemistry, Genetics and Evolutionary Trends, May 2011, © CCEA 2013

Chapter 12 – Gene Technology

Gene technology is at the forefront of current biologically-related research. Once the structure and function of DNA had been worked out, it was only a short step to try to manipulate the functioning of DNA in organisms or even to transfer DNA from one organism to another.

DNA technology has huge potential in many areas including food production, drug development and medicine. However, it is an area where progress should always be considered within the wider ethical framework.

One of the key aspects of gene technology is the ability to obtain a section of DNA from one cell (or organism) and transfer it into another cell or organism. The techniques involved in this gene transfer will be covered in the next part of this chapter.

Gene transfer – obtaining the required gene

As part of the AS course we have already come across the terms **restriction endonucleases** and **reverse transcriptase**. Both refer to types of **enzymes** that can be used in obtaining a desired gene for transfer.

Restriction endonucleases

Restriction endonucleases (restriction enzymes) occur naturally as defensive bacterial enzymes that cut up foreign DNA injected by bacteriophages.

Many restriction endonucleases have been isolated and are used in gene technology to cut specific sections of DNA. Each restriction endonuclease cuts the DNA double strand, by a hydrolysis reaction, at a specific sequence of bases called a **recognition sequence**. Sometimes the enzyme cuts straight across the two strands (i.e. between opposite adjacent bases) to leave the cut section of DNA with **blunt ends**. Some restriction enzymes make a staggered cut to leave **sticky ends**. This happens when the cuts in each DNA strand (within the recognition sequence) are between adjacent bases that do not lie opposite each other (due to the nature of base pairing). Two examples of how restriction endonucleases work are shown on the next page.

Restriction endonucleases

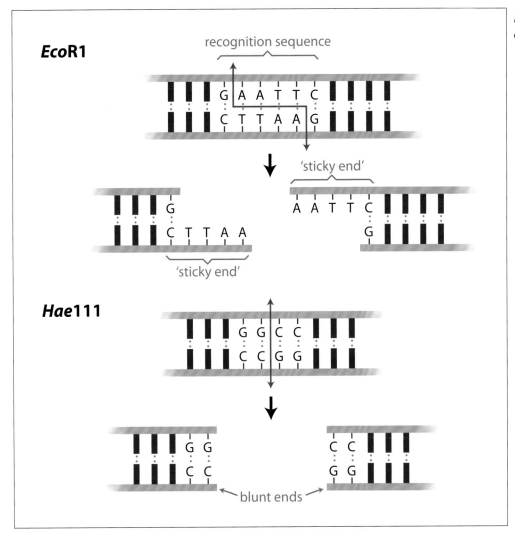

In **EcoR1** the recognition sequence is **GAATTC** and the cut is made between the adjacent bases **G and A** (or A and G) that lie beside each other on the same DNA strand. As the complementary base pairs of G and A on the opposite DNA strand will be C and T (and not G and A) the *Eco*R1 will not cut directly across the DNA – instead the cut is deflected along the DNA to where the bases G and A do lie beside each other on the opposite strand.

In the **Hae111** the recognition sequence is **GGCC** with the cut taking place between adjacent **G and C** (or C and G) bases.

In this example G and C bases lie opposite C and G bases due to base pairing rules therefore a straight cut will take place.

Sticky ends are in fact short sections of DNA where there is one only strand and the bases in that section are unpaired and therefore exposed. The advantage in using restriction enzymes that produce sticky ends is that DNA with sticky ends will easily join with another section of DNA if it has complementary sticky ends. This knowledge has been widely used by genetic engineers when inserting DNA sections into the DNA of other organisms.

Reverse transcriptase

During the AS course and in the previous chapter there has been reference as to how retroviruses, which store genetic information in the form of RNA, use enzymes to make DNA from the RNA. The enzyme involved is **reverse transcriptase**.

In gene technology, reverse transcriptase is used to make a desired section of DNA (gene) from the gene's mRNA.

The technique involves:

- Isolating and extracting the **mRNA** of the desired gene. The search can be made easier by analysing those cells in which there is likely to be a lot of the relevant mRNA (i.e. a cell in which the desired gene is very active). For example, the mRNA of the genes that produce digestive proteases, lipases and amylases, will be found in certain secretory cells in the pancreas whereas the mRNA of insulin will be found in the pancreatic endocrine regions.

- **Reverse transcriptase** can be used to make a single strand of DNA (**complementary DNA** or **cDNA**) using the mRNA as a template and following normal base pairing rules.

- The enzyme **DNA polymerase** is then used to make the double stranded DNA (gene) from the single strand of cDNA.

It is obviously important to check that the correct section of DNA (or mRNA) is being targeted when using the technologies described above. One way of checking a section of DNA (or mRNA) is to use a gene probe.

DNA (gene) probes

DNA probes can be used to identify sections of DNA that contain a **specific sequence of bases**. If a section of DNA can be identified, then restriction endonucleases can be used to cut out the desired section by cutting the DNA immediately outside the desired section.

The probes are **short single strands of DNA** (e.g. 20 nucleotides in length). This short section will be complementary to the target section of DNA so that its bases will bind (**hybridise**) to the target section if it is present.

It is also important to be able to identify exactly where this target section is on the targeted DNA, therefore the DNA probe is usually 'labelled' in such a way that it can be identified. The two most common types of labelling are **radioactive** labelling (that can be detected using **X-ray film**) or **fluorescent** labelling (detected using **UV light**).

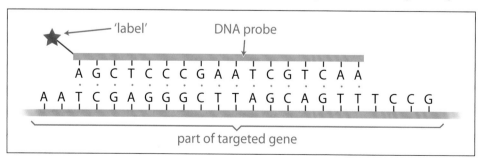

Targeting a specific gene with a DNA probe

Note : A DNA probe can be made **radioactive** by labelling the 5' end with ^{32}P.

Using DNA probes – the following section is an example of how fluorescently labelled DNA probes can be used to identify specific DNA sequences.

DNA that is expected to contain the target sequence is hydrolysed into sections using **restriction endonucleases** with the DNA fragments being subsequently separated by **gel electrophoresis**.

The DNA sections, now separated by gel electrophoresis, are transferred to a **nylon membrane**. At this stage the fluorescently labelled DNA probe is added. If the target sequence is present the DNA probe will hybridise (bind) with it; if not it will then be 'washed off' and removed. If the nylon membrane is then exposed to UV light the DNA probe (and target sequence) will appear as a **fluorescent band**.

Note: In some types of contemporary gel electrophoresis the transferring to another membrane stage is bypassed, i.e. the gel itself is subjected to UV light. With this, the probes are added earlier and the target sequences are visible *in situ*.

A A A T G C C A G G G T A T C G C T T ← DNA section

↓ treatment with restriction endonucleases

A A A T G
G G G T A T C
G C T T
C C A

} DNA fragments

fluorescently labelled DNA probe added
C G A A

DNA fragments separate based on size (length)

well

gel electrophoresis → nylon membrane → fluorescent band

UV light

Using a fluorescent DNA probe

Gel electrophoresis and fluorescent labelling in action

Note 1: It is important to 'wash off' any DNA probes that do not attach to their target sections – fluorescently labelled probes will show up whether they have hybridised with their target sequences or not!

Note 2: The gel electrophoresis separates the DNA sections on the basis of size (length). Shorter sections of DNA travel further (and faster) through the gel. The series of bands on the gel will represent a series of sections of DNA of different lengths (shortest sections closest to the positive electrode (anode at the top of diagram) and longest sections closest to the negative electrode (cathode) and the well (origin) at the bottom of the diagram.

Note 3: In the diagram above the fluorescent band is the second from the top as the sequence GCTT is the second smallest and also is the sequence that is complementary to the fluorescent probe CGAA.

Note 4: DNA probes will attach to single strands of DNA, not the normal double stranded form. Therefore when using DNA probes it is usually necessary to treat the DNA in a way that splits the two strands along its length.

Note 5: If a radioactively labelled probe is used (instead of a fluorescent one) the nylon membrane is exposed to an X-ray film. If the probe and target sequence combine, this will cause the fogging of the X-ray film.

Gene transfer – transferring the donor gene into the recipient cell

Normally once a desired section of DNA (gene) has been identified and isolated, it is not transferred directly into the target cell (or organism). Instead, the DNA is usually transferred into a **vector**; in due course the vector will transport the donor DNA into the host cell. Therefore transferring the donor DNA into recipient cells involves two stages – **inserting the gene into a vector** and **inserting the vector into the host cell**.

Inserting the gene (desired section of DNA) into a vector

The main type of vectors, which are in effect 'gene delivery tools' are **plasmids** and **viruses**.

Note: Plasmids are short lengths of DNA found in bacteria, separate from the main loop of bacterial DNA. The plasmids typically contain genes that provide antibiotic resistance.

Plasmids as vectors – As the bacterial plasmid is a closed loop of DNA, it must be cut to create the ends to which the donor DNA can be joined. If the *same* **restriction endonuclease** is used to cut the bacterial plasmid as was used to excise the donor DNA (gene), it will mean that the plasmid and donor DNA will have complementary sticky ends.

Therefore the donor DNA will make a perfect join (in terms of matching base pairs) with each end of the cut plasmid. Once the bases have

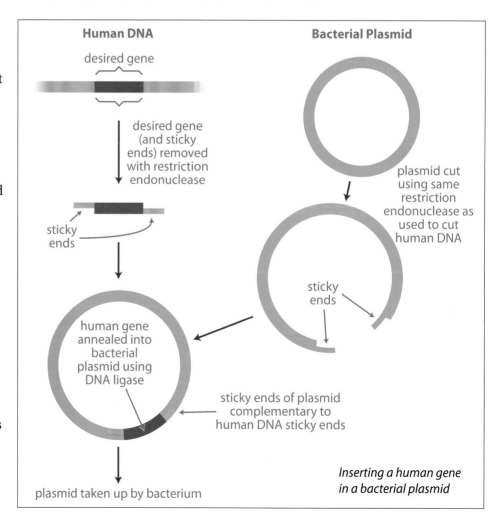

Inserting a human gene in a bacterial plasmid

200

paired up, the enzyme **DNA ligase** is used to **anneal** (join) the DNA backbones together through the formation of **phosphodiester bonds** between the sugar-phosphate backbones of the donor DNA and the plasmid DNA. The end result is that the donor DNA is seamlessly **spliced** into the plasmid which becomes a closed loop again.

The plasmid DNA is now referred to as **recombinant DNA** as it contains 'foreign' DNA from another source; the plasmid itself can be referred to as a **recombinant plasmid**.

Note: If the donor DNA does not have sticky ends through:

- being formed using reverse transcriptase converting mRNA into cDNA

- or through using a restriction endonuclease that does not produce sticky ends, e.g. *Hae*111, then sticky ends can be added to the donor DNA. If sticky ends are added, it is important that their bases are complementary to the bases of the sticky ends on the cut plasmid.

Viruses as vectors – viruses are naturally adapted to 'shoot' their genetic material into a host cell and this makes them ideal vectors. A bacteriophage virus can have donor DNA spliced into its DNA with the result that the donor DNA will also be fired into the host bacterial cell together with the viral DNA.

Inserting the gene (desired piece of DNA) into the host cell – the role of plasmids

After incorporating the donor DNA into the plasmid vector as described earlier, the next step is to encourage the host cell to take up the plasmid. In many genetic engineering processes (recombinant DNA technology) the host cell is a bacterial cell that can then be cloned and then used as 'factories' to produce the desired product.

If the bacterial cells are incubated with **calcium ions** and subjected to **heat shock** (a rapid temperature rise from 0° – 40 °C) then they are more likely to take up the recombinant plasmids. This treatment makes the bacteria more permeable, therefore reducing the barrier to them taking up the plasmids. Even with this treatment, only a very small proportion of bacterial cells will actually take up a recombinant plasmid.

The key thing following the inducement of plasmid uptake is to **identify** the **transformed bacteria**, i.e. the bacteria that contain the donor DNA and therefore will be able to produce the desired product.

The use of **marker genes** (other genes on the recombinant plasmid apart from the donor DNA) that can be identified is a common technique used to identify recombinant or transformed bacteria.

Using marker genes – Bacterial plasmids almost always contain genes involved in the development of antibiotic resistance in the bacteria. Some plasmids have genes that confer resistance to two (or more antibiotics). One example is the **R-plasmid** which has the genes for resistance to the antibiotics **tetracycline and ampicillin**.

When cutting R-plasmids prior to inserting donor DNA, a restriction enzyme is used that cuts the bacterial plasmid within one of the genes that provides antibiotic resistance (e.g. the resistant gene for tetracycline). This is important as if the donor DNA anneals effectively into the plasmid, i.e. a recombinant plasmid is produced, the plasmid will no longer have a gene that confers resistance to tetracycline (the gene will have been cut in two by the restriction endonuclease). However, the gene that confers resistance to ampicillin is unaffected.

The following diagram shows how it is possible to identify the transformed bacteria (the assumption is made that none of the bacteria have the R-plasmid initially).

Detecting the transformed bacteria by replica plating

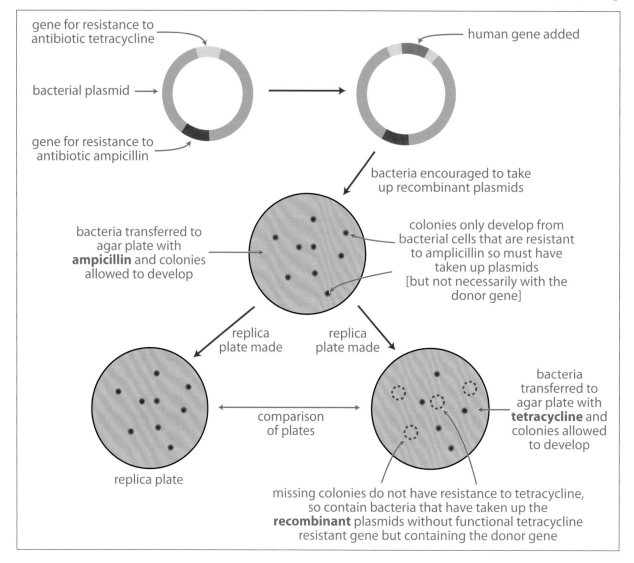

In the diagram above the colonies that do not survive in the tetracycline (missing in bottom right diagram) are formed of transformed bacteria with the human gene – i.e. the bacteria required. These transformed bacteria will be present on the plate in the bottom left hand corner (not treated with tetracycline) and can be identified and subsequently cultured.

Replica plating involves 'blotting' the original plate carefully with an absorbent pad and then pressing this against the surface of a fresh plate allowing some of the cells of each colony to be transferred. The key thing is that colonies will form (or not) on equivalent positions on the new plate.

Note: Other markers are now available that are quicker and more straightforward than replica plating. For example, a gene that produces protein that fluoresces in certain conditions can be incorporated into a plasmid. The donor DNA can be added to the 'already' recombinant plasmid by using a restriction enzyme to cut the plasmid in the centre of the gene that codes for the fluorescent protein (similar principle to the tetracycline above). When tested, the host cells that have taken up the donor DNA will not be able to fluoresce.

Using DNA probes – DNA probes can be used to identify if host DNA is recombinant. The principle of using DNA probes is discussed on page 198.

Once it has been confirmed that a colony of bacteria contain recombinant DNA, the next phase is usually to clone the bacteria to ensure that large numbers are produced. They are typically grown in large fermenters where conditions are ideal for rapid growth and the production of the desired product.

Transformed bacteria as described in the previous sections are examples of **genetically modified organisms (GMOs)** in general, and specifically **genetically engineered microorganisms (GEMs)**. Some of the benefits, and potential hazards, in using GMOs are reviewed in the following sections.

Genetically Modified Organisms (GMOs)

It is convenient for explanatory purposes to split genetically modified organisms into genetically modified microorganisms and other genetically modified organisms (plants and animals).

Genetically Engineered Microorganisms (GEMs)

Bacteria have proved to be the ideal (but not the only) microorganisms suitable for genetic modification. Unlike most other organisms, it is relatively straightforward to insert donor DNA into the bacterial DNA (aided by the presence of plasmids).

The bacterium *Escherichia coli* has been widely used in genetic engineering as have a range of other microorganisms including the yeast *Saccharomyces cerevisiae*.

The general public is more accepting of the use of GEMs including bacteria than they are about the genetic modification of crop plants and animals. For this reason, and as it is less complex, scientific research and commercial development in the field of GEMs is at a more advanced stage of development.

Many important chemicals and other products have been produced by GEMs over the last forty years. Examples include:

A modern insulin 'pen' containing genetically engineered human insulin for the treatment of diabetes

- **Insulin** – insulin produced by transformed bacteria can be produced in sufficient quantities to meet the needs of the growing numbers of people who have diabetes. Additionally, as the bacteria use the 'human' insulin gene to produce the insulin, it is identical to the hormone naturally produced by humans. Previously, insulin had to be extracted from the bodies of dead domestic animals (e.g. pigs and cattle) in abattoirs, a time-consuming and ineffective process, by comparison.

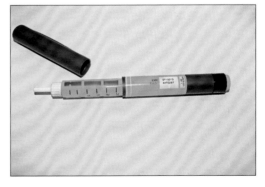

203

Furthermore, non-human insulin is slightly different to human insulin and therefore has the potential to cause allergic reactions – cow insulin differs from human insulin by three amino acids and pig insulin differs by one amino acid.

- Other important products produced by GEMs include the **human growth hormone**, **enzymes**, **adhesives**, **lung surfactant protein** and **interferon** (a drug used in the treatment of certain cancers).

Note: Although we have used the term transformed bacteria in the sections above, a more recent term used to describe an organism (or type of organism) that has had its DNA deliberately altered is '**transgenic**'. In the next section we will cover examples of transgenic plants and animals – the term transgenic is generally used when referring to plants or animals that have had their DNA altered by recombinant DNA technology.

Other Genetically Modified Organisms

Transgenic plants – transgenic crop plants have enormous potential commercial, health and other benefits. Before reviewing some of the benefits we will review the methods that can be used to insert donor (foreign) DNA into plants.

The soil bacterium *Agrobacterium tumefaciens* causes the growth of tumour-like plant galls in plants that it infects. The bacteria enter the plant at a point where the plant has been damaged in some way and then integrate bacterial DNA (from a plasmid) into the DNA of the plant. The bacterial DNA causes the very rapid cell growth that leads to the formation of the galls.

In genetic engineering, the gall-forming genes are removed from the bacterial plasmids and replaced with donor DNA using the techniques already described in this chapter. Recipient plant cells are specially treated so that they will readily take up the recombinant plasmid.

Note 1: The recombinant plasmids retain the ability to become integrated into the host (plant) DNA but will not cause the galls.

Note 2: Rather than introduce the donor DNA into mature plants (where its effect would be localised and therefore limited), the donor DNA can be added to a small number of cells in tissue culture – the result being that as the cells in the culture grow into mature plants, all the cells in the plant will contain the recombinant DNA.

'**Gene guns**' can also be used to insert the donor DNA into the host cells. By coating microscopic (tungsten or gold) pellets with the donor DNA it can be fired (using compressed air) into the host cell – it is a bit 'hit or miss' whether the donor DNA will actually become incorporated into the host DNA. Although much less reliable than using *Agrobacterium*, it can be used with species that are resistant to infection by the bacterium.

Most transgenic plants are more commonly known as **Genetically Modified (GM) Crops**. Up to now GM crops have had a bad press in Europe but is this really a fair assessment of their potential?

Case study - GM Crops

Transgenic crops have tried to address the issues of crop quantity and quality. The benefits of producing more crops and crops with less wastage are obvious at a time when there is a world shortage of food.

GM crops have been produced that have:

- **Herbicide resistance** – GM plants that are resistant to herbicides will be unaffected by herbicide applications, therefore allowing more effective applications without the need to avoid spraying near the crops. Maize (corn) and soybeans are examples of species that have GM varieties resistant to herbicides.

- **Pesticide properties** – The bacterium *Bacillus thuringiensis* (Bt) produces a protein that is toxic to insect pests (it has an additional advantage in that it is not toxic to other types of animals). Many species of crop plants now have varieties with the Bt gene incorporated into their DNA; examples include maize, potato and cotton. Obvious advantages are a reduction in losses to insect pests and also a reduction in the use of insecticides with benefits including less expense, less harm caused to non-pest insects and less pollution.

- **Disease resistance** – GM crops can be produced that are resistant to fungal and viral pathogens.

- **A greater ecological range** – For example, plant varieties have been produced that are more drought resistant. Ryegrass plants have been developed that have a drought tolerance gene added from another species.

- **Nutritional enhancement** – many GM programmes have improved nutritional composition and content as their goal. One of the best examples is the genetic manipulation of rice ('Golden' rice) to provide enhanced levels of vitamin A and iron. The 'Golden rice' has been genetically engineered to contain up to 30 micrograms of beta-carotene per gram (ordinary rice has none).

Note: Several billion people across the world are at risk of iron deficiency and nearly half a million people each year have suffered blindness as a result of vitamin A deficiency (the effects of both deficiencies are greater in the developing world). Of those that go blind in the developing world a very significant number die within months.

Other examples of 'nutritional enhancement' include the development of GM plants that have an increased 'shelf life', increased protein content, improved texture and improved flavour (e.g. Flavr-Savr tomatoes are an interesting case – by adding a gene that produced mRNA that was complementary to the mRNA of the gene responsible for fruit softening, the two mRNA molecules became 'neutralised' as they combined, thus fruit softening was reduced making transport easier and increasing 'shelf life').

GM crops have also been developed that produce compounds beneficial to man, e.g. **vaccines** and **drugs**. Transgenic plants can produce vaccines, drugs and other chemicals that are difficult or very costly to produce.

The ethical issues – the benefits of using GM crops are obvious, and only some of the benefits are outlined above.

Some of the arguments that have been used against GM crops by its opponents include:

1. **It is not natural** – this is a very debatable point. The insulin produced by transgenic bacteria involves the same principles and saves millions of lives each year yet it does not have the level of opposition GM crops have. Why? Crop species (and their DNA indirectly) have been manipulated by man for around 10 000 years by selective breeding. Transgenic manipulation differs in extent but not principle.

GM Maize – can you really tell the difference?

2. **The creation of 'superweeds'.** While it is possible that genes could be transferred from GM crops to other species by cross-pollination, this is no more likely than between other plant species. However, rigorous risk assessments and safety precautions ensure that the risk is kept as low as possible.

3. GM crops have a **greater ecological range** than non-GM crops. Some species of GM crops can grow in a wider range of habitats and may therefore outcompete non-crop species in certain ecological situations. This is a risk but has to be weighed against producing more food (particularly in developing countries where there may be food shortages).

4. **Some insects are becoming resistant to the toxic effects of GM crops with the Bt gene** – but then again many more populations of insects are resistant to insecticides.

5. There is a worry that some of the compounds produced by GM crops could cause **allergies**. While this is possible, it is no more likely than allergies being caused by the production of other 'new' products.

GM crops are extensively used in many countries including the USA (in 2011, 94% of the soyabean planted was genetically modified) and Argentina. However, the focus for much of the resistance to GM crops has been in Europe.

The benefits that GM crops can provide are so great that the scientific community is firmly of the opinion that opposition is political (driven by largely uninformed public opinion) rather than scientific.

Transgenic animals – As with transgenic plants there are several techniques for inserting donor DNA into animal cells. These include encapsulating the donor DNA in lipid vesicles called **liposomes**. The use of a lipid carrier makes it easier for the DNA to cross the lipid bilayer of the cell-surface membrane.

Another method involves the technique of electroporation. **Electroporation** involves disrupting the cell membrane (and making it more permeable) by the use of high voltage treatment. **Viruses** can also be used to insert donor DNA into animal cells – we will review the potential of viruses as vectors in the next section on gene therapy. By inserting the donor genes directly into the **fertilised eggs** of the animal this will ensure that all the cells in the animal will contain recombinant DNA. This technique has been used to produce many valuable products listed in the following table.

The mouse is probably the animal that has been genetically engineered to the greatest extent; transgenic mice are produced for many reasons including disease modelling –see later sections.

However, many transgenic animals produce products of value to man as summarised in the following table. In general, the donor gene (**transgene**) can be added to the fertilised egg at the one-cell stage. This ensures that the donor gene will be present in all the daughter cells of the developing organism.

Transgenic organism	Genetic modification and consequence
Chicken	Human gene for the production of the antibody mi-R24 inserted. The mi-R24 antibody is obtained from eggs and used in the treatment of skin cancer.
Cow	Human gene added that codes for the protein alpha-lactalbumin, leading to milk that is more similar in composition to human milk. Other genes can be added to increase milk production or milk with reduced lactose content (for individuals with lactose intolerance).
Sheep	Have the human gene that codes for Factor VIII (blood clotting factor). Factor VIII can be purified from ewes' milk and used to treat haemophilia. Transgenic sheep can also produce the serum protein alpha-1-antitrypsin, important in regulating the activity of proteases and used in the treatment of individuals with cystic fibrosis.
Goat	A human gene added to produce the anticoagulant anti-thrombin. Can be given to individuals deficient in anti-thrombin due to a defective allele.

Knowledge of gene transfer technologies raised the prospect of tampering with the human DNA complement. The most obvious place to start was to look at the possibility of inserting functional donor alleles (genes) into human cells that are not functioning as well as they should due to the presence of a single defective allele. This is **gene therapy**.

Gene therapy

Human conditions such as **cystic fibrosis** and **muscular dystrophy** are caused by the presence of a single defective gene. In these examples the defective alleles are recessive so the condition is only fully expressed when the individual has both recessive alleles at the relevant gene locus (cystic fibrosis) or is present as a single allele on the (single) X chromosome present in males (muscular dystrophy).

If a functional allele can be inserted into the cells affected by the condition, theoretically the cells will function as normal – this is the principle behind **gene therapy**.

There are two distinct approaches to gene therapy as outlined below:

- **Somatic-cell gene therapy.** This is where the gene therapy only targets the affected tissues. This technique can be used when a condition caused by defective gene(s) affects specific, and easily reached, parts of the body, e.g. lungs. Additionally, somatic-cell gene therapy can be used at any stage of an individual's life.

- **Germ-line gene therapy.** This approach involves replacing the defective gene(s) in the fertilised egg (or theoretically in a defective gamete). In germ-line gene therapy, all the cells of the developing individual are normal (in terms of the defective gene under consideration) and there is no issue with targeting affected tissues in the body, which is a problem with somatic-cell gene therapy. Additionally, with germ-line gene therapy the defective gene will not pass on to future offspring as the gametes produced will not contain the defective gene.

Currently it is only somatic-cell gene therapy that is used. Germ-line gene therapy is (probably) beyond current technological capability and raises so many moral and ethical issues that it is presently not permitted.

Therefore, the remainder of this section on gene therapy is focused on the progress and limitations of somatic-cell gene therapy. As with any aspect of gene technology, a good place to start is to review how the donor (functional) DNA can be inserted into recipient cells.

Getting the functional allele into recipient cells

Other gene technologies use **viruses** as one type of vector in gene transfer, so it is a logical place to start for gene therapy. Different types of viruses have proved effective.

- **Adenoviruses** are viruses that cause respiratory infections. They are ideal for gene therapy involving lung tissue as adenoviruses are able to inject their DNA into lung epithelial cells. However, before adenoviruses can be used in gene therapy they have to have their 'harmful' disease-causing genes removed as well as the donor DNA being spliced in. Adenoviruses are not without problems though, as it is difficult to remove the disease-causing genes without dismantling the genes that allow the virus to enter cells and insert their genetic material. They may cause **infection**. Additionally, some individuals may be immune to adenoviruses and they are **unable to penetrate** the respiratory cells.

- **Retroviruses** can be used to target host cells. When the host cells are affected by the retrovirus, its RNA and any additional donor RNA is converted by reverse transcriptase into DNA in the host cell. If the donor DNA replaces or supplements the defective DNA in the host cell, then gene therapy is possible.

- **Liposomes** are artificial lipid vesicles containing the donor DNA. The lipid coating of the vesicle protects against degradation and helps the donor DNA bind to the appropriate target cells. This process can be aided by using specific marker cells, e.g. monoclonal antibodies, that help the liposome target the appropriate recipient cells. Having a lipid coat means that the liposome can pass relatively easily through the lipid part of the phospholipid cell-surface membrane.

Note: Liposomes are less effective at getting the donor DNA into the host cell nucleus compared to viruses but they are often safer in that they do not have some of the problems associated with deliberately inserting viruses into human cells (e.g. infection, allergies and other immune responses).

When the donor DNA is in the appropriate host cells it can function in two distinct ways – the donor DNA can become incorporated into the host DNA or can function as independent DNA units (**episomes**) in the nucleus that are **not** incorporated into the main nuclear DNA.

Although still at the early stages of its development, gene therapy has huge potential in replacing (or supplementing as with episomes) defective DNA that causes many of the major genetic diseases today. Major difficulties still surround the ability to target all the affected areas of the body for a particular condition, the fact that treatment is often short-lived as any new and replacement cells will not have the donor DNA, and also that offspring of treated individuals may still be affected, depending on the genetics involved. Additionally, the defensive strategies employed by cells may destroy the introduced DNA or prevent it being 'switched on'.

Another problem is that as many genetic disorders (or disorders with a genetic pre-disposition) involve many genes across a range of chromosomes (e.g. Type 1 diabetes), it can be very difficult to both identify the genes involved and effectively incorporate all the donor DNA necessary into host cells.

A good way to review progress to date is to use one particular example as a case study.

Case study – gene therapy and cystic fibrosis

Cystic fibrosis, the condition - Cystic fibrosis is the most common inherited genetic condition in the western world. In Europe approximately 1 in 2500 are affected. The condition is due to the malfunctioning of a protein of around 1500 amino acids in length. The protein malfunction is caused by a mutant recessive allele – in the dominant or heterozygous state the individual concerned functions normally, but if both recessive alleles are present cystic fibrosis will be the result.

The affected protein is the **trans-membrane-conductance regulator (CFTR)** protein. This protein is responsible for keeping epithelial membranes in good condition. In an individual with cystic fibrosis, the protein will not function as normal and the membranes become covered with thick sticky mucus. This affects several parts of the body including:

- The buildup of mucus in the **lungs** affects **gaseous exchange** and leads to a much higher risk of **lung infection**.

- The buildup of mucus in the **pancreatic duct** prevents the pancreatic enzymes reaching the duodenum leading to problems with **food digestion**.

Delivering the donor DNA - The use of gene therapy to improve lung function in patients with cystic fibrosis has an obvious advantage – it is relatively straightforward to target and get access to the cells affected.

The main vectors in delivering the functional CFTR gene are **adenoviruses** and **liposomes**. These are prepared as reviewed earlier and can be sprayed into the respiratory system of the patient as an **aerosol**.

The benefits and drawbacks – If the donor DNA enters enough host respiratory cells and is expressed (works!) in producing functional protein, then the debilitating lung symptoms associated with cystic fibrosis can be reduced and the quality of life for the patient improved.

However, there are many reasons why the process is less effective than hoped for in many patients. While lung function may improve, this technique does not affect the **other parts** of the body, e.g. the pancreas, also affected by cystic fibrosis. Adenoviruses may cause **infections**, **immune responses** or **allergies**. Patients may develop **immunity** to the adenoviruses (therefore they are unable to enter the respiratory cells or are destroyed when they do) and the aerosol may **not reach all parts** of the lung (making its effect localised).

A major problem of course is that the donor DNA functions as an episome. It reaches the nucleus but **does not become incorporated into the host DNA** – the donor DNA masks the effect of the defective allele but does not replace it – therefore is only effective for the life of the cell. With lung epithelial cells being very short-lived, this means the functional donor gene is not passed on to new cells (and is certainly not passed on to offspring); therefore regular **repeat treatments** are necessary.

> **Note:** The example of cystic fibrosis highlights a key feature of DNA. The same DNA (same 46 chromosomes) is present in all the cells of an individual human (excepting sex cells). However, in different parts of the body different genes are active or expressed. This explains that although the defective CFTR gene is present in all the cells it has its major effect in those parts of the body where the gene is particularly important and is expressed.

Gene therapy is used to treat a range of disorders and many more are coming on-stream. A treatment for pancreatitis has just recently been approved for use in Europe (November 2012). Gene therapy is a fast-changing area of gene technology with both huge medical potential and almost certainly complex underlying ethical issues, particularly as the boundaries between addressing genetic malfunction and genetic enhancement become blurred.

The potential of gene therapy can only be realised when there is an excellent knowledge of the total DNA complement with all relevant genes being effectively mapped.

Genome sequencing and genetic mapping

Throughout this chapter we have referred to all the DNA in an organism being the total DNA complement, or used similar terms. The **complete DNA (base or nucleotide) sequence** is its **genome**. In very simple terms, the genome is a 'map' of the DNA in an organism.

> **Note:** The genome includes **all** the DNA, i.e. exons and introns.

There is a subtle distinction between genome sequencing and genetic mapping. **Genome sequencing** is working out the base sequence in an organism, i.e. the order of bases along each chromosome. Genome sequencing has many applications including its use in DNA fingerprinting in forensic analysis and the analysis of ancestral relationships between organisms.

Note: If the sequence of bases can be worked out along one chromosome in a homologous pair, it will be possible to work out the majority of bases in its partner chromosome by assuming that they will be the same. The exceptions will be in the relatively small number of cases where the alleles at a particular gene locus are different (heterozygous). We are familiar with heterozygous genes from genetics at GCSE; however, it is important to understand that heterozygosity is relatively rare with most genes being homozygous.

Genetic mapping is identifying exactly where particular genes are on chromosomes (without necessarily knowing the base sequence within the genes). Genetic mapping has been important for many reasons, including the location of defective genes and the identification of 'useful' genes that could be used in recombinant DNA technology.

Genome sequencing – key steps

While the genome sequencing of man was the ultimate target, it is not surprising that in the early stages of genome sequencing scientists targeted more straightforward organisms. Key early stages in identifying the complete DNA nucleotide sequence in organisms included:

- **Yeast** was the first eukaryotic organism to be fully sequenced – it has approximately 16 000 genes and 16 chromosomes.

- The **roundworm** (nematode) was the first multicellular organism to be sequenced – it has 20 000 genes but only 6 chromosomes.

- Other organisms that have been sequenced include virus phage λ, the bacterium *Escherichia coli*, the plant *Arabidopsis thaliana* and the fruit fly *Drosophila melanogaster*.

The **Human Genome Project** was a massive multinational project, started in 1990 and largely completed by 2003; a project that took over a decade and billions of pounds to work out the DNA nucleotide sequence in the human genome.

The Human Genome Project showed that the human genome is just over **three billion base pairs** in length. Further analysis showed that the human genome contains around **21 000 genes**, very similar to the number in other mammals. Furthermore, only around 2% of this DNA actually codes for polypeptides or protein with the remainder having a regulatory role through acting as gene switches or having no known function as yet (commonly, although not entirely accurately, referred to as 'junk' DNA).

The benefits of genome sequencing (the Human Genome Project) and the creation of 'genome libraries'

Some of the benefits of the Human Genome Project (and genome sequencing in general) are summarised in the following bullet points.

- More detailed **mapping of genes** was possible and the benefits this can bring in terms of the diagnosis and treatment of genetic disorders. Specific genes, or sections of DNA, can be identified using DNA (gene) probes as described earlier in this chapter. **DNA 'chips'** are DNA sequences that act as probes by being complementary to the nucleotide sequences associated with genetic disease – consequently they can be used to identify the presence of a defective allele or not, a very valuable technique in identifying if someone is a carrier of a condition.

Note: DNA 'chips' can also be used to identify specific sections of mRNA (rather than DNA). This can identify if genes are actually being **expressed** (are working) in a particular cell, i.e. if the gene is actually functioning, as the mRNA is only produced by functioning genes.

- The development of genome sequencing increases the potential of **gene therapy**. An understanding of the difference between functional and defective genes in terms of base pairs is important in identifying exactly what donor DNA is required and also with the possibility of artificially making donor DNA in 'gene machines'.

- Drug development can be matched to the genomes of individuals (or groups of people) so that drug treatments can be more effective in the individual(s) concerned, and importantly be modified to reduce side effects and allergies. There is huge potential in the use of '**designer drugs'**. However, the realisation of their potential is likely to be a compromise between scientific capability and the economics of 'personalised medicine'. Nonetheless, there is progress such as linking the specific treatment for some breast cancer patients to the actual gene that is defective. The same principle applies to the genome sequencing of pathogenic microorganisms. Knowledge of the genome of the different strains of pathogenic bacteria and viruses enables antibiotics and vaccines to be developed that specifically target these strains.

- DNA (genetic) profiling or **fingerprinting** – DNA fingerprinting is dependent on the differences in repeat DNA sequences - microsatellite repeat sequences (MRSs) or short tandem repeats (STRs). Different individuals have different numbers of repeat sequences. These repeat sequences occur in introns and probably form a part of the DNA that does not have a (known) function, i.e. 'junk' DNA.

- Knowledge of gene sequence allows the **primary structure** of **proteins** to be worked out. For example, if a certain sequence of DNA has been mapped to show that a particular gene lies between two specific points, then knowledge of the bases between those points will allow the mRNA codons and amino acid sequence to be determined. Molecular modelling software can then be used to predict secondary, tertiary and quaternary protein structure based on predicted bonding and folding arrangements.

- A greater understanding of the **ancestral links** between organisms and their **evolutionary development**. Prior to the arrival of genome sequencing similarities in morphology, anatomy, biochemistry and even ecology have been used to work out ancestral relationships. Genome sequencing has been able to confirm, or even modify, these relationships.

Case study – the evolutionary development of Man

The relationship between the different species of primate, and the relationship between man and other primates has been advanced through genome sequencing and related investigations. At the DNA level, humans and chimpanzees are 98 – 99% similar with a slightly greater divergence between humans and the other great apes such as the gorilla. There is even less genetic divergence between humans and 'Neanderthal Man' (*Homo neanderthalensis*), our closest relative, that became extinct around 30 000 years ago.

It has long been known that modern man evolved in Africa and subsequently (perhaps as recently as 50 000 years ago) migrated from there to other parts of the world. Genomic analysis shows that there is much more genetic divergence in Africa than in more distant areas, e.g. Arctic Europe and Australasia – exactly the pattern expected to fit the migration 'out of Africa' theory.

Note: Chimpanzees have the ABO blood grouping system (as did *H. neanderthalensis*). What can we conclude from this? That the ABO system evolved before the split between modern man and the chimpanzees 6-7 million years ago.

As already noted, one consequence of the Human Genome Project is that it is apparent that we have many fewer genes that have more than **one type of allele** (can be heterozygous) than we thought. In reality, most of our genes have two identical alleles. Additionally, **humans are 99.9% similar** in terms of DNA sequences. Much of the variation (the 0.1%) involves differences in single nucleotides. These are referred to as **single nucleotide polymorphisms** (**SNPs**) – assuming the frequency of these variants reaches 1% in the population and they are not just very isolated mutations in small groups – there are as many as **10 million SNPs** in human populations.

Note: It is the other 0.1% that provides much of the variation among different humans. Much of this is provided by the small number of genes that have more than one type of allele, with different people having different combinations of alleles, but this is not the whole story – mutations (and we all have at least some mutated genes) also contribute to variation.

The **HapMap Project** involved an international consortium that analysed the genomes of nearly 300 people across the world with the intention of mapping the locations of SNPs. The aim of the researchers was to identify a set of genetic markers that can be used to screen genetic data. Obvious examples include the use of **genetic screening** to match specific DNA sequences with the risk of genetic disease.

There are many other projects linked to genome sequencing. The **1000 Genomes Project**, launched in January 2008 and involving the USA, England, China and others, identified the genetic variation present in the genomes of 1000 people. Following the identification of the initial variation, the potential of the project is the mapping of variations to medical histories and a greater understanding of the genetic basis to disease.

Note: While some medical conditions such as cystic fibrosis can be clearly attributed to the inheritance of two defective alleles of one gene, the genetic basis of many medical conditions is much more complex. Conditions such as Type 1 diabetes, heart disease, many forms of mental illness and many others are linked to a 'genetic pre-disposition' in individuals involving many genes across a number of chromosomes. Gene sequencing and its many spin-off projects offer the possibility of progress with these more complex conditions.

Considerable genetic data has been generated by genome sequencing projects and stored in **biobanks** – data that is being used for many purposes including, but not only, medical research. For example, the data in some biobanks is being used to work out human migration patterns in our distant past.

Inactivation or replacement of genes (knockin and knockout technology)

The deliberate removal or addition of a gene (or other sequence of DNA) can enable the organisms concerned to function as model organisms for the study of genetic disease or drug therapies.

A **gene knockout** is a transgenic organism in which a gene (or genes) has been removed or made inoperative.

With gene knockouts, the principle is that the effect of loss of gene function can be modelled in non-human living organisms. This technology has obvious potential in furthering progress in the understanding of genetic diseases such as cystic fibrosis, Huntington's disease and muscular dystrophy. Most vertebrate knockout technology has involved the mouse. The mouse has many advantages in this setting: it is a mammal and biochemically and physiologically very similar to humans; it has a short life cycle and can be easily kept in laboratory conditions. The International Mouse Knockout Consortium was established in 2007 with the aim of making data available from the knockout of all the protein-coding genes available to the scientific and medical community. Another advantage with using mice is that most people are not as ethically opposed to using mice than they would be to using larger mammals.

A **gene knockin** is where a particular gene has been added. Knockin technology has been used to deliberately add a defective gene in order to study in detail disease progression.

As with many aspects of gene technology, progress is underpinned by ethical considerations.

The benefits and risk of gene technology – the ethical imperative

Reference to ethical issues has often been made in this chapter. With gene technology the benefits and risks must always be considered in tandem.

GMOs (or more specifically **GEMs**) appeared around 40 years ago with the use of transformed (transgenic) bacteria in the development of products e.g. insulin, useful to man. Generally most (informed) people have few ethical issues with this technology. The benefits far outweigh any potential risk. Nonetheless there are very strict regulations concerning the containment of transgenic microorganisms with considerable resources used to prevent their escape into the wild. The level of containment required has a positive correlation with the perceived risk.

These containment measures include:

- Appropriately licenced and **purpose-built laboratories** that have very effective **air filters** including 'negative – pressure' atmospheric gradients that 'sucks' air back into the laboratory.

- Very tightly controlled procedures for staff in terms of access and cleaning.

- Special disinfectant procedures in place.

- Using bacterial strains that are **poorly adapted** to survive outside controlled laboratory conditions, and in particular, poorly equipped to survive in humans.

These strains will typically have optimum temperature ranges very different to human body temperature.

- Using strains that have **'suicide genes'** that are activated if conditions do not remain within specific pH or temperature limits.

However, no matter how good the containment measures or how tight the legislation is, there is always the *possibility* that genetically engineered microorganisms could escape and survive beyond the confines of the laboratory.

GM Crops are another matter in the public consciousness. Perhaps it is that they are more visible or that people have to consider eating a GM crop that has helped create the much greater level of opposition here (compared to GEMs). We have already noted the arguments that they are not 'natural' or that the escape of their pollen or seeds could create 'superweeds'. 'Superweeds' can also be created through normal natural selection processes so while it cannot be discounted, GM technology is no more likely to cause the development of 'superweeds' than could occur naturally – particularly if appropriate legislative controls are in place.

Nonetheless, field trials with GM crops are held in the open and not in closed containers as with GEMs. Legislation does require that appropriate controls are in place such as the completion of the trials (and the removal of the crop) before flowering takes place.

With the potential of producing disease-resistant, more nutritious and more productive crops in a greater range of habitats (including in arid and salty soils that currently cannot be used without considerable treatment and investment) do the benefits not outweigh the disadvantages? Particularly at a time with a severe world shortage of food – nearly a billion people worldwide go hungry because they cannot produce or buy food. The problem can only get worse as the human population continues to grow out of control, climate change renders more land each year unsuitable for agriculture and pesticide resistance is increasing.

Genetic screening is another technology with huge potential. Genetic screening can take place before birth or after a child is born. Genetic screening before birth raises huge genetic issues for some people. It is possible to screen for many conditions including Down syndrome. What if the screening provides a positive result? The issue of whether to have an abortion or not is a complex ethical issue. Individuals concerned have to weigh up the possibility of bringing up a child with a medical disability (and the quality of life the child would have) against the possibility of destroying the foetus; a very difficult choice for many.

Usually (but not always) genetic screening **after** birth has fewer ethical implications. All newborn children in Britain are tested for the presence of **phenylketonuria** (**PKU**). PKU is a recessive inherited condition that affects about 1 in 10 000 people. Affected individuals lack an enzyme, a consequence of which is that the amino acid phenylalanine accumulates in the blood which, if allowed to continue, will lead to severe mental handicap. The advantage of early screening ensures that children with the condition are given a diet low in phenylalanine and PKU does not develop.

Some types of genetic screening are less straightforward. Take the case of Huntington's disease.

Case study – Huntington's disease

Huntington's disease is caused by a single defective allele. In DNA a base sequence of CAG is repeated many more times in individuals with Huntington's disease than in unaffected individuals. The condition causes progressive brain deterioration in middle age with complete neurological dysfunction and death the inevitable outcome.

> **Note:** We have come across repeating sequences of DNA before – the **MRSs** (STRs) in non-coding ('junk') DNA that can be used in DNA fingerprinting. The repeating sequences in Huntington's disease are certainly not 'junk' DNA as they have a very significant effect in controlling metabolism in individuals affected.

The defective allele in Huntington's disease is unusual compared to some of the other genetic diseases we have reviewed (e.g. cystic fibrosis and Duchenne muscular dystrophy); the Huntington allele is **dominant** not recessive – there are no carriers; people either have the condition or do not. Therefore if even one parent is heterozygous for Huntington's disease, each child has a 50% chance of inheriting the condition.

Individuals who suspect that they might be affected can get a test to confirm, or otherwise, the presence of the defective allele (i.e. will the individual tested develop the condition). Suppose that in a particular family an elderly grandparent has the condition but his / her forty year old son / daughter does not want to take the test – he / she prefers not to know. However, the twenty year old grandchild does want to know and opts for the test. If the grandchild is shown not to have the defective allele, this is obviously a huge relief to the grandchild but does not tell whether the forty year old parent has the allele. However, if the Huntington allele is confirmed in the grandchild, his / her parent will then know that he or she will develop the condition as the Huntington's allele must be present (the option of ignorance was removed by the grandchild taking the test).

With genome sequencing now much faster (hours rather than a decade as with the Human Genome Project) and much less expensive, the possibility of individuals being routinely screened for a wide range of genetic conditions is feasible – it is possible that in a generation each 'newborn' will have his / her genome as just another part of their medical notes. But as genetic screening becomes more common other ethical issues arise. Should information gleaned through genetic screening be made available to insurance companies? How easy would it be to get life insurance if a genetic condition was confirmed that could affect quality or length of life? Yet another point for consideration is the huge gap in our ability to identify the presence of a genetic defect and our ability to do anything about it as is the case with Duchenne muscular dystrophy and Huntington's disease. Also what if as a consequence of screening for a particular disease, the alleles that predispose for another totally unrelated disease were discovered – should the individual be informed?

However, **pre-implantation genetic diagnosis** (PGD) is an effective screening method at the emybro stage for potential parents in 'at risk' groups. In PGD, conception is by IVF and a number of embryos are screened for genetic abnormality. Only 'healthy' embryos are implanted in the uterus. In the UK over sixty inherited conditions are licensed for PGD.

This takes us on to **gene therapy**. Issues specific with gene therapy for cystic fibrosis were reviewed earlier but there other more general issues. Gene therapy is expensive;

would the money used be better spent in reducing hospital waiting lists or even spent on antibiotics and vaccines for developing countries – decisions that would save many lives?

The introduction of donor DNA into human cells is not without risk. The deliberate introduction of viruses into cells and the introduction of donor DNA has the potential to disrupt the host DNA. In the French trial of gene therapy for **SCID** (severe combined immunodeficiency) in 2002, two of the eleven babies in the clinical trial died from **leukaemia** – the assumption being that the gene therapy disrupted the host DNA leading to the leukaemia. Following the death of the children, all research in this area was stopped for nearly ten years. In the last few years research has started again with more positive results so far.

Although germ-line gene therapy is banned, the potential and probably the technological know-how of creating designer babies, or even human clones, exists. Not surprisingly, strict legislation regulates the whole area of reproductive biology.

> **Note:** An interesting take on human cloning is a central theme in *Perfect People*, a novel by Peter James (2011).

Detailed knowledge of the human genome and progress in drug development raises the possibility of **personalised medicine**. Personalised medicine is already in use with very specific drug treatments being tailored to the genome of the individual and even the genome of specific cancer tumours caused by the presence of specific genes. While one aim of personalised medicine is a more effective targeting of the problem, another aim is to reduce side effects of treatment – the same drug or treatment can affect different individuals in very different ways. Again the potential is enormous but often the more specific the treatment, the greater the expense.

The development of **biobanks** that store genetic data for some (or all) in a population is a step on the way to personalised medicine but it is not without its problems. If the gathering of data is mandatory (e.g. through the collection of blood, urine or even tissue samples) there are issues with consent. If it is not mandatory but an opt-in arrangement, certain ethnic minority groups and the less well educated are likely to be under-represented. Either way there are issues with data security.

The biggest obstacle is probably the complexity as the conditions that can have a genetic pre-disposition that affect large groups in the population often involve many genes with each one contributing only a very small factor towards the pre-disposition. Additionally, the genetic pre-disposition can often be a small part of the picture with environmental influences being more important. For example, most would argue that diet, obesity and lack of exercise are major factors in the development of coronary heart disease (CHD) with genetic pre-disposition playing a relatively minor role in individuals who are very obese, have fat-rich diets and do not take exercise. Most people would agree that attention to obesity, diet and exercise would have a far greater effect than focusing on the genetics of this condition. Nonetheless, it is thought that there are as many as 100 genes involved in the degree of genetic pre-disposition involved – too many to make personalised medicine in this area anything other than very complicated.

The complex nature of many apparently 'straightforward' genetic diseases also complicates matters. Seventy percent of cystic fibrosis sufferers have the same mutation (the same three bases missing) but the other thirty percent of cases are caused by up to a thousand different mutations.

There is no doubt that gene technology is a very fast moving part of biology with huge potential benefits: there is no doubt either that it is steeped in increasingly more complex ethical issues.

Exam questions

1. Bacterial plasmids may carry genes that provide resistance to naturally occurring antibiotics.

   (a) (i) What is a plasmid? [1]

      (ii) In recombinant DNA technology, plasmids are often used as vectors. Explain what is meant by the term 'vector' in this context [1]

   Diagram 1 illustrates a naturally occurring plasmid that contains genes for resistance to two antibiotics. When this plasmid is not present in a particular bacterium, the bacterium would be killed in the presence of either of these antibiotics.

   Diagram 2 illustrates a recombinant plasmid, which has had a human gene inserted at the point shown.

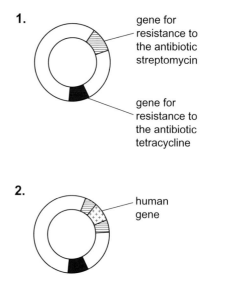

   (b) (i) Describe **two** methods by which a specific gene could have been obtained from human cells. [4]

      (ii) Describe how the human gene could then have been inserted into the original plasmid **(diagram 1)** to produce the recombinant plasmid **(diagram 2)**. [3]

   The human gene, referred to previously, codes for the production of a medically important hormone. In order to mass produce the hormone, *E. coli* cells (lacking any plasmids providing antibiotic resistance) are encouraged to take up plasmids. Those *E. coli* cells which have taken up the recombinant plasmids are identified and cloned in a nutrient medium and the hormone then separated and purified.

   (c) (i) Explain how the *E. coli* bacteria might be encouraged to take up the recombinant plasmids. [1]

      (ii) Outline the procedure by which the bacteria that have taken up the recombinant plasmid **(diagram 2)**, might be identified. [2]

      (iii) Explain how the elimination of other bacteria would increase the efficiency of the production of hormone. [1]

   Using bacteria to manufacture hormones has many advantages. For example, an increasing number of people with diabetes has increased the demand for the hormone insulin. This increased demand is met by producing insulin from genetically modified bacteria rather than extraction from the pancreas of cattle or pigs.

   (d) Suggest **one** health and **one** ethical advantage of using bacteria to produce insulin. [2]

Question taken from CCEA's Biology Assessment Unit A2 2, Biochemistry, Genetics and Evolutionary Trends, May 2012, © CCEA 2013

2. (a) The pedigree diagram below shows the incidence of cystic fibrosis in a family. Cystic fibrosis is a recessive autosomal condition.

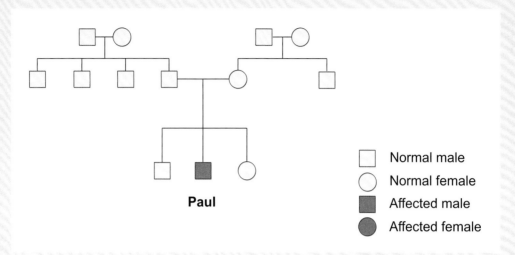

☐	Normal male
○	Normal female
■	Affected male
●	Affected female

Paul

(i) Ignoring the possibility of a recent mutation, explain the genetic basis for Paul having cystic fibrosis. Your answer should relate to the two earlier generations. [2]

(ii) Cystic fibrosis results in a thick, sticky mucus accumulating in the lung passages as a consequence of the malfunctioning of the surrounding respiratory passage cells. This makes patients more prone to infection.

Research is ongoing into the use of gene therapy to treat cystic fibrosis. One technique is to use aerosols to spray normal alleles (within liposomes) into the respiratory passages. The normal alleles provide normal functioning but do not become integrated into the host cell's DNA. Another technique involves the use of viruses as vectors to enable the normal alleles to gain entrance to cells.

The use of gene therapy in treating cystic fibrosis highlights issues surrounding somatic cell gene therapy in general, since it is difficult to modify genes in an already developed organism. Therefore, while gene therapy has huge potential it is still of limited use as a successful treatment.

Using cystic fibrosis as an example, give **three** reasons why the technique of gene therapy is of limited use. [3]

(b) The transfer of genes from one organism to another produces genetically modified organisms (GMOs). However, the production of GMOs involves certain risks and, in order to reduce these risks, a number of safety precautions have been devised. Describe **two** safety precautions used to reduce the risks involved in the production of GMOs. [2]

(c) Human genome sequencing raises the possibility of producing 'designer drugs'.

(i) Define the term 'genome'. [1]

(ii) Explain what is meant by a 'designer drug'. [1]

Question taken from CCEA's Biology Assessment Unit A2 2, Biochemistry, Genetics and Evolutionary Trends, May 2011, © CCEA 2013

3. The Human Genome Project was organised to sequence all the nucleotides and map the genes present in human DNA. The graph below shows the number of mapped genes for different sized chromosomes.

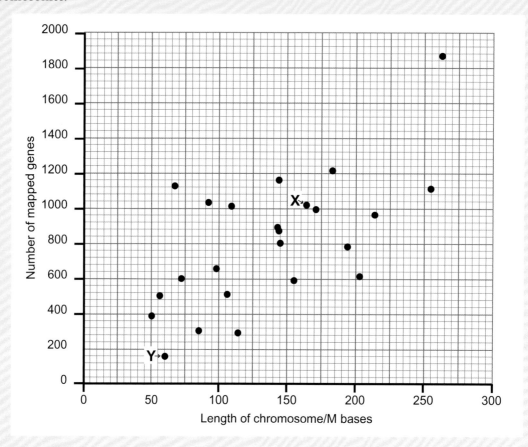

(a) Describe the trend evident in the graph. [1]

(b) The sex chromosomes, **X** and **Y**, are identified in the graph. Compare the number of genes in these chromosomes with other similar sized chromosomes. [2]

(c) Explain the significance for males of the difference between the number of the genes on the **X** and **Y** chromosomes. [1]

Question taken from CCEA's Biology Assessment Unit A2 2, Biochemistry, Genetics and Evolutionary Trends, June 2010, © CCEA 2013

4. Quality of written communication is awarded a maximum of [2] marks in this section.

(a) Write an account of the role of nucleic acids in the synthesis of proteins. [10]

(b) Knowledge of the role of nucleic acids has been exploited to provide new sources of medically important proteins and new crops from genetically modified organisms.

Discuss the safety precautions currently employed to overcome potential hazards of using genetically modified organisms and some of the ethical issues regarding the benefits and risks of gene technology. [6]

Question taken from CCEA's Biology Assessment Unit A2 2, Biochemistry, Genetics and Evolutionary Trends, June 2010, © CCEA 2013

Chapter 13 – Genes and Patterns of Inheritance

Genetics is the science of heredity; the way in which characteristics pass from parents to offspring. Chromosomes in the cell nucleus carry the genetic material in short sections called **genes.** We already know that each gene codes for a particular polypeptide (or protein). As proteins, mainly in the form of enzymes, control metabolic pathways, they control the characteristics of an organism. In summary, at its simplest level, each gene controls a particular characteristic, e.g. flower colour. However, it is important to remember that in complex living organisms such as humans, most characteristics are controlled by many more than one gene.

Genetics, chromosomes and genes

As chromosomes occur in homologous pairs, each chromosome of a pair will carry the same gene (e.g. for flower colour) but the gene for flower colour may have different forms **(alleles)** in the two chromosomes (e.g. one allele may be for red flowers and one for white flowers).

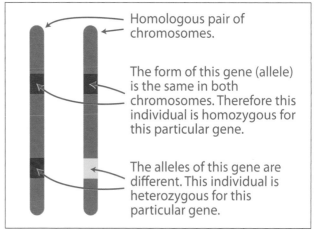

Homologous pair of chromosomes.

The form of this gene (allele) is the same in both chromosomes. Therefore this individual is homozygous for this particular gene.

The alleles of this gene are different. This individual is heterozygous for this particular gene.

A homologous pair of chromosomes with the positions of two genes shown

Note: Apart from the sex chromosomes (and ignoring mutations), there are the same genes (and number of genes) on each chromosome of a homologous pair. However, the number of genes on different homologous chromosome pairs is very variable. The wide variation is due to many factors including chromosome length and the relative proportions that are coding (exons) and non-coding (introns).

Some important genetic terms are defined below.

Term	Definition
Gene	Short section of chromosome that codes for a particular polypeptide / protein / characteristic
Allele	A particular form of a gene
Homozygous	Both alleles of a gene are the same
Heterozygous	The alleles of the (same) gene are different
Gene locus	The position of the gene on the chromosome

Gregor Mendel – the founder of genetics

Gregor Mendel (born in 1822) lived as a monk in what is now part of the Czech Republic. His work on the breeding of peas (*Pisum sativum*) has formed the basis of the subject we now know as genetics. Mendel noticed that in pea plants there were many characteristics that varied in a discrete way from plant to plant, e.g. plant height, flower colour, pea shape or size. By crossing (mating) plants in a series of breeding investigations, (lasting over ten years), he was able to study the inheritance of particular characteristics.

Monohybrid inheritance – the inheritance of alleles at one gene locus

One characteristic that Mendel investigated was pea height – pea plants can be normal sized (tall) or exist as a short variety. While peas, as with all living organisms, vary to the extent that 'tall' (or 'short') plants were not all exactly the same size, he could clearly categorise plants as either tall or short. Mendel was careful to consider only one characteristic (e.g. height) at a time (**monohybrid inheritance**) to gain an understanding of the principles involved.

Before Mendel carried out his investigation by crossing tall and short pea plants, he allowed the tall plants to interbreed with each other for many generations to ensure that they always produced tall plants, i.e. they were **pure breeding** (homozygous). Mendel did the same with the short plants to ensure they were also pure breeding.

When Mendel crossed the tall plants with the short plants (**parental generation**), he observed that **all** the offspring of this cross (the first filial or F_1 **generation**) were tall.

However, when he crossed any F_1 plant with any other F_1 plant, their **progeny** or offspring, (the F_2 **generation**) contained a mixture of both tall and short plants. Further analysis, following many of these crosses, showed that approximately 75% of the progeny were tall with approximately 25% short.

When trying to explain the results of his monohybrid cross, Mendel used the symbol **T** for tall plants and the symbol **t** for the short plants. The capital is used to designate the **dominant** condition (all the F_1 plants were tall and three quarters of the F_2 plants were tall, suggesting that the tall state was dominant relative to the **recessive** short state). These symbols represent the alleles which determine the height in the plants. Consequently as genes (alleles) occur in pairs (one on each homologous chromosome) the genetic makeup of each individual is represented by two symbols, e.g. TT, Tt or tt, depending on the combination present. The gene arrangement (symbols) represents the **genotype**, and the outward appearance (whether tall or short) is the **phenotype**.

Mendel further deduced that only one of the two factors (genes / alleles) in the parental genotype pass into a **gamete**. This is consistent with our understanding of **meiosis** – only one homologous chromosome from each pair can pass into a gamete. He also concluded that it was totally random which of the two 'factors' (genes / alleles on homologous chromosomes) will enter a particular gamete.

Consequently **Mendel's first law of inheritance** (the **law of segregation**) can be summarised as *the two alleles of each gene separate during meiosis with only one entering each gamete.*

The genetic crosses discussed in the previous sections are summarised in the following diagram. As is traditional with genetic crosses, gametes are represented by a symbol inside a circle. In the following crosses the gametes are within filled boxes for clarity.

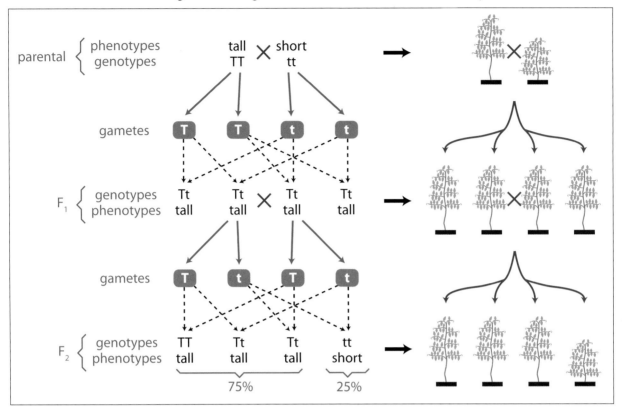

Note 1: Although crossing very large numbers of plants the 3: 1 didn't work out as an exact ratio. This is because it is totally random which gametes (and therefore which allele of a particular gene) join during fertilisation.

Explanation as to how the 3:1 ratio for flower colour is produced in peas

Note 2: Our understanding of monohybrid inheritance can be expanded to be defined as the inheritance of the alleles of a single gene at one gene locus.

More genetic terms are summarised in the following table.

Term	Definition	Example from Mendel's cross involving height in peas
Genotype	The two alleles for a particular characteristic (trait)	The original parents were either TT (if tall) or tt (if short) as they were pure breeding (homozygous)
Phenotype	The outward appearance of an individual in terms of the trait under consideration	The original parents had either a tall or a short phenotype
Dominant	In the heterozygous condition the dominant allele will override the non-dominant (recessive) allele	The F_1 progeny are all tall even through they are heterozygous and have a short allele
Recessive	The recessive allele will be dominated by the dominant allele – it will only show itself in the phenotype if there are two recessive alleles	Only 25% of the F_2 progeny are short as only 25% have no dominant (T) allele present

As Mendel crossed different traits (characteristics), he noted similar ratios as found when studying pea height. He also noted that many of his crosses gave a **1 : 1** offspring ratio.

This can be explained by one of the parents being **heterozygous** for the trait concerned and the other **homozygous recessive**. In our example of height in peas their respective genotypes are **Tt** and **tt**.

The 1 : 1 ratio arising from a monohybrid cross is explained on the right using height in peas as an example.

The test cross

Homozygous dominant and heterozygous individuals have different genotypes (e.g. TT and Tt) but have the same phenotype (e.g. tall). To determine the genotype of an individual with dominant phenotype but unknown genotype a test cross can be carried out. This involves crossing the unknown individual with an individual that is homozygous recessive. The ratio of phenotypes in the progeny can be used to determine the unknown genotype.

Explanation of the 1 : 1 ratio in monohybrid crosses

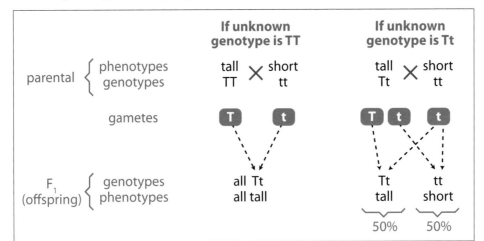

The test cross

With the test cross if **any** of the offspring show a recessive phenotype, then the unknown parent must have been heterozygous (it is not necessary to confirm a 50/50 ratio, particularly if numbers of offspring are low).

Note: For many years test crosses have been used to confirm (or otherwise) pedigree status in plants or animals. In recent years, genomic sequencing or DNA fingerprinting gives faster and more conclusive results.

Monohybrid inheritance throws up other possibilities. For example, instead of one allele being dominant and the other recessive, co-dominance can arise.

Co-dominance

In co-dominance the two alleles at a particular gene locus are different, but neither has a dominant or masking effect over the other. Due to the absence of dominance, the heterozygous phenotype is different to both homozygous phenotypes.

Snapdragons (*Antirrhinum*) show co-dominance for flower colour. The pink flower (intermediate between the homozygote red and white colours) is a consequence of co-dominance in the flower colour trait.

The flower colour genotypes and phenotypes possible in snapdragons are shown in the following table.

Genotypes	Phenotypes
C^RC^R	Red flowers
C^RC^W	Pink flowers
C^WC^W	White flowers

Note: The genotypes are represented as shown in the table because using the 'traditional' capital and lower case symbols, e.g. R and r, would confuse in terms of dominance and recessiveness.

A **1 : 2 : 1** ratio is produced when two heterozygote parents are crossed for a trait that displays co-dominance. The following diagram explains how the 1 : 2 : 1 ratio is produced.

Although crosses can be set out as shown earlier, it is traditional and often more straightforward to represent crosses as Punnett squares as shown below (particularly if there is more than one type of gamete possible from both parents).

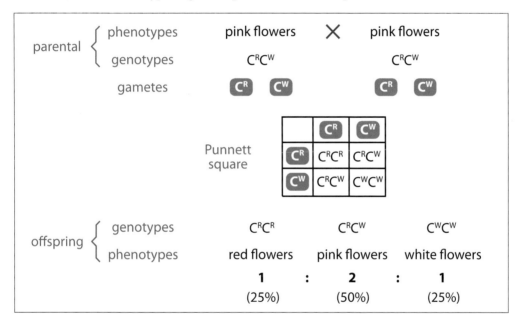

Co-dominance in snapdragons

Note: We will come to another example of incomplete dominance in the next chapter. Individuals with sickle-cell anaemia have two recessive alleles and 'normal' individuals have two dominant alleles for the relevant gene. The heterozygote has sickle-cell trait (but not the full condition). Individuals with sickle-cell trait have a phenotype somewhere between the two homozygote conditions.

Multiple alleles

For some traits there are more than two possible alleles for a particular gene at the gene locus, i.e. the inheritance of the trait is multiple allelic.

There are many examples of multiple alleles in inheritance with many of the examples being further complicated by co-dominance or a hierarchy of dominance across the range of alleles.

Take for example, the inheritance of **human blood groups**. There are four blood groups in the **ABO** system with each individual being one of blood group A, B, AB or O. Allele A is co-dominant with allele B, and both A and B are dominant to O. Taking this into account, the possible genotypes of each group are shown in the following table.

Blood group	Possible genotypes
A	$I^A I^A$ and $I^A I^O$
B	$I^B I^B$ and $I^B I^O$
AB	$I^A I^B$
O	$I^O I^O$

There are a range of possible crosses and outcomes with the different blood groups. However, the only possible cross that can produce offspring showing the range of the four blood groups is a cross between a parent heterozygous for blood group A and a parent heterozygous for blood group B as shown below.

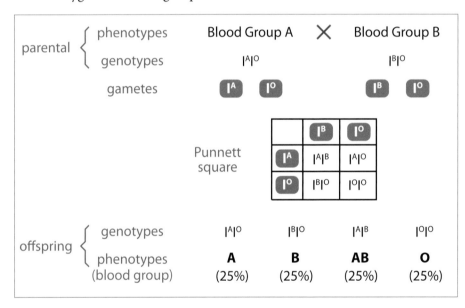

Inheritance of blood groups showing how parents with blood groups A and B respectively can produce children with all four possible blood group types

In **coat colour in rabbits** there are four different alleles (full colour or agouti, chinchilla, himalayan and albino). Full colour is dominant over the other three alleles and albino is recessive to the other three with chinchilla and Himalayan being in the middle.

In some species, the outworking of certain allele combinations result in a genotype that is not viable, i.e. **lethal alleles**. This is explained in the next section.

Lethal allelic combinations

The affects of a lethal combination of alleles can be seen in the inheritance of coat colour in mice. Mice can have yellow or grey coloured (agouti) fur. The allele that gives the yellow fur colour is dominant to the allele that codes for agouti fur colour. Cross-breeding two heterozygous yellow mice would be expected to give a ratio of 3 (yellow) : 1 (agouti) if normal Mendelian inheritance patterns, as reviewed earlier, were evident.

However, a ratio of 2 (yellow) : 1 (agouti) occurs. This can be explained by the occurrence of two alleles coding for yellow fur being a lethal combination as shown in the diagram on the right. Offspring that have the lethal combination (approx 25% in this example will have it) fail to develop properly as embryos. Therefore only the non-lethal combinations (heterozygotes and non-lethal homozygotes) survive long enough to be counted in the progeny.

Most often, lethal allelic combinations result in the spontaneous abortion of embryos or foetuses at a very early stage and most often are recessive, only being expressed when both alleles are present. However, there are exceptions. The allele for Huntington's disease is inherited as a dominant autosomal (non-sex chromosome) lethal allele as its presence will always lead to the death of affected individuals. The key (and very distressing) difference with most other lethal allelic combinations is that its effects only manifest themselves in an adult, and often without prior warning during childhood and young adulthood.

Lethal alleles in mice

Note: Lethal allelic combinations are usually recessive in that the presence of two recessive alleles (and the absence of a dominant allele) often results in an essential metabolic pathway not functioning. Huntington's disease is not strictly an example of a 'lethal allelic **combination**' in that it only requires a single dominant allele to be present rather than the presence of a particular genotype.

Sex determination and sex linkage

Humans have 46 chromosomes organised as 23 pairs. Twenty two pairs (44 chromosomes) are referred to as **autosomes** with the other pair being the sex chromosomes.

Sex determination - It is the **sex chromosomes** (designated X and Y), that determine the sex of an individual. Although different systems exist across the animal kingdom, in humans two X chromosomes lead to the development of a female and an X and a Y sex chromosome lead to the development of a male.

Sex determination in humans

Following the normal rules of segregation in meiosis, only one of the sex chromosomes will enter a gamete. Consequently, all females produce gametes with an X chromosome (and 22 autosomes) and half the gametes produced by a male will have an X chromosome and half will have a Y chromosome. This pattern of sex determination shows why approximately 50% of children are males and 50% female as shown in the diagram (right).

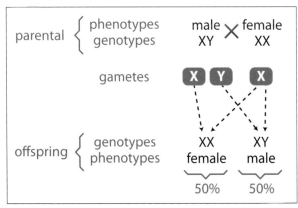

Sex linkage – All the genetic traits we have covered so far in this chapter are independent of the sex of the individuals, e.g. in a typical heterozygote x heterozygote cross we get a 3 : 1 progeny ratio of the trait investigated independent of the gender of the offspring.

For some genetic traits, there is a close correlation between the trait and the sex of the individual, i.e. the conditions are said to be **sex-linked**.

In humans, the Y sex chromosome is almost 'genetically empty' with fewer genes and these are largely concerned with the development of 'male' characteristics. Therefore, the X chromosome has large sections (and many genes) that are non-homologous, with no corresponding genes on the Y chromosome.

The non-homologous nature of much of the X chromosome explains the sex-linked nature of several human conditions. **Red-green colour blindness**, **haemophilia** and **Duchenne muscular dystrophy** almost always occur in **males** only. Each of these conditions can be caused by the presence of a single recessive allele on the X chromosome.

While females can carry the recessive allele for any of the above conditions on an X chromosome, it is almost always masked by the dominant allele on their other X chromosome – they can be carriers but very rarely have the condition (they would need both sex chromosomes to have recessive alleles). However, males only need to have one recessive allele on their X chromosome to have the condition, as they do not have the gene on their Y chromosome to mask the effect of the recessive allele.

However, for a male child to get a sex-linked condition as described above, his mother will have invariably been a **carrier** (someone who carries the allele but who is phenotypically 'normal'). The following diagram shows why sex-linked conditions such as haemophilia are almost always restricted to males.

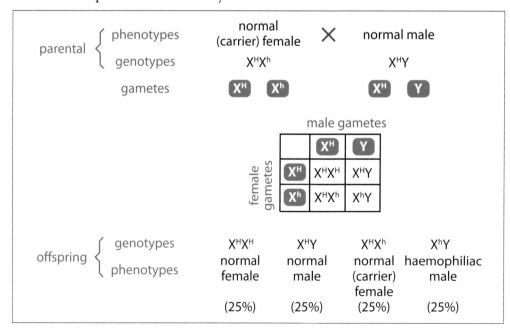

The inheritance of haemophilia from a carrier female

Note 1: In crosses involving sex-linkage, it is important to identify the sex chromosome and the alleles they contain by using superscripts (see cross above).

Note 2: With crosses involving sex-linkage it is useful to identify which gametes are from the male and which are from the female (see earlier cross).

Note 3: It is possible (although very rare) for females to phenotypically express sex-linked conditions. To have a recessive allele on each of their X chromosomes, their father would have to show the condition (have the recessive allele on his X chromosome) and their mother would need to be a carrier (or have the condition).

Note 4: Sex linked alleles can also be **dominant**. The key difference from the cross showing the inheritance of haemophilia is that there would be no carriers – if the allele is present (in the male or the female) the condition would appear.

Pedigree charts

Pedigree charts or diagrams can be used to chart the inheritance of a condition or trait through several generations of a breeding group (using the wider family grouping in human examples). There are some important conventions associated with pedigree charts including:

- males are represented by squares

- females are represented by circles

- shading within a square or a circle indicates that the trait under consideration, e.g. haemophilia, is expressed in the phenotype

- sometimes (but not always) carriers can be identified by e.g. cross hatching, - if so, there will be a key to make this clear

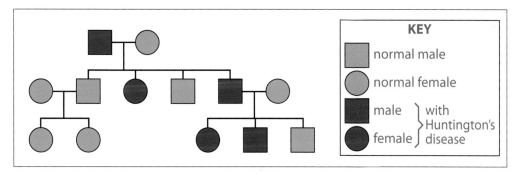

The inheritance of Huntington's disease across three generations of the same family

Huntington's disease is autosomal dominant so the condition cannot skip a generation. As it is not sex-linked it is equally likely to appear in males and females. In the example above the male in the first generation must have been heterozygous for Huntington's disease (if he had been homozygous for the condition all of his children would have been affected).

If you get a pedigree chart in an examination question, it is important to try to deduce the nature of the inheritance under consideration. It will almost always be one of the following situations.

- **autosomal recessive** – in a pedigree diagram this can often be identified by the trait only appearing in some generations (i.e. it is 'hidden' in some generations). If autosomal, then (approximately) even numbers of males and females will be affected.

- **autosomal dominant** – it is impossible to pass the condition on without at least one parent having the trait. Again, if autosomal, (approximately) even numbers of males and females will be affected (see example of Huntington's disease on page 229).

- **X-linked recessive** – more common (or only present) in males but not present in all males (a carrier mother will pass the trait on to around half of her sons).

- **X-linked dominant** – if dominant, not mainly restricted to males the way X-linked recessive traits are. For example, a father with the condition will pass the trait on to all his daughters.

Note: Use the information in the bullet points above to focus in on the most likely mechanism of transmission. However, once you have predicted the mechanism, it is important to confirm by checking some of the crosses in the pedigree to ensure they fit with your prediction.

A review of monohybrid inheritance in humans

There are many examples of monohybrid inheritance in humans, e.g. the Rhesus factor, ABO blood group, albinism and the examples of genetic disease that we have covered in this or the previous chapter.

Monohybrid inheritance involves genes where there are at least two alternative forms of an allele. However, most genes occur in only one form with both alleles being identical, therefore monohybrid inheritance is associated with only a small proportion of the total gene complement.

If there are two or more alternative forms (alleles) of the same gene, this is due to genetic change (mutation) and most often, but not always, the mutated allele is recessive. Mutations frequently result in loss of function and it for the reasons above that many of the examples of monohybrid inheritance we have used are of genetic diseases, most of which have very harmful consequences to the individuals involved.

The examples we have referred to include cystic fibrosis, albinism, phenylketonuria, (all **autosomal recessive**), Huntington's disease (**autosomal dominant**), sickle cell anaemia (**incomplete dominance**), haemophilia, red-green colour blindness and Duchenne muscular dystrophy (**X-linked recessive**).

Returning to the principles of the genetic transmission of traits, Mendel was not content with just investigating monohybrid inheritance; he carried out investigations on the inheritance of two traits (characteristics), e.g. height in peas and whether the seeds were round or wrinkled. This is the study of **dihybrid inheritance**.

Dihybrid inheritance – the inheritance of alleles at two gene loci

When investigating the transmission of height of peas **and** seed shape **together** (dihybrid inheritance), Mendel noticed that the ratios started to become more complex. Nonetheless, when considering the inheritance of two different traits together they tended to form ratios that held true when the cross was repeated.

When Mendel crossed pure breeding pea plants that were both tall and had round seed shape with pure breeding plants that were both short and had wrinkled seed shape, he observed that all the F_1 generation (the offspring / progeny of the parental cross) were tall and had smooth seeds. However, when he crossed F_1 plants he found that the F_2 plants occurred in the ratio:

9 – tall with smooth seeds
3 – tall with wrinkled seeds
3 – short with smooth seeds
1 – short with wrinkled seeds

Based on his work with monohybrid inheritance Mendel knew or could deduce that:

- Tallness and smooth seed shape are dominant with short plants and wrinkled seeds being recessive

- All the plants in the F_1 generation were heterozygous for both height and seed shape

Furthermore, the cross could only be explained by assuming that both traits (e.g. height and seed shape) were inherited independently. In effect, the outcome is a consequence of two monohybrid crosses occurring simultaneously.

This forms the basis of **Mendel's second law**, the **law of independent assortment**. In effect this means that *during the formation of gametes, the segregation of the alleles of one gene is independent to the segregation of the alleles of any other gene.*

In terms of meiosis, the law of independent assortment can be explained by the fact that homologous pairs of chromosomes (bivalents) arrange themselves independently of other homologous pairs on the equator of the spindle at **metaphase 1**.

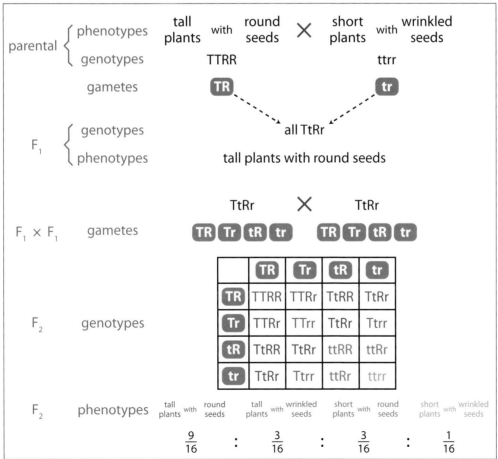

Dihybrid inheritance – the 9 : 3 : 3 : 1 ratio

Mendel discovered that another common ratio with dihybrid crosses was **1 : 1 : 1 : 1**. This can be explained by crossing the double heterozygote with the double homozygous recessive. See below.

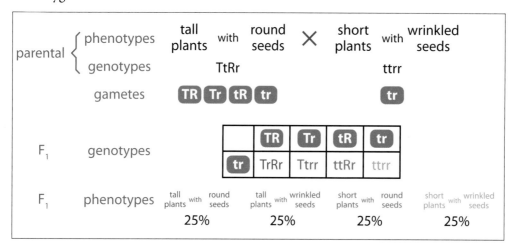

Explanation of the dihybrid 1 : 1 : 1 : 1 ratio

Note 1: When working out dihybrid crosses, most mistakes are made in working out the gametes. Remember, only one allele of each gene can go into a gamete and that there is an equal chance of either of the alleles from one gene entering a gamate with either of the alleles from another gene (due to segregation and independent assortment during meiosis in the formation of gametes).

Note 2: Dihybrid inheritance only holds true to the ratios discussed above if the genes are on different chromosomes. If two different genes are on the same chromosome, they tend to transmit between the generations as if it was a monohybrid cross. If the genes are on different chromosomes they are said to be **independently inherited**.

The ratios 9 : 3 : 3 : 1 and 1 : 1 : 1 : 1 are classical dihybrid rations when each of the two genes involved has a dominant and a recessive allele. However, the inheritance (and the ratios of progeny produced) can be clouded by any the presence of multiple alleles, co-dominance, sex linkage or any of the variations we reviewed in monohybrid inheritance.

It may be that the two genes under consideration inherit independently but when certain allelic combinations (from the **different** genes) are present they **interact** to produce a range of phenotypes. This is an example of **gene interaction**.

Gene interaction

There are a number of different types of gene interaction as summarised in the following sections.

The additive effect of the alleles across two gene loci - Some traits are a consequence of the **cumulative effect** of certain alleles in two (or more) genes. The phenotype is thus dependent on a genotype straddling across two genes.

For example, if the thickness of fur in a particular mammal is controlled by two independently assorted genes A and B. The double homozygous recessive (aabb) codes for the base thickness with each dominant allele present in the genotype contributing another ten percent in terms of thickness. The additive effects that different genotypes produce, above the base thickness, are listed in the following table.

Genotypes	Fur thickness
aabb	base thickness
Aabb / aaBb	base + 10%
AAbb / aaBB / AaBb	base + 20%
AABb / AaBB	base + 30%
AABB	base +40%

The following diagram represents a cross between two individuals, each heterozygous for both genes.

parental genotypes	AaBb ✕ AaBb
gametes	AB Ab aB ab AB Ab aB ab

The additive effects of gene interaction

F₁ genotypes

	AB	Ab	aB	ab
AB	AABB	AABb	AaBB	AaBb
Ab	AABb	AAbb	AaBb	Aabb
aB	AaBB	AaBb	aaBB	aaBb
ab	AaBb	Aabb	aaBb	aabb

F₁ phenotypes

genotypes	fur thickness	ratio of offspring phenotypes
aabb	base (0)	$^1/_{16}$
Aabb/aaBb	+ 10	$^4/_{16}$
AAbb/aaBB/AaBb	+ 20	$^6/_{16}$
AABb/AaBB	+ 30	$^4/_{16}$
AABB	+ 40	$^1/_{16}$

Relative frequency of the different phenotypes in fur thickness

The relative proportions of the different offspring phenotypes are shown in the histogram on the right.

The additive effect of more than two genes can lead to **polygenic inheritance**. In polygenic inheritance the combined effect of a number of genes results in a **normal distribution** similar to the diagram above but there will be many more categories. If enough genes are involved there might be so many different categories, and the differences between them become so small, that the trait displays **continuous variation** (rather than the discontinuous variation shown by the other examples we have reviewed so far).

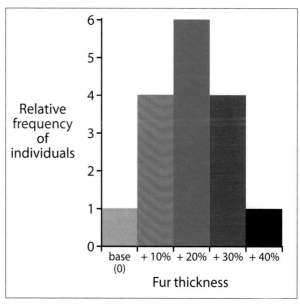

233

Epistasis – This is a form of gene interaction where one gene **interferes** with the expression of another gene or **influences** it in some way but is not merely additive as discussed in the previous example.

Note: For epistasis it is important to remember that it is a **gene** interfering with the expression of another **gene** (and not alleles as with dominant and recessive alleles).

Comb type in the domestic chicken is an example of epistasis where the phenotype is dependent on the genotype of two different, independently inherited, genes. The two genes responsible for comb formation are designated P and R. The four phenotypes possible for comb type, their possible genotypes and an explanation of the link between genotype and phenotype are listed in the following table.

Comb type	Possible genotypes	Explanation
Walnut	PPRR, PpRR, PPRr, PpRr (i.e. P_R_)	At least one dominant P and one dominant R allele present
Pea	PPrr, Pprr (i.e. P_rr)	At least one dominant P allele but no dominant R allele
Rose	ppRR, ppRr (i.e. ppR_)	At least one dominant R allele but no dominant P allele
Single	pprr	Both genes homozygous recessive (no dominant alleles at all)

The diagram below shows how a cross between a particular chicken with a pea comb and a particular chicken with a rose comb can produce progeny showing all four possible phenotypes.

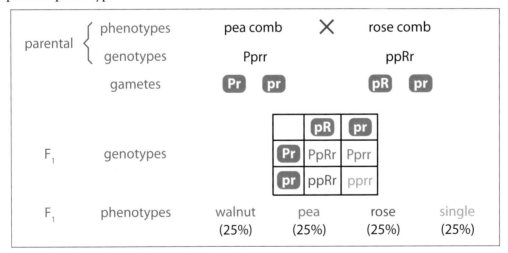

Epistasis in the domestic fowl – the development of the walnut phenotype is an example of epistasis

Note: In the above cross, reference was made to it being between 'particular' chickens with pea and rose combs. You should be able to work out why it was worded like this rather than stated that a cross between a pea and a rose chicken could produce all four phenotypes in the offspring.

Flower colour in sweet pea is another example of epistasis. In this example there are two genes (C and P) responsible for flower colour. If each of the two independently assorted genes has at least one dominant allele present (C_P_) then purple flowers will result. However, if only one (or neither) of the genes is present in its dominant state

(C_pp or ccP_ or ccpp) then the flowers are white. The ratio of offspring produced when crossing two double heterozygotes is shown in the diagram on the right.

The ratio shown (**9 : 7**) is a variation on the normal 9 : 3 : 3 :1 dihybrid theme and is explained below.

Gene interaction, in general, normally arises when two or more genes are involved in the control of a metabolic pathway leading to a particular phenotype. Each gene may control an enzyme

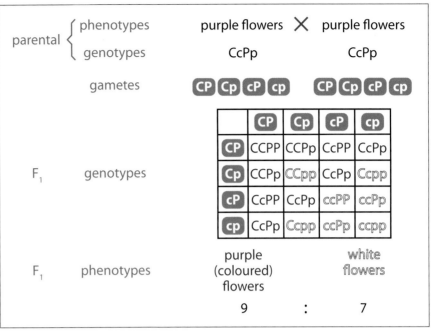

Flower colour in sweet pea (a 9:7 epistatic ratio)

important at a particular stage of the pathway; consequently both (or all if more than two) genes need to be functional to achieve the 'normal' phenotype. In the above example of colour in sweet pea, at least one dominant allele in each gene must be present to make the gene functional and able to metabolise the two steps in the process (if either gene is homozygous recessive, the enzyme is not produced by that gene and therefore the metabolic pathway cannot be completed).

The metabolic pathway involved is summarised in the following diagram.

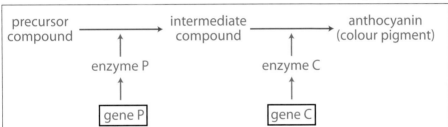

The **9 : 7** ratio can be explained by the requirement for at least one **dominant allele** to be present in **each gene**. This ensures that each of the steps in the metabolic pathway can be completed as both the P and C genes will produce the necessary enzymes.

These are only two examples of epistasis. In comb type in chickens, two loci **interact** to create a new phenotype (e.g. walnut) and in flower colour in sweet pea, the two loci also interact to produce the purple flower colour. In other examples, e.g. wheat kernel colour, two (or more) genes can **duplicate** (substitute for) the work of each other producing a **15 : 1** phenotypic ratio, with the '1/16' representing the double homozygous recessive.

Additionally, an allele at one locus could **mask** an allele (or alleles) at another locus. Squash can be yellow, green or white with colour controlled by two genes (1 and 2) with alleles (W or w) and (Y or y) respectively. If there is at least one dominant W allele present (W-) the squash will be white irrespective of the genotype of gene 2. If gene 1 has only recessive alleles (ww) then it will be coloured, but the actual colour produced depends on gene 2. Genotypes of wwY- give a yellow colour and wwyy gives a green colour. A cross between two plants producing white squashes, but both heterozygous for each gene, produces a offspring phenotypic ratio of **12 : 3 : 1** as shown in the following diagram.

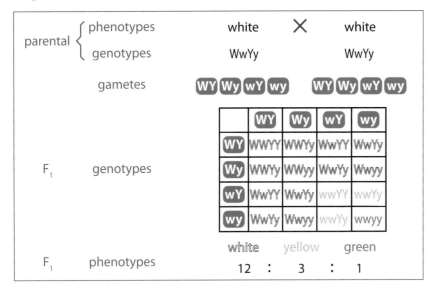

In this example, gene 1, if homozygous dominant or heterozygous, **masks** the effect of gene 2.

Epistasis in squash

The effect of the environment

Most of the examples we have covered in this chapter involve phenotypes that are directly dependent on their genotypes. In effect, this means that particular genotypes produce particular phenotypes irrespective of environmental influences. An individual with two recessive alleles for cystic fibrosis will have the condition irrespective of environmental influences.

But in truth, in complex living organisms (and certainly in humans) most traits are not inherited in typical Mendelian fashion as demonstrated by monohybrid or dihybrid crosses or any of their variations. Most traits are polygenic and controlled by many genes. In the last chapter we have already noted that predisposition to CHD can be affected by as many as one hundred genes. Similar numbers have an influence on human height. The polygenic picture is further complicated by the fact that many traits are also influenced by the environment. For example, a particular individual may have a suite of alleles that predispose towards 'tallness', but the actual height reached will be influenced by many environmental factors including diet.

If we look at overall development of many traits in a human (and many other species), e.g. personality, the actual trait produced is a result of the complex interactions between genetics (nature) and the environment (nurture).

At the cellular level, it is relatively straightforward to understand how the environment may have an influence on genetic expression. Certainly DNA in the nucleus controls cell development (and ultimately the development of the organism) through the production of the proteins (enzymes) that control metabolic pathways. However, it is the cell (sometimes through environmental influences) that determines which genes are switched on in the first place. The role of the environment in affecting gene expression (**epigenetics**) is a branch of biology that is currently attracting considerable interest.

Mendel revisited

It is nearly 150 years since Mendel published his conclusions on the inheritance of characters in peas. In his investigations he analysed the inheritance of seven traits (length of stem, shape of seed, colour of seed, shape of pod, colour of pod, colour of flower and position of flower). Since that time our understanding of genetics has developed, but this understanding has built on, rather than contradicted, his original ideas. At the time of his research he did not know about chromosomes or genes, referring to 'factors' inside the plant.

Nonetheless, his work was meticulously planned and he spent over ten years carrying out his research. He also used many replicates allowing him to produce offspring in the numbers that allowed him to calculate ratios (the same argument holds true today with genetic investigations: a large number of offspring are often required to identify ratios due to the random nature of gamete production and fertilisation).

He also had the wisdom (or luck) to choose the pea. The pea has a range of easily observable traits (including the seven traits he studied) that are subject to straightforward monohybrid or dihybrid inheritance patterns.

Exam questions

1. The terms 'polygenic inheritance' and 'epistasis' are used to describe particular patterns of inheritance. State **one** way in which they are similar and then distinguish between the terms. [3]

Question taken from CCEA's Biology Assessment Unit A2 2, Biochemistry, Genetics and Evolutionary Trends, May 2012, © CCEA 2013

2. Labrador retrievers are dogs with black, brown or yellow coats. The coat colour is controlled by two independently-inherited genes which are not sex-linked.

   The alleles of a pigment gene at the **B/b** locus determine the amount of black pigment produced. The presence of a **B** allele results in a black coat. A brown coat is produced by the **bb** genotype.

   A second gene at the **E/e** locus influences the expression of the alleles at the **B/b** locus. The presence of the **E** allele allows the alleles at the **B/b** locus to be expressed. A yellow coat is always produced if the genotype is **ee**, no matter which alleles are present at the **B/b** locus.

   (a) (i) State the genotype of a pure breeding brown Labrador. [1]

   (ii) State the genetic term which describes the relationship between the **B/b** and **E/e** loci. [1]

   (b) Two black dogs known to be heterozygous for both genes (**BbEe**) were crossed. Determine the expected proportions of the offspring produced with respect to both genotypes and phenotypes. Show your working in a genetic diagram.

   (c) A litter of pups, which resulted from a cross between a yellow male Labrador and a black female, consisted of 7 yellow and 3 black pups.

   (i) With respect to the alleles at the E/e locus only, state the genotypes for the male and female parents (yellow male and black female). Give a reason for each of your answers. [2]

   (ii) Suggest an explanation for the lack of brown pups in the litter. [2]

Question taken from CCEA's Biology Assessment Unit A2 2, Biochemistry, Genetics and Evolutionary Trends, June 2010, © CCEA 2013

3. Haemophiliacs possess a non-functional form of the gene responsible for the production of blood clotting factors. The pedigree diagram below shows the incidence of haemophilia in an affected family.

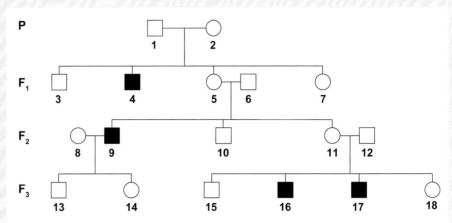

Individuals within the pedigree are numbered. Males are represented by squares and females by circles. Those who have haemophilia are represented by solid symbols.

(a) On the basis of the information provided, is the inheritance of haemophilia:

   (i) autosomal or sex-linked? Justify your answer. [1]

   (ii) dominant or recessive? Justify your answer. [1]

(b) Using the symbols h to represent the allele for haemophilia and H for the normal allele, state the genotype of:

   (i) individual **2**

   (ii) individual **4** [2]

(c) Individual **14** carries a recessive allele for albinism (lack of normal body pigment) which is not sex-linked. She marries a man who is also a carrier for albinism but who does not carry the haemophilia allele. The genes exhibit independent inheritance.

Using the symbol **a** for albinism and **A** for normal pigmentation, show, by means of a suitable genetic diagram, the probability of this couple producing a male child who has both haemophilia and albinism. [5]

(d) There is no evidence of haemophilia in previous generations of this family. State the most likely reason for the condition appearing in the family pedigree shown. [1]

Question taken from CCEA's Biology Assessment Unit A2 2, Biochemistry, Genetics and Evolutionary Trends, May 2012, © CCEA 2013

Chapter 14 – Mechanism of Change

Students should be able to:	
5.6.1	Understand the concept of the gene pool
5.6.2	Understand the Hardy-Weinberg equation and apply it to calculate allele and genotype frequencies in an outbreeding population
5.6.3	Understand the source and maintenance of genetic variation
5.6.4	Understand selection and its contribution to the maintenance of polymorphic populations and evolutionary change in populations
5.6.5	Understand the concept of species and the process of speciation

In the previous chapter the effect of gene and allelic combinations in individuals was studied. Inheritance, as studied in the last chapter, involves analysis of how genes and alleles pass through the generations producing the classic genetic offspring ratios generated.

Population genetics involves genetic analysis at the **population** level, i.e. the distribution of particular genes across entire populations rather than just at an individual or family grouping level. Some important terms are listed below.

- The **gene pool** is the term used to describe the sum **total** of all the **genes** (and alleles) in a **population** (or species) at a particular time.

- The **allele frequency** is the proportion of a particular allele in a population (or species) at a particular time.

- The **genome** refers to **all** the DNA in an individual - it is the entire genetic complement in any one organism.

  Note 1: The Human Genome Project was so called because it worked out the complete DNA sequence of each chromosome in a (typical) human individual.

  Note 2: Some textbooks refer to the genome as being the total of all the DNA in a haploid set of chromosomes (as the alleles for most – but not all – genes will be identical in homologous chromosomes).

Population geneticists are interested in the ways in which allele frequency changes between populations and over time. To investigate these changes it is important to be able to work out the allelic frequencies in populations. One way of doing this is by using the **Hardy-Weinberg equation**.

The Hardy-Weinberg equation

The Hardy-Weinberg equation can be used to calculate allele and / or genotype frequencies in a population with respect to a trait that shows Mendelian inheritance patterns.

Suppose that alleles **A** and **a** represent alternative alleles of a particular trait with **A** representing the dominant allele and **a** representing the recessive allele. Across the population under consideration, **A** and **a alleles** have frequencies represented as **p** and **q** respectively (with **p** representing the frequency of the dominant allele and **q** the frequency of the recessive allele.

Therefore the frequency of the alleles in the population can be represented as:

p + q = 1 (frequency of alleles)

In the above equation 1 represents 100% of the population meaning that each individual in the population will have two alleles which can be two dominant alleles, two recessive alleles, or one of each, for a particular trait.

In terms of the **individuals** in the population, they can only be homozygous for the dominant allele (**AA**), homozygous for the recessive allele (**aa**), or heterozygous (**Aa**).

The frequency of homozygous dominant individuals (genotype **AA**) is represented as p^2 with the frequency of homozygous recessive individuals (genotype **aa**) being represented as q^2. Heterozygous individuals (**Aa**) have a frequency of **2 pq**.

	Ap	aq
Ap	AA p^2	Aa pq
aq	Aa pq	aa q^2

Therefore the frequency of individuals with the different genotypes can be represented as:

$p^2 + 2pq + q^2 = 1$ (frequency of individuals)

In the above equation 1 represents 100% of the population meaning that each individual in the population can only have a genotype that is homozygous dominant, homozygous recessive, or heterozygous, for a particular trait.

Therefore, if some of the population information is available in terms of either the frequency of a particular allele or genotype, or the frequency of a particular phenotype, the two equations above allow the allele and genotypic frequencies to be calculated.

Worked example

In the fruit fly (*Drosophila melanogaster*) wings can either be normal or vestigial (dramatically reduced). Wing type is inherited in typical monohybrid fashion with normal dominant to the recessive vestigial. In a particular population, 16% of the flies have vestigial wings.

Question - In a population of 200, calculate how many flies are heterozygous for wing type and also the frequency of the normal (W) and vestigial (w) alleles.

> **Note 1:** In this question as in many calculations involving the Hardy-Weinberg equation, you are given the number of individuals that are homozygous recessive – they can be identified by phenotype, but the homozygous dominant and heterozygous individuals cannot be identified by phenotype as they have the same phenotype.

> **Note 2:** Although given percentages in the stem of the question, the Hardy-Weinberg calculations are based on proportions of 1.

16% represent the homozygous recessive individuals, so must have a **ww** genotype.

Therefore **$q^2 = 0.16$**

q = 0.4

Using p + q = 1   **p = 0.6**
continued on next page

Therefore the frequency of the W allele = 0.6 (60%) and the frequency of the w allele = 0.4 (40%).

Using $p^2 + 2pq + q^2 = 1$

$0.36 + 2pq + 0.16 = 1$

Therefore $2pq = 0.48$ (48% of the population are heterozygotes).

In a population of 200 this represents **96** flies.

Although the Hardy-Weinberg equation can be used for calculating genotype and allele frequencies in populations this only applies if the population is in Hardy-Weinberg equilibrium. To be in equilibrium certain assumptions are made. These include:

- **The population is large**. In small populations random variations can skew the distribution of alleles and genotypes in the same way that genotypic offspring ratios only hold true if large numbers of progeny are considered.

- **Mating is random.** This means that there is an equal chance of an individual of any one genotype mating with an individual of the same or any other genotype. Obviously, if there was increased frequency of mating within a particular genotype group (or between specific genotype groups) then the population would not be in equilibrium.

- **Individuals are diploid** and the trait in question is inherited in typical Mendelian pattern.

- **Differential selection is not taking place based on the three genotypes under consideration.** In other words, no particular genotype is more likely to survive (or reproduce) than any other genotype – all genotypes (and alleles) are equally 'favoured'.

- **Mutation is not taking place.** Although mutation rates vary in different genes, under normal circumstances the rate is so low at a particular locus, that it can usually be discounted when investigating allele frequencies at a particular point in time.

- **There is no migration.** Loss of individuals from a population or the gain of individuals from other populations will affect the Hardy-Weinberg equilibrium of populations. For this reason, many studies of population genetics involving the Hardy-Weinberg equation have involved isolated populations (e.g. island populations).

The many assumptions surrounding the Hardy-Weinberg equation do **not** apply to the populations of many species. Migrations and mutation do happen. Differential selection is a fact of life in most species in that some individuals will be better adapted than others and therefore more likely to survive and pass on their alleles to offspring. However, selection only happens if there is variation across the population for certain phenotypes (and genotypes) to be favoured over others. Before looking at the process of selection, it is important to review the range of mechanisms that contribute to the variation that exists among the individuals of a population.

1. Sources of genetic variation (meiosis and fertilisation)

Meiosis as a source of variation

Meiosis (as reviewed in detail in AS1) is a major source of variation in sexually reproducing organisms and it contributes to variation in a number of very important ways.

Independent assortment is a crucial source. Remember that the golden rules in meiosis are that only one chromosome from each homologous pair enters a gamete and that which of the two chromosomes from each pair enters a particular gamete is dependent on how the homologous pairs line up at the equator of the cell at the start of metaphase 1. As the way in which a homologous pair lines up at the equator in meiosis is random and independent of how any other pair aligns there are 2^{23} potential chromosome arrangements in a gamete in humans – obviously huge potential for variation.

Crossing over which occurs in prophase I of the first division of meiosis is another source of variation as it facilitates the exchange of genetic material between homologous chromosomes.

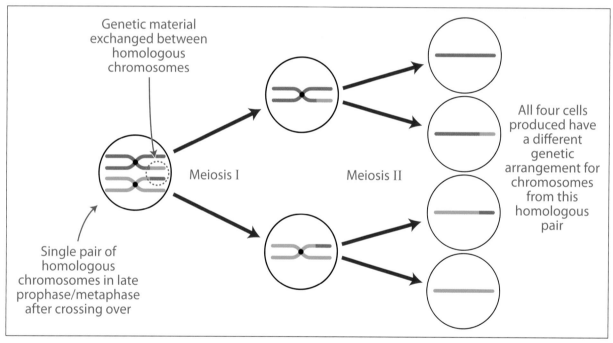

Crossing over can produce entirely new allele (but not gene) arrangements along the length of the chromosomes and it produces allelic combinations that were not present in either parental chromosome.

Crossing over in meiosis

Cross-fertilisation

Meiosis ensures that there is considerable variation in the gametes produced by any one individual. However, the process of cross-fertilisation provides further opportunity for variation.

Normally the male (whether producing sperm in animals or pollen in flowering plants), produces very large numbers (often millions) of gametes each with different chromosome and allele arrangements, for the reasons described earlier. Females are usually more frugal with egg production as each egg is larger and usually requires more investment but also because the female can only provide support and nourishment for a small number of developing young. Nonetheless, the fusion of male and female gametes is an entirely random process further shuffling the possibilities so the actual genetic material that recombines together in the new individual during cross-fertilisation (fertilisation involving two parents) will further add to the variation produced.

Independent assortment and crossing over during meiosis and the random nature of fertilisation, mixes up allelic combination possibilities but does not produce genetic novelty in the sense that there are no new alleles or genes produced in the process.

Mutation can produce genetic novelty and is therefore a very important source of variation in living organisms.

2. Sources of genetic variation (mutation)

Mutation is a permanent change to the DNA in an organism. There are many different types of mutation: mutation can affect chromosome number or structure or can be more localised (and smaller) in scale affecting a gene or even a single base pair.

The significance of mutations not only depends on the type of mutation but also when and where they occur. A mutation in a skin cell in an adult will only affect that cell or any daughter cells produced should the affected cell divide mitotically. A mutation in a gamete will affect all the cells in any offspring produced should that gamete remain viable and be involved in fertilisation.

Types of mutation

Gene mutations – These are mutations that are restricted to a single gene. Many affect only one base – these are **point mutations**. Point mutations can involve **substitution** and **deletion** of single bases.

Substitution is when one base is **replaced** by another as represented by the diagram on the right.

Clearly the consequence of a point mutation involving substitution will be limited to one amino acid (taking account of base triplet rules and the non-overlapping nature of the DNA code). If the substitution occurs in the third base of the triplet it may produce no effect at all due to the **degenerate** nature of the DNA code. In these circumstances the mutation is described as neutral.

Sickle cell anaemia is an autosomal recessive condition caused by the presence of two recessive alleles. The sickle cell allele is an example of a gene (point) mutation caused by substitution. The normal allele contains the DNA base triplet CTT,

Substitution

DNA before substitution of base	DNA after substitution of base
T, A, C } amino acid 1	T, A, C } amino acid 1
A, T, A } amino acid 2	A, T, A } amino acid 2
G, C, G } amino acid 3	G, G, G } amino acid 5 — base substitution
T, T, A } amino acid 4	T, T, A } amino acid 4
G, G, G } amino acid 5	G, G, G } amino acid 5

which codes for the amino acid glutamate at a particular position. In contrast, the mutated sickle cell anaemia allele has the DNA sequence CAT, which codes for valine.

Deletion is a second example of point mutation. With deletions, one base is **removed** (deleted) from the DNA sequence. The consequences of this can be very significant as they cause **'frameshift' mutations**. As the DNA sequence is read in threes, the deletion of one base changes the base triplet template along the rest of the gene, after the point of mutation, as shown in the following diagram.

This means that all the **amino acids** after the point of mutation may be changed or that the protein can be shortened if a 'stop' codon is produced earlier in the sequence than intended.

Note 1: Substitution (gene) mutations may still produce the original or (largely) functional protein but mutations caused by base deletions can lead to changes so large that a non-functional protein is produced.

Note 2: Many of the genetic conditions discussed in the last two chapters are caused by gene mutations and in some cases point mutations.

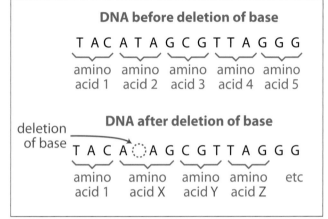

Deletion

Note 3: Point mutations (or gene mutations involving a small number of bases) are relatively common. It is estimated that each human embryo may have as many as between fifty to one hundred new mutations in its genome. The vast majority will be neutral or have very little effect.

Chromosome mutations – Chromosome mutations involve change to large sections of DNA (several genes) or even whole chromosomes. Large sections of chromosome can break off (possibly during cell division) and attach to another chromosome or even get lost.

A relatively common mutation affecting chromosome number, rather than structure, is the mutation that gives rise to Down syndrome. If one of the parental homologous pairs (chromosome 21) fails to segregate properly during gamete formation, this results in some gametes being produced with 24 rather than 23 chromosomes. If an affected gamete is involved in fertilisation a zygote (first cell of new individual) will be produced with 47 chromosomes resulting in Down syndrome.

The chromosome mutation described above that leads to Down syndrome is an example of **aneuploidy**, the situation in which **one** chromosome pair fails to segregate. Aneuploidy can also lead to affected individuals having a missing chromosome (e.g. Turner's syndrome in humans is caused by having one X chromosome missing giving the genotype XO).

If **all** the homologous chromosome pairs fail to segregate then **polyploidy** results. Polyploidy can result in individuals with three sets of chromosomes (triploid) or even four sets (tetraploid).

Some other features of mutations are listed below.

- **What causes mutations?** Mutations can occur spontaneously for no obvious reason. However, the rate at which they occur can be accelerated if the individual is exposed to particular environmental stimuli. An example seldom out of the headlines is the link between **UV light** and the mutations that give rise to the uncontrolled cell division that leads to **skin cancer**. **X-rays** and **gamma rays** can also increase mutation rates.

- **How often do they happen?** Rates of mutation vary from species to species and within the genome of a particular species. The mutation rate in humans has been estimated at one error every 100 million base pairs per generation. However, some types are much more common. The errors that give rise to Down syndrome occur much more frequently.

- **Are all mutations harmful?** As mutation involves a change to the DNA it will most often have harmful (and often fatal) consequences – revisit the genetic diseases over the last two chapters. As noted earlier, some mutations can be neutral (e.g. some substitutions in the third base of a base triplet) in that they have no effect on the phenotype. Variation in human blood groups (the ABO system) and in eye colour has been caused by mutation and appears to be neutral. A very small number of mutations can be beneficial. Although very rare, these beneficial mutations can be very important as seen later in this chapter.

Selection

As we have seen with genetic diseases, the alternative forms of a particular trait may not be equally beneficial to the organism concerned. In nature, variation is subject to **selection** pressure with beneficial variations increasing the chances of survival and harmful variations harming the chances of survival of the individual concerned.

In any given environmental situation, the better adapted individuals will **survive** at the expense of the less well adapted individuals (the *survival of the fittest*). This is particularly likely to happen if there is competition for resources (the *struggle for existence*). The 'struggle for existence' and 'survival of the fittest' summarise key tenets of Charles Darwin's theory of **natural selection**.

While selection can act on any type of variation, whether caused by genetic or environmental factors, it is only the genetic variation that can contribute to change in allele frequencies over time. Some key points about selection are listed in the points below.

- Selection acts on **populations** of organisms through its effect on **individuals**. Individuals may survive or die because they or more or less well adapted in a particular environment. Over time, the genetic makeup of the populations may change as particular alleles increase in frequency and others reduce in frequency.

- Selection is **environmentally dependent**. The thick white fur of the polar bear only gives a selective advantage in the Arctic.

- For selection to lead to change in a population or species over time, the basis of the variation must be **genetic** (not just environmental).

- If selection leads to a change in a population or species over time (a change in allelic frequencies), it does so through **differential reproductive success**. If the better adapted individuals are more likely to survive, it is also very likely that they will produce more offspring (and perpetuate their beneficial alleles).

- Selection is an **ongoing process**. It is always taking place although not always obvious.

In the AS book we reviewed a number of examples of selection including pesticide resistance in insects and the development of narrow leaves in wild garlic. These changes took place because in particular environments (a pesticide-rich environment and soils with low nitrogen levels respectively) insects with mutations that confer resistance and garlic plants with very narrow (but long) leaves are more highly adapted (fitter) and are more likely to survive and pass their genes to their offspring.

Again in the AS book we did look at the difference between **stabilising selection** (favouring the *status quo*) and **directional selection** (favouring one of the extremes of variation). It is important to review the key points of stabilising and directional selection and the differences between them.

Stabilising selection

Many traits in living organisms show normal distribution. In humans, height and mass are two obvious examples of traits that are normally distributed with most individuals being close to average and fewer individuals approaching the extremes.

In stabilising selection, the average individuals are best adapted in terms of the trait under consideration (i.e. selection favours the modal variants). The 'extremes' are less well adapted and likely to be selected against; consequently it is the average individuals that are more likely to survive and pass on their genes to their offspring.

The example used at AS is certainly one of the best known examples of stabilising selection. The analysis of births in a London hospital in the 1930s showed that the babies with the best chance of survival were those close to average mass. Mortality rates were higher for the babies with low birth masses (they were often premature) and those with the highest birth masses (their large size often led to complications at birth). In this example the selection pressure was much greater at the extremes of body mass as babies with very low, or very high, body masses at birth were less well adapted.

Stabilising selection

This example of stabilising selection also shows that selection pressures can change over time. As a consequence of modern medical advances, very small and very large babies are much more likely to survive; therefore the selection pressures contributing to the stabilising selection are much reduced.

In **highly adapted populations** in **stable ecosystems**, almost all the selection taking place will be stabilising. Over many years, organisms in an ecosystem have become highly adapted as a consequence of selection. In this situation, there will be no obvious change in phenotype over time therefore it appears as if selection is not taking place! Stabilising selection is **not** a force for evolutionary change.

Directional selection

With directional selection the average individuals are not those most highly adapted. The best adapted individuals have phenotypes that lie closer to one of the extremes of variation.

Directional selection is most likely to take place in one of the following two scenarios.

- The environment is changing

- A population or (species) colonises a new habitat

There are many examples of directional selection in nature. Most GCSE textbooks use the example of the **peppered moth** (*Biston betularia*) with which you are probably already familiar.

Another example is the development of **pesticide resistance** in insects – the resistance is caused by mutation. In insect populations not subject to pesticide control, insects that have the resistance mutation are selected against (the metabolic 'cost' of the mutation may cause the insects to grow slower and be less 'fit' in other respects) and therefore the frequency of the mutation(s) in the population will be low. However, in insect populations subject to pesticide applications, the presence of alleles that confer resistance to pesticide is a significant adaptive advantage. These insects will be selected for – they will be the ones that survive and pass their (resistant) alleles on to their offspring, ensuring that the frequency of the resistant alleles rapidly spreads through the population.

A very contemporary example is the earlier flowering times of some populations of plants subject to climate change. Although climate change in Britain appears to mean more storms, wetter weather and more flooding; in much of the world, areas that already have a shortage of rain are becoming even drier (i.e. increased 'desertification'). The populations of many species of flowering plants are flowering earlier in these increasingly dry habitats, ensuring that they reproduce in the increasingly short window where growth is possible. In this example, aridity is the **selection pressure** and those plants able to flower at an earlier stage in their growth are more highly adapted than those that exhibit later flowering times.

> **Note:** This example is an interesting one as the scientists involved in collecting the data had to check that it wasn't just the change in environment (and nothing to do with genetic change) that caused the plants to flower earlier (as will happen with many plant species). To confirm that **genetic change** was taking place, plants of the same species, but from different populations, were grown in the **same environmental conditions**. When grown in the same conditions, plants from populations from the more arid habitats still flowered earlier showing that flowering times were under genetic control.

Antibiotic resistance in **bacteria** is yet another very common example of directional selection.

Case study – antibiotic resistance in bacteria

The antibiotic **penicillin** was first produced in commercial quantities in the early 1940s. Penicillin's anti-bacterial properties are due to its ability to disrupt bacterial cell wall formation. When it was first used to combat bacterial infections less than 5% of the strains (varieties) of *Staphylococcus aureus* (a common bacterium responsible for many types of infection) were resistant. Now over 95% of strains are resistant to penicillin.

Resistance to penicillin (or related antibiotics) is caused by random mutation in the bacterial genome. Resistance can come in many ways; some mutations lead to the production of enzymes that break down the penicillin, other lead to changes in cell wall structure that prevents the penicillin gaining entry and even new metabolic pathways in cell wall formation that bypass the effects of the antibiotics.

When a new generation of antibiotics was produced including **methicillin** these initially proved successful against penicillin-resistant strains. However, as could have been anticipated, some strains became resistant to the methicillin, hence **methicillin-resistant *Staphylococcus aureus* (MRSA)**. MRSA is now resistant to a range of antibiotics and other drugs, and it and other similarly resistant bacteria (e.g. *Clostridium difficile*) are widely referred to as 'superbugs'.

Antibiotic resistance in bacteria is an example of directional selection with the use of antibiotics as the selection pressure. Evolutionary change in the *Staphylococcus aureus* species has occurred over time. The change in phenotype (resistance) is underpinned by genetic change.

Note: The examples of pesticide resistance in insects and antibiotic resistance in bacteria are very obvious in the populations concerned – insects and bacteria will either survive or not when subject to pesticide or antibiotics respectively. Most examples of directional selection, e.g. the development of slightly earlier flowering times of some plant species in drought conditions, changes in fur thickness in mammals in response to changing climate are much more subtle and gradual. Nonetheless, directional selection leads to evolutionary change over time.

A key feature of all of the examples used in this section is that the directional selection is associated with **environmental change** (change also including introduction of pesticides and antibiotics). Unlike with stabilising selection, directional selection does tend to lead to **evolutionary change** in populations.

Note: Although directional selection may be the main source of evolutionary change in populations, it is not the only source. For example, if a species is decimated by disease or predation leaving only a small number surviving, these may not be genetically representative of the original population as a whole. As numbers increase again the new population may be very different genetically from the earlier population; the gene pool is limited to the range of genes in the survivors (excepting any new mutations). This random evolutionary change is called **genetic drift**.

Polymorphism – In many examples of directional selection there are two or more discrete genotypes that produce distinct phenotypes (e.g. black or light coloured pepper moths, bacteria that are resistant or not to antibiotics). Populations where there is more than one alternative for a particular trait are described as being **polymorphic**.

A typical definition for polymorphism is the presence of two or more genotypes, the rarest of which exceeds 1%.

Other examples of polymorphism include human blood groups and eye colour, banding in snails – polymorphism in living organisms is very common with no shortage of examples. However, polymorphic populations are effective tools for the study of natural selection. One example is the incidence of sickle cell anaemia in different human populations.

Case study – sickle cell anaemia

Sickle cell anaemia is a blood disorder that affects many people in parts of Africa and a number of Mediterranean countries. The allele that codes for sickle cell anaemia leads to red blood cells that are sickle shaped and less well adapted to flow through narrow capillaries.

The condition is caused by a point (gene) mutation where the normal DNA base triplet CTT, which codes for the amino acid glutamate is replaced by the base triplet CAT, which codes for the amino acid valine.

Individuals who are heterozygous for sickle cell anaemia (one normal allele and one allele that codes for sickle cell anaemia) do not have sickle cell anaemia but are described as having sickle cell trait. Individuals heterozygous for the sickle cell allele have haemoglobin that is less efficient than normal haemoglobin, but is more efficient than that in individuals with two sickle cell alleles. The genotypes and phenotypes are summarised in the following diagram.

phenotype	genotype
normal	$Hb^A Hb^A$
sickle cell trait	$Hb^A Hb^S$
sickle cell anaemic	$Hb^S Hb^S$

In most human populations, the sickle cell allele (whether homozygous or heterozygous) is selected against and its frequency in the population is very low. However, it has been found that in those regions where the incidence of sickle cell anaemia (and the sickle cell allele) is high, malaria is also common. This can be explained by the fact that the malformed red blood cells, formed as a consequence of sickle cell anaemia (or sickle cell trait in heterozygotes) offer a degree of protection against malaria. The protection is due to malarial parasite being less able to complete its life cycle in the sickle shaped red blood cells.

Consequently, while the homozygote sickle cell condition ($Hb^S Hb^S$) can lead to ill health and often death at an early age, in Africa the presence of the sickle cell allele in the heterozygous condition ($Hb^A Hb^S$), due to its protective effects against malaria, gives a selective advantage over the 'normal' genotype ($Hb^A H^A$). In areas of Africa affected by malaria, the relative fitness of the three genotypes has been estimated as $Hb^A Hb^A = 0.90$; $Hb^A Hb^S = 1.00$; and $Hb^S Hb^S = 0.20$. In effect, 'normal' individuals are only 90% as likely to survive and pass on their genes compared to an individual heterozygous for sickle cell anaemia.

This is an example of **balanced polymorphism** as the adaptive advantage of the heterozygote (**heterozygosity**) ensures that in the African populations the relative proportion of the three different genotypes remains stable.

> **Note:** Although the homozygous sickle cell condition is strongly selected against, there will still be a high proportion of individuals born with sickle cell anaemia as a consequence of the offspring ratios produced by unions between the more favourably adapted heterozygotes.

Species and Speciation

Selection in a particular population of a species can cause this population to diverge to an extent that it is very different genetically from the ancestral (original) species (i.e. all the other populations). A point could be reached where the population concerned actually forms new species – the process of speciation.

The Species

But what exactly is a species? There are many definitions of a species but most are broadly similar to the following.

A species is a group of individuals of common ancestry that are normally capable of interbreeding to produce fertile offspring. Each species is **reproductively isolated** from other species.

> **Note: Reproductive isolation** means unable to interbreed.

Using this definition we can see why horses and donkeys are classified as different species even though they can interbreed but produce sterile mules. Similarly, a number of large cat species have been able to interbreed in captivity (e.g. male tigers and lionesses) and a number of their offspring (e.g. the tiglon) have proved to be fertile. However, tigers and lions are still classified as separate species as the hybrids tend not to occur in the wild.

There can be a blurring at the edges when determining if a particular species has split into two (or more) species as separate populations diverge. For example the dog (*Canis canis*) is still regarded as being one species but there are over 300 different breeds, many of them very different in physical appearance and character. As divergence continues to increase, a point may be reached where 'natural' interbreeding between some breeds becomes increasingly unlikely.

> **Note:** The domestic dog and the wolf share a common ancestor. Unlike the other examples of directional selection used in this chapter, the selection (and continued divergence) of particular traits in dogs has been accelerated by selective breeding by man – **artificial selection** rather than natural selection.

Speciation

Speciation is the formation of new species that are reproductively isolated from other species.

Speciation can occur in a number of ways, but in most cases there are two distinct processes.

- The original species becomes separated into two or more populations that become reproductively isolated from each other (i.e. breeding is restricted to **within** each isolated population).

- Different forms of directional selection take place in each of the isolated populations with the result that, over time, the populations become so different that they remain reproductively isolated from each other even if they subsequently come into contact.

The initial isolation is usually **geographical**. For example populations can get isolated on oceanic or even small offshore islands or by mountains or rivers. Many species of small, and relatively sedentary invertebrates, have been effectively isolated by the building of motorway networks.

Note: In the initial geographical isolation the key feature is not mechanism of separation, or the distances involved, but the **effectiveness** of the barrier in preventing gene exchange between the different populations.

Once separation occurs there will almost certainly be **genetic divergence** between the different populations as even slightly different environmental conditions will encourage natural selection to act in different ways in the isolated areas. In time, as a consequence of directional selection and genetic divergence, a number of reproductive isolating **mechanisms** develop that prevents interbreeding and gene exchange should the isolated populations overlap. At the stage when interbreeding between the formerly isolated populations becomes impossible, **speciation** will have occurred.

Reproductive isolating mechanisms that can develop include:

- Barriers to the **reproductive process** including mechanical barriers to mating / fertilisation, offspring infertility, reproductive cycles no longer synchronised.

- **Behavioural isolation** – different populations can develop different courtship rituals (important in speciation in birds).

- **Ecological isolation** – different populations can become ecologically isolated. Examples include different habitat or food preferences (e.g. the different types of leaf (tree) used by leaf mining insects).

Note: The term sub-species is often used to classify separate populations that have not quite diverged enough to become separate species but may do so in the future. Sub-species usually differ from each other in several significant aspects (although they are potentially capable of interbreeding and producing fertile young).

Speciation that involves initial geographical separation followed by genetic divergence is described as **allopatric speciation**.

The most studied and most widely known example of allopatric speciation is the finches of the Galapagos Islands, first studied by Charles Darwin.

Case Study – The Galapagos Finches ('Darwin's finches')

The Galapagos Islands are a group of volcanic islands, 600 miles to the west of Ecuador in the South Pacific Ocean. The islands formed relatively late in geological history. Initially the islands were barren of life but a primary succession developed as plant seeds and other terrestrial organisms were carried to the islands by strong currents, winds or driftwood.

Eventually a number of finches (probably of one species) reached the island from the South American mainland. In time populations of finches developed on most of the islands. However, although very occasionally birds could travel between islands it was very rare due to the strong currents and winds in the area – in effect, the finches on each island were reproductively isolated from the finches on other islands.

Over time, the finches on the different islands diverged from the finches on the other islands (and from the South American mainland) to become different species. One key area of divergence is in beak size and shape as the finch beaks on the different islands evolved as they became adapted to the food sources available on each specific island.

There are two factors that have been critical in allowing the finches to evolve into a number of different species on the islands.

- There were very few other species of birds on the islands. This reduced competition and any adaptations in terms of beak shape had a greater chance of being advantageous in manipulating new food sources.

- Finches are poor fliers. Although this makes their initial arrival in the islands the more remarkable (they must have travelled the 600 miles from the South American mainland on driftwood or were supported by very favourable winds), it meant that the finches on the different islands were more effectively reproductively isolated.

The evolution of the finches on Galapagos is an excellent example of **adaptive radiation**. This describes the process of a range of species rapidly evolving to fill the abundant **ecological niches** available. Adaptive radiation is most likely to occur when there is little competition from other species and when there is a range of (uncolonised) habitats available to be exploited.

Speciation, particularly in plants, can also arise due to polyploidy.

Polyploidy and speciation – It is thought that polyploidy may be responsible for the formation of more than half the known species of flowering plants. Polyploid species have more than the normal two complete sets of chromosomes – three complete sets produces the 'triploid' condition and four complete sets the 'tetraploid' condition.

Tetraploids can form if chromosomes duplicate during cell division but the putative 'daughter' cells fail to divide. If this happens in the zygote then all the cells of the new individual will be tetraploid. Sometimes if it is the failure of chromosomes to segregate in a gamete, then the triploid condition will result.

An example of speciation involving polyploidy can be seen in the cord grass *Spartina*. In the 1820s, a non-native species *Spartina alterniflora* (normal chromosome number $2n = 62$) was accidentally introduced into Britain near Southampton. The species hybridised with the closely-related, native species *Spartina maritima* ($2n = 60$).

The offspring from this cross had 61 chromosomes (the two parents producing gametes with 31 and 30 chromosomes respectively). These plants, (named *Spartina x townsendii*) were sterile (reproducing only vegetatively) but through polyploidy and chromosome doubling in each cell produced a new tetraploid species (*Spartina anglica*) that had 122 chromosomes ($4n$) in each cell.

Spartina anglica is fertile with meiosis taking place as normal. As with many polyploid species it is vigorous and able to spread rapidly and colonise new habitats.

Note: A feature of speciation by polyploidy is that it is **very rapid** – often taking place within one generation. Allopatric speciation invariably takes much longer.

As well as being important in plant speciation, polyploidy is very important in **plant breeding**. As well as producing vigorous plants, the extra genetic information in each cell (typically making the cells larger than in non-polyploids) can produce increased variability (an advantage for plant breeders) and allow the species to extend its ecological range.

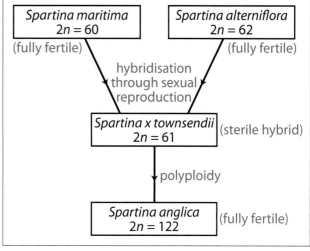

Speciation in Spartina

The disadvantage with many polyploids is defective meiosis and consequent sterility. Triploids (3*n*) are unable to perform meiosis and are sterile but some tetraploids are also sterile due to the 'un-natural arrangement' of chromosomes in the nucleus. For example, the common woodland species, lesser celandine (*Ranunculus ficaria*), is normally a diploid (2*n* = 16) but triploid (3*n* = 24) and tetraploid variants (4*n* = 32) are **both** sterile.

Exam questions

1. *Allium ursinum* (wild garlic) is a common plant found throughout damper areas of the British Isles.

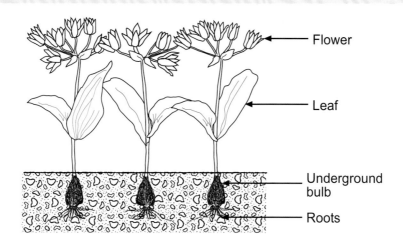

(a) An investigation was carried out to determine if leaf size in wild garlic was associated with soil nitrate levels. Measurements were taken of the length and width of leaves at various sites in Northern Ireland along with soil nitrate levels. Fifty leaves were measured at each site and the mean values calculated.

The scattergrams below show the results. (Two of the sites investigated, Ballinderry and Marble Arch, are identified on the graphs – these relate to sub-part (ii) of the question.)

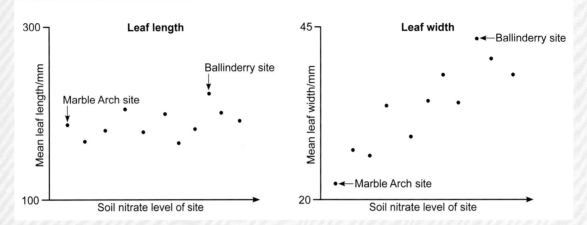

(i) Describe the trend shown by each of the above scattergrams. [2]

There is an obvious difference in the mean leaf width of the plants in Ballinderry and Marble Arch. An experiment was devised to investigate the relative contributions of the genotype and the environment in determining this difference. Seeds from wild garlic plants in Ballinderry and Marble Arch were collected and planted in an experimental garden, where soil nitrate levels were controlled and kept constant.

After a number of years, when the plants in the experimental garden had reached maturity, 50 leaves from each site of origin were sampled and their width measured. The graph below shows these results along with the results of mean leaf width in the natural habitats.

(ii) Using the information provided, state whether the difference in leaf width between the two sites is mainly genetic or environmental. Explain your answer. [2]

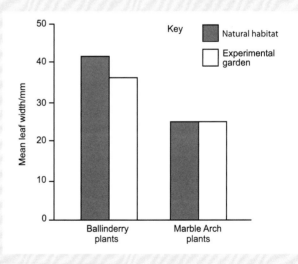

(b) Asexual reproduction in wild garlic occurs via bulb formation while sexual reproduction produces seeds. The seeds are heavy and are rarely dispersed more than a few centimetres away from the parent plant. The result is that populations of wild garlic are effectively isolated. However, DNA analysis shows that the wild garlic populations in the Ballinderry and Marble Arch sites have evolved from the same ancestral population.

(i) Explain how evolutionary change has contributed to the differences in leaf width between the sites. [5]

(ii) It is possible that the wild garlic in the two sites has evolved into different species. Suggest how you could investigate whether this has happened or not. [2]

Question taken from CCEA's Biology Assessment Unit A2 2, Biochemistry, Genetics and Evolutionary Trends, May 2011, © CCEA 2013

2. Read the following passage concerning the gene coding for the muscle protein, dystrophin. Mutant alleles of this gene result in a lack of dystrophin, which leads to the progressive muscle-wasting disease, Duchenne muscular dystrophy (DMD).

> The gene for dystrophin is located on the X-chromosome. Sequencing techniques have shown that the gene contains 2.4 million nucleotide pairs. However, only 11,055 nucleotides codes for a dystrophin. The 79 coding regions (exons) within the gene are interrupted by non-coding regions (introns). 5
>
> The disease DMD, is inherited as a sex-linked trait. DMD is rarely found in females, although they can be carriers of the mutant allele. Affected males show symptoms at five years old and most are wheelchair dependent at 12 years old.
>
> However, in a study of 77 cases of DMD, 43 had no family history of the 10 disease. Mutations in the female ovary can result in ova (eggs) having the allele causing DMD. This is not detected in DNA analysis of other tissues of the female, such as blood.
>
> An analysis of the DNA, using blood samples, from two families with DMD sons is shown below. The restriction enzyme BglII was used to cut the 15 DNA in the region of the dystrophin gene and cDNA probes were used to detect the different genetic markers (RFLPs). The diagrams below show the genetic markers (RFLPs) found in the parents and offspring in the two families. In family **A** the probe used identified markers i to vi. In family **B** the probe used identified markers **vii** to **xi**. 20

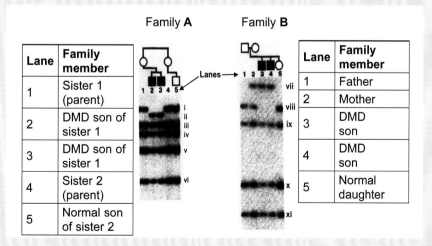

Using this information, and your own understanding, answer the questions which follow.

(a) Calculate how many amino acids are in the protein, dystrophin [line 3]. (Show your working.) [1]

(b) Explain the term 'family history' [line 10]. [1]

(c) Mutations in the gene involve the deletion of a nucleotide [line 11]. Describe how the deletion of a nucleotide will change the gene and explain how the primary structure of the protein is altered. [2]

(d) (i) In family **A**, compare the genetic markers identified by the genetic probe in the DMD sons and other members of the family. [2]

(ii) In family **B**, the genetic marker **vii** is present in both the DMD sons and their mother. Explain why their mother does not suffer from DMD. [2]

(iii) Comment on the inheritance of DMD in the two families. [3]

Question taken from CCEA's Biology Assessment Unit A2 2, Biochemistry, Genetics and Evolutionary Trends, June 2010, © CCEA 2013

Chapter 15 – Classification

Students should be able to:

5.7.1	Describe the form (level of organisation) and life cycle in Division Bryophyta
5.7.2	Describe the form (level of organisation) and life cycle in Division Tracheophyta
5.7.3	Compare the divisions of Plantae
5.8.1	Describe the body form and feeding in Phylum Cnidaria
5.8.2	Describe the body form and feeding in Phylum Platyhelminthes
5.8.3	Describe the body form and feeding in Phylum Annelida
5.8.4	Describe the body form and feeding in Phylum Chordata

Kingdom Plantae

The Kingdom Plantae ('true' plants) encompasses species that are **multicellular**, have **eukaryotic cells** with **cellulose cell walls** and **photosynthesise** using **chlorophyll** contained in **chloroplasts**. Additionally, species in the kingdom Plantae show distinct **differentiation** with the cells in the different parts of plant specialised for specific functions, e.g. leaf cells specialised for photosynthesis.

Plants also have a life cycle featuring an alternation of generations. This means that there are two distinct phases, a sexually reproducing **haploid gametophyte** (the stage that produces the gametes) and an asexually reproducing, **diploid sporophyte** (spore producing stage).

A generalised plant life cycle is shown in the diagram on the right.

The relative importance that the two phases (the haploid gametophyte and the diploid sporophyte) have in the life cycles of the different major plant groups varies as will be seen in the following sections.

Note: Animals are normally diploid but produce haploid gametes. However, there is no distinct haploid stage or generation.

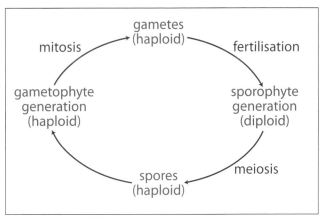

A generalised plant life cycle

The two major plant groups are the **bryophytes** and the **tracheophytes**.

Division Bryophyta

This division is represented by the **mosses**.

Structure – Mosses **lack true roots**, **stems** and **leaves** and they **do not possess vascular tissue** (xylem and phloem) – support is by **turgor**. However, the cells in the moss plant are organised into structures that have a superficial similarity to stems and leaves and there are filamentous-like structures called **rhizoids** that anchor the moss to the ground. Not being true roots, the rhizoids are unable to penetrate the substratum to any great degree and have no specific role in water uptake. Water and minerals can be gained (or lost) over the entire surface of the moss plant. Additionally, the leaf-like structures **do not possess** a **cuticle** or **stomata**.

As a consequence of the absence of vascular tissue and a very restricted ability in reducing water loss, moss plants seldom reach a significant size and are usually restricted to moist habitats.

Note: In the photograph (right) note the leaf-like appearance of the visible parts of the moss.

Moss growing in the crevices in a wall

Note: By growing on the stone walls and the roof in the photograph (left) the mosses avoid competition from grasses and other plants and avoid damage by trampling. This upland area in the Yorkshire Dales has high annual rainfall levels so forms an ideal habitat for the moisture-requiring mosses.

A typical representation of a moss plant is shown in the following diagram.

Life Cycle – The dominant phase in a moss is the **haploid (*n*) gametophyte** (i.e. the visible moss plant is the gametophyte).

In the moss plant, gametes are produced in very small sex organs called **antheridia** and **archegonia** that produce the male gametes (sperm, or can be called antherozoids) and the female gametes (ova or eggs) respectively. As the gametophyte is haploid, gametes are produced by **mitosis** (not meiosis – meiosis cannot take place in haploid cells). When mature, the flagellated sperm swim in a film of water that often covers the surface of the gametophyte (moss plant) into the archegonia. This process is often aided by rain splash that helps transport the sperm to the archegonia. As only the male gametes are mobile, fertilisation takes place inside the archegonium.

As fertilisation involves the fusion of two haploid gametes, the resultant zygote and the structure it

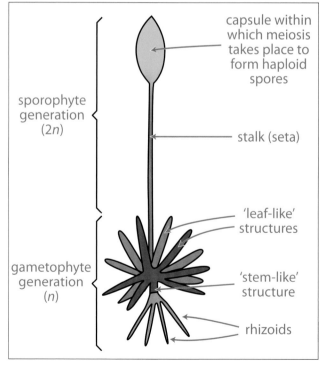

forms following mitotic division forms the **sporophyte generation (2*n*)**. The sporophyte grows into a **spore-producing capsule** that extends above the moss plant and in due course produces **haploid spores**

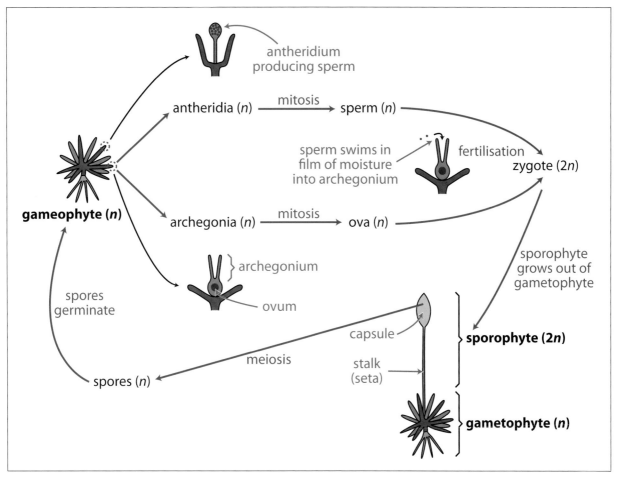

The moss
life cycle

by **meiosis**. Eventually the spores are released and normally dispersed by wind. They later germinate in suitable conditions to form new moss plants (gametophytes). A generalised moss life cycle is shown in the diagram above.

Note 1: The sporophyte in a moss is a shorter lived, reproductive phase, and is totally dependent on the gametophye for nutrition (it cannot survive on its own so there is no free living sporophyte stage). The photograph below shows sporophytes consisting of green capsules and red seta (capsule stalks) extending out of the moss plant (gametophyte).

Moss (showing both gametophyte and sporophyte generations) growing on a wall

259

Note 2: In some species, antheridia and archegonia may be on different plants ensuring cross-fertilisation; alternatively, in species that produce both types of gamete on the same plant, cross-fertilisation may occur through sperm being splashed from one plant to another.

Note 3: The sporophyte possesses stomata and a cuticle which provides a degree of protection for the stalk and capsule that extends above the gametophyte into the drier air.

Note 4: The requirement of water for the transport of the sperm to the archegonium is another reason why mosses are restricted to damp environments.

Division Tracheophyta

The tracheophytes are **vascular plants**; they have a vascular system (xylem and phloem). There are two major sub-divisions, the **ferns** (pteridophytes) and **flowering plants** (spermatophytes).

Sub-division Pteridophyta (ferns)

Structure – Ferns have **true roots**, **stems** and **leaves** (which are typically subdivided into leaflets called pinnae).

Ferns possess **vascular tissue** in the roots, stems and leaves. The presence of **xylem** and **phloem** ensures that there are well developed systems for water / ion transport and organic nutrients respectively. The presence of vascular tissue is a very important factor in ferns being able to grow to considerable sizes. Support is both by turgor within the cells and by the presence of xylem cells thickened by lignin.

The presence of a **waterproof cuticle** and **stomata** (with fine control allowing the stomata to be closed if the plant is subject to water stress) in the leaves, in addition to true roots and stems with vascular tissue, allow ferns to colonise drier areas than mosses characteristically do.

A typical fern

In many ferns the stem (rhizome) runs horizontally underground with the leaves being the only part that extends above ground as shown in the diagram on the right.

Life Cycle - The structures we recognise as fern plants are **sporophytes** - the phase in the life cycle that produces (haploid) spores.

In ferns, **spores** are produced on the lower

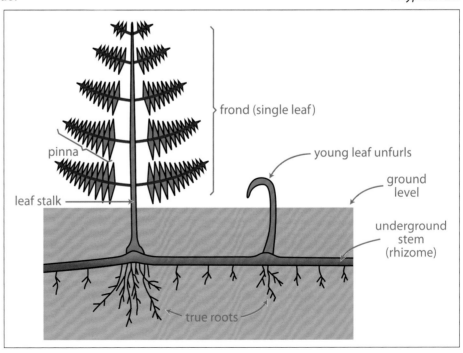

surface of the leaves. They are produced in special structures called **sporangia**. Sporangia are grouped together to form a **sorus** (pl. sori). Typically, each sorus is protected by an inverted umbrella-like structure called an **indusium**.

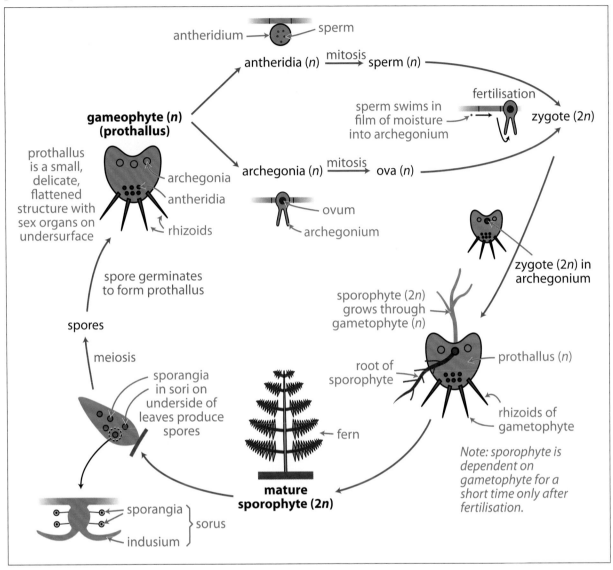

The fern life cycle

The **spores** are produced in the sporangia by **meiosis**. Spores are released in dry conditions as a consequence of the wall of the sporangium drying differentially and splitting to release spores. The spores are dispersed through a combination of the 'catapulting' effect of the splitting of the sporangium and air currents.

If the spore lands in a suitably moist area, it will germinate and grow into a **prothallus** (the **gametophyte (n)** generation). This is a very small, heart shaped, thin and delicate structure that has no cuticle, no stomata or vascular tissue and is consequently restricted to damp areas – they are so small and almost transparent that they are very hard to see. Being the gametophyte, the prothallus produces the gametes: as with mosses, these are produced in **antheridia** and **archegonia** – in the prothallus these are usually located on the more moist lower surface. As the gametophyte is **haploid**, the gametes are produced by **mitosis**.

As with bryophytes, the **flagellated sperm** swim from the antheridia to the archegonia in a film of moisture (again possibly aided by rain splash) and **fertilise** the **egg** (ovum).

The zygote develops into the **diploid sporophyte**. Although *initially* dependent on the gametophyte (the prothallus) for food and support, it quickly grows through the delicate prothallus (destroying it in the process) and forms true roots that can penetrate into the soil. The diploid sporophyte starts to photosynthesise, becomes independent and becomes recognisable as a fern plant.

> **Note 1:** In ferns (pteridophytes) the **diploid sporophyte** is the **dominant phase** of the life cycle. The gametophyte is much reduced (in comparison to mosses).

Lower side of a single fern leaf (frond) showing pinnae which are further subdivided into pinnules. The small brown dots on the pinnules are sori, each containing a number of sporangia, within which spores are made

> **Note 2:** Although the sporophyte (typical fern plant) is well adapted to life on land, pteridophytes are usually restricted to damp environments. This is for two main reasons. The **gametophyte (prothallus) is a delicate stage** (with little in the way of strategies to reduce water loss – it has no stomata, cuticle or true roots with water and ions being absorbed over the entire surface) and **water is required to enable fertilisation** to take place (allowing the sperm to swim from the antheridia to the archegonia).

Ferns in a dark and damp hedgerow – a typical habitat

Sub-division Spermatophyta (flowering plants)

Angiosperms (flowering plants) are spermatophytes that produce flowers and seeds.

Structure – Flowering plants are the most dominant vegetation in the world today and include herbaceous flowering plants and broadleaved deciduous trees.

As with ferns (the other branch of the tracheophytes) spermatophytes have **true roots**, **stems** and **leaves** with a **waterproofed cuticle** and **stomata** that are subject to fine control. Vascular tissue is highly developed. As with the sporophyte (but not the gametophyte) generation of ferns, the roots are able to penetrate deep into the ground to absorb water and minerals.

Life cycle – in spermatophytes the **sporophyte** is the dominant generation with the gametophyte not existing as a separate plant but is restricted to the product of a few mitotic divisions within the sporophyte (i.e. the gametophyte is a developmental phase within the flower).

Angiosperms produce flowers which contain the **sporangia**. There are two types of sporangia (microsporangia and megasporangia), each of which produces a different type of spore. Consequently, flowering plants (angiosperms) are **heterosporous**.

The male parts of the flower, the **anthers**, contain **pollen sacs** which represent the **microsporangia**. The pollen sacs (microsporangia) produce **microspores (pollen grains)** within which the **male gametophytes**, and in turn the **male gametes**, develop.

Diploid cells in the pollen sacs (microsporangia) divide by **meiosis** to produce the **haploid pollen grains** (microspores).

The female parts of the flower, the **carpels** (comprising stigma, style and ovary) produce **megasporangia (ovules)** in the **ovary**. The **megaspore mother cell** in the ovule (2*n*) divides by **meiosis** to produce the **megaspore (embryo sac)** (*n*).

  Note: The **style** is the part of the carpel that extends between the stigma and the ovary.

The **embryo sac** undergoes three successive **mitotic** divisions to produce eight cells. The three cells at the top are called antipodal cells, the two in the middle are polar nuclei, with an egg (female gamete) and two synergids at the base.

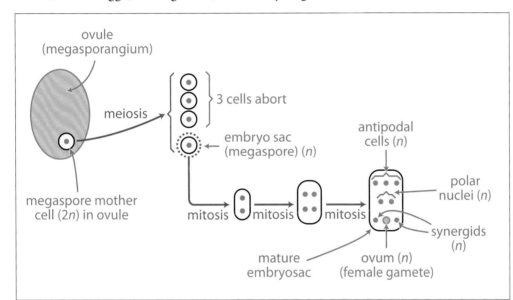

The development of the embryo sac

The mitotic divisions involved and the mature embryo sac formed represent the **female gametophyte** generation. At this stage the female part of the flower is ready for fertilisation.

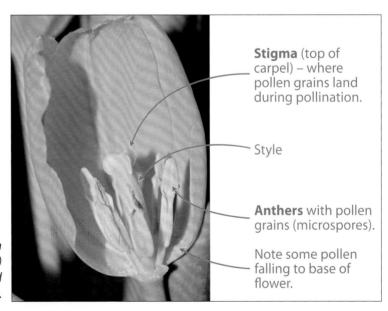

A tulip flower (with some petals removed) showing anthers and a central carpel.

Stigma (top of carpel) – where pollen grains land during pollination.

Style

Anthers with pollen grains (microspores).

Note some pollen falling to base of flower.

263

Note 1: Daffodil ovaries have many ovules – many species have only one ovule per ovary.

Note 2: The female part of the flower (the carpel) extends from the stigma, through the style down to the ovule-containing ovary.

Pollination and fertilisation – Pollen grains are released by anthers and may be transferred by **wind** or **insects** to a stigma on the flower of a plant of the same species. This is **pollination**.

The **pollen grain nucleus** divides **mitotically** to produce a **generative nucleus** and a **pollen tube nucleus**. Following pollination on a receptive stigma, the **pollen tube** grows down though the style in the direction of an ovule in the ovary. The **generative nucleus** divides again by **mitosis** to form **two male gametes**. The germinating pollen grain represents the **male gametophyte generation**.

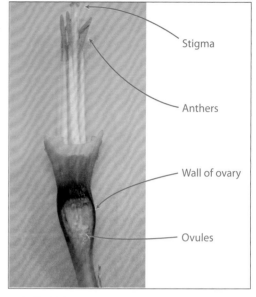

A daffodil flower with leaves removed and part of ovary wall removed to show anthers with pollen grains (microspores), and the ovules (megasporangia) within the ovary

Formation of the male gametes

The growth of the pollen tube (below) – showing events in the ovary between the processes of pollination and fertilisation.

As the pollen tube enters the ovary it links with an ovule and subsequently transfers the male gametes into the ovule (and subsequently into the embryo sac). One male gamete (nucleus) fuses with the egg to produce a diploid zygote (**'true' fertilisation**). The other male gamete fuses with **both polar nuclei** to produce a **triploid endosperm** which may develop into a food storage zone in the developing seed. As a consequence of this second 'fertilisation' event, flowering plants are said to exhibit **double fertilisation**.

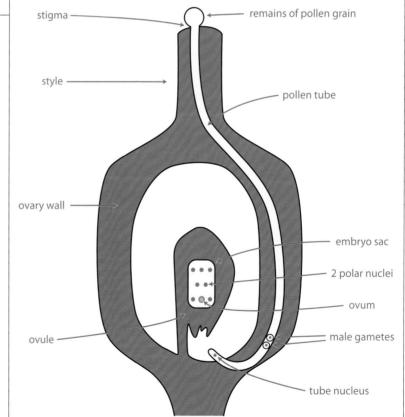

Note 1: Flowers are usually either adapted for **wind** or **insect pollination**. For example, insect pollinated flowers are usually brightly coloured, are often scented, and may have a nectary to attract insects.

Note 2: It is possible to have pollination without fertilisation but it is not naturally possible to have fertilisation without pollination.

Fruits on a hawthorn tree are attractive to birds

Following fertilisation, the zygote (and the rest of the ovule) develops into a **seed** which may eventually be dispersed and subsequently germinates to produce a new plant. The ovary may develop into a **fruit** which is often adapted for dispersal of the seed(s). For example, many fruits are brightly coloured to attract birds. The birds eat the nutritious fruit and discard the relatively indigestible seeds, often considerable distances away from the parent plant.

Comparison of divisions in the plant kingdom

There is a progression across the different divisions in the plant kingdom in terms of:

- The dominance of the sporophyte generation

- Adaptation for life of land

Dominance of the sporophyte generation – in **mosses** (bryophytes) the gametophyte is the dominant generation with the sporophyte being only a spore-producing stage that is totally dependent on the gametophyte. In **ferns** (pteridophytes) the sporophtye is the dominant stage with the gametophyte (prothallus) much reduced, although it does exist as an independent stage. In **flowering plants** (angiosperms) the sporophyte is also the dominant stage but the gametophyte is very much reduced (degenerate) and only exists as a very localised gamete-producing phase within the sporophyte (plant) – it does not exist as a separate independent phase or plant.

Adaptation for life on land – Mosses are very poorly adapted for life on land. They have no waterproof cuticle or stomata for control of water loss, no true roots, stems or leaves and no vascular tissue. Ferns and flowering plants do have all these in their sporophtye generations (dominant phase) and are consequently much better adapted for life in drier areas.

However, ferns are largely restricted to life in moist habitats due to the inability of the fragile prothallus (gametophyte) stage to restrict water loss or to gain water (no true roots or vascular tissue and no cuticle or stomata) and the requirement for moisture in enabling the male gametes to swim to the female gametes for fertilisation.

Flowering plants can be particularly well adapted for life in dry terrestrial environments for the following additional reasons:

- The gametophyte does not exist as an independent stage – there is no vulnerable haploid phase as it remains protected within the sporophyte (plant).

- The male gamete does not swim to the female gamete. Therefore a film of external moisture surrounding the plant is not necessary. Instead the male gamete is initially protected within protective pollen grains and following pollination transported to the female gamete within the pollen tube.

- Seeds are dispersed rather than spores. Seeds are much more able to withstand desiccation due to their tough outer coat compared to spores.

However, the great diversity of flowering plants means different species are adapted for virtually all the habitats available on Earth and can be highly adapted for anything between very moist environments (or even life in water – hydrophytes) to extremely dry environments (xerophytes) as seen in the photographs (right).

Kingdom Animalia

Animals are **eukaryotic multicellular** organisms that **do not** possess a **cell wall**. They are **heterotrophs** feeding on organic food that they can **digest internally**. Most animals are capable of **locomotion**.

Marsh marigold – adapted for wet or very damp habitats

The major groupings within the kingdom Animalia are the various phyla. In this specification students are required to know the body form and nature of feeding in the phyla Cnidaria, Platyhelminthes, Annelida and Chordata (a representative sample of the phyla that exist within the animal kingdom).

Phylum Cnidaria

Cnidarians include the marine jellyfish, sea anemones and the freshwater *Hydra*.

Cactus – a xerophyte adapted for hot and dry conditions

Body form – Cnidarians are relatively simple animals formed of two body layers separated by a non-cellular jelly layer (mesogloea). The outer layer is the **ectoderm** and the inner layer, lining the gut cavity, is the **endoderm**. As cnidarians have two body layers, they are referred to as being **diploblastic**.

Although there is a range of different cell types, there is relatively **little differentiation** (there are no organs).

Cnidarians are **radially symmetrical** and they are restricted to an aqueous medium for support – they have a **hydrostatic skeleton** formed by the fluid-filled enteron (gut cavity). Apart from support, they need an aqueous medium to allow food to drift within reach (most species are not very mobile and those that are tend to drift in water currents, e.g. jellyfish) and they have virtually no means of restricting water loss across the body surface.

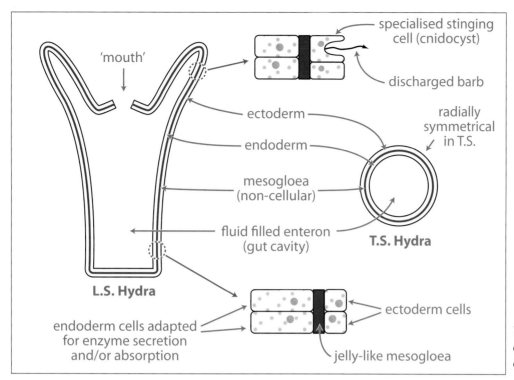

The body structure of a typical cnidarian (Hydra)

Feeding – Jellyfish, sea anemones and *Hydra* possess **tentacles** with **stinging cells** (cnidocysts). The tentacles and the stinging cells serve to immobilise prey – the stinging cells shoot out barbs that penetrate the prey delivering a toxin that paralyses it. The tentacles then sweep the food into the fluid filled enteron (gut cavity) through the single opening ('mouth').

Special **digestive cells** in the endoderm **secrete digestive enzymes** into the enteron which begin the process of digestion. Following this initial phase of **extracellular digestion**, partly digested food is absorbed into the endodermal cells by endocytosis. Digestion is then completed **intracellularly**.

> **Note:** Corals are also members of the phylum Cnidaria. Unlike the other examples discussed in this section, they are colonial in that many individual animals congregate together to form what we know as coral (or a coral reef).

Phylum Platyhelminthes

Platyhelminthes are the flatworms.

Body form - Platyhelminthes are **triplobastic**. In addition to the ectoderm and endoderm layers present in cnidarians, they have a **mesoderm** that lies between the other two layers. Parts of the mesoderm become differentiated, e.g. to form basic nerve or reproductive tissue.

> **Note:** The mesoderm is a genuine body layer that contains cells. It should not be confused with the acellular mesogloea of the cnidarians which is not a true layer as such.

The three body layers are solid – there are no spaces (**coelom**) within the layers, therefore platyhelminthes are described as being **acoelomate**.

267

The triploblastic condition allows greater development and differentiation. For example, simple 'organs' can develop within the mesoderm. However, a disadvantage is that there there are many cells per unit volume involved in metabolic activity. This means that there are high demands for oxygen and other metabolites. Consequently, platyhelminthes (flatworms) are **flattened dorso-ventrally** (top to bottom) which gives them a **high surface area – volume ratio**. This dorso-ventral flattening both:

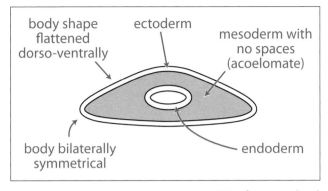

T.S. of a generalised platyhelminth

- Increases uptake of oxygen due to the increased surface area – volume ratio

- Decreases the diffusion distance from the body surface to body cells

A common platyhelminth is the **planarian**.

As seen in the representation of a planarian in the following diagram, the body is **bilaterally symmetrical**. An advantage with this form is that the animals have a 'front' where sensory receptors can be accumulated, allowing platyhelminths to 'test' the environment into which they are entering. The streamlined bilaterally symmetrical shape makes movement much easier compared to the radial symmetry of the cnidarians.

The body is supported by the aqueous medium and the bulk of the cells in the mesoderm provide support through acting as 'packing' tissue.

Feeding – Some types of planarians are carnivores feeding on small prey and others are detritivores. Planarians have a **single opening to the gut**, meaning that the indigestible food waste has to be egested through the opening through which the food enters the gut (mouth). The gut is branched and extends throughout the body. Consequently food can be brought to all parts of the body by the gut. Therefore there is no requirement for a circulatory system (particularly as the flattened shape means that no cell is far from the permeable ectoderm, therefore respiratory gases can diffuse the short distances involved directly to the body cells).

Enzymes are secreted into the gut cavity and digestion is initially extracellular. The partially digested food is absorbed into the endodermal cells by endocytosis (a process basically similar to cnidarians).

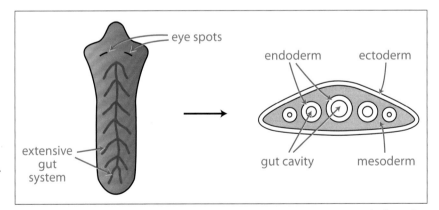

A planarian

Note: The planarian is a typical free-living flatworm that 'swims' through the development of undulating wave-like movements. However, some species in the phylum Platyhelminthes are highly adapted as parasites. An example of a parasitic platyhelminth is the tapeworm.

Phylum Annelida

Annelids include the earthworm, the lugworm and the ragworm. They are also known as roundworms.

Body form – Annelids are **bilaterally symmetrical** but tend to be much more rounded in cross-section (TS) compared to the platyhelminthes. They are also triploblastic but unlike the flatworms the mesoderm is not a solid layer; there are spaces or a **coelom**. Consequently, annelids are **coelomate triploblasts**.

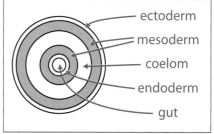

The coelomate triploblastic condition

There are a number of **advantages** with possessing a coelom:

- The ratio of **surface area to metabolically active tissue** is much **increased**. This is largely why annelids can be round in TS – there is not the same requirement to maximise surface area to volume ratio for respiratory purposes.

- As the coelom can be fluid filled, it can function as a very effective **hydrostatic skeleton**.

- The muscles involved with **locomotion** are separated from the **gut muscles**. This allows movement of the organism and peristaltic gut movements to occur independently.

- It provides room for the development of **organs**.

Annelids are **metamerically segmented** meaning that the body is divided into (usually) a large number of structurally similar segments. Most of the segments are similar in structure with their own coelomic space including rudimentary organs such as excretory and nervous structures.

Note: Although metameric segmentation results in a number of structurally similar segments, the different segments do not function independently of other segments.

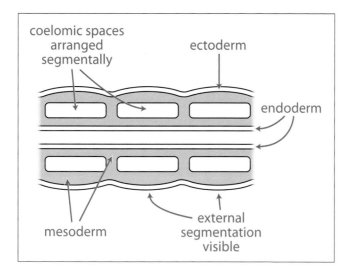

Annelid in longitudinal section

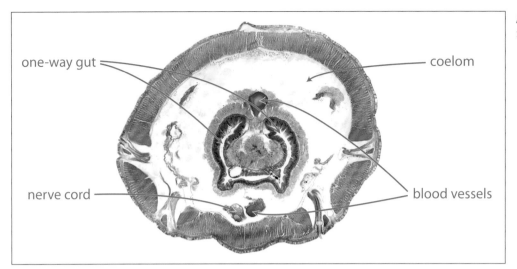

Earthworm, transverse section

one-way gut

coelom

nerve cord

blood vessels

Locomotion usually involves the antagonistic action of circular and longitudinal muscles in the ectoderm contracting in turn against the fluid filled hydrostatic skeleton. External **chaetae** (bristles of chitin) are able to produce the friction against the ground enabling movement to occur.

Feeding – Earthworms and many other annelids are detritivores. There is a **one way gut** with a **separate mouth** and an **anus**. This allows **regional specialisation** and prevents food waste following digestion being mixed with incoming food. Within the gut, there is a muscular pharynx (adjacent to the mouth), an oesophagus, a crop (storage area), a muscular gizzard (for mechanical digestion) and an intestine for absorption.

Unlike cnidarians and platyhelminthes, digestion is completed in the gut (totally **extracellular** digestion). Undigested food waste is egested via the anus and for many species deposited as visible worm casts.

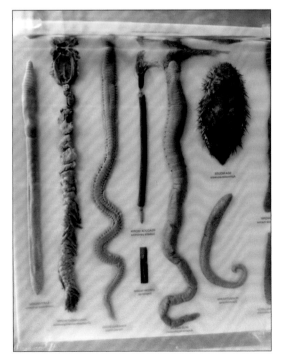

Some preserved annelids

Note 1: The earthworm is on the left of the photograph.

Note 2: If you look carefully you will see evidence of (metameric) segmentation in several of the worms.

Note 3: The annelid second from left has been partially dissected showing the specialisation of gut regions.

Note 4: The smaller oval worm (sea mouse) on the top right does not look worm-like in appearance but is an annelid as it has the diagnostic characteristics of the phylum (some of which have been covered in this section).

Phylum Chordata

Vertebrates (animals with backbones) are chordates. The main groups within the Chordata are the fish, amphibians, reptiles, birds and mammals.

Body form – Chordates have a **coelomate triploblastic** organisation. They are also **bilaterally symmetrical**, possess a **one way gut** with a mouth and an anus. Although **metamerically segmented**, this is less obvious in chordates than in annelids.

The body cavity (**coelom**) is much greater in extent proportionally and more continuous than in annelids and contains much more extensively developed and complex organs which are usually organised into complex systems, e.g. digestive, circulatory, excretory and reproductive.

In vertebrates there is a **vertebral (spinal) column** with **segmented muscle blocks** and a **post-anal tail** with the skeleton consisting of an **internal jointed system of calcified bones**.

> **Note:** In non-vertebrate chordates (a very small group of relatively rare animals) that in terms of evolutionary development are a bridge between invertebrates and vertebrates, there is a stiff dorsal rod (**notochord**) instead of a true backbone (vertebrate column).

Feeding – Mammals may be active predators, omnivores (eat both plant and animal food) or herbivores. There is a complex gut with a high degree of regional specialisation. Digestion is **extracellular** and the absorbed food products are distributed to all the body cells by a well developed circulatory system.

Evolutionary trends in the Kingdom Animalia

The sequence from the cnidarians, through the platyhelminthes and annelids to the chordates shows a number of evolutionary trends including:

- The gradation from **radial symmetry** (cnidarians) to **bilateral symmetry** (other phyla). Radial symmetry gives sessile organisms living in the open the opportunity to obtain food from all directions but it has many limitations. Bilateral symmetry allows streamlining to develop and the development of an anterior (and posterior) end that is more suitable for movement and allows for the concentration of sensory receptors (sense organs) that can test out the environment in front of the organism.

- The gradation from the **diploblastic** to the **triploblastic** condition and within the triploblasts the evolutionary progression from **acoelomate** to **coelomate**. Coelomate triploblastic groups (annelids and chordates) have a coelom that reduces the volume of metabolically active tissue to surface area and provides the body cavities necessary for the development of complex organs and body systems.

- The development of a **one way gut** as opposed to a gut cavity (cnidarians) or a gut with only one opening (platyhelminthes).

Exam questions

1. Photograph **A** below shows moss of the genus *Polytrichum*.

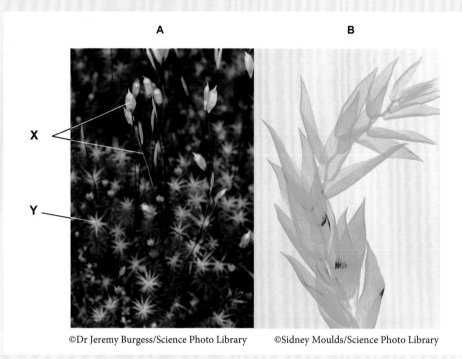

A   B

©Dr Jeremy Burgess/Science Photo Library   ©Sidney Moulds/Science Photo Library

(a) (i) Identify the stages in the moss life cycle indicated by **X** and **Y**. [2]

(ii) State the ploidy of the cells in stage **X** shown in photograph **A**. [1]

Plants of the genus *Polytrichum* are upright and have well-developed rhizoids. They form dense tufts as shown in photograph **A**. These features allow *Polytrichum* species to grow on rocks and walls, both of which are relatively dry.

(iii) Suggest how the following features allow these plants to grow in relatively dry areas.

• Well-developed rhizoids

• Growth in dense tufts [2]

(iv) Explain how the plant is supported to keep it upright. [1]

(b) Photograph **B** shows a moss plant of the genus *Sphagnum*. This moss covers the waterlogged soils of peat bogs. The lower part of the plant is dead and there are no rhizoids. Water and mineral ions are absorbed directly through the 'leaf-like' structures.

Suggest reasons for the following features, characteristic of *Sphagnum*.

• The absence of rhizoids and the dead lower part of the moss

• The ability to absorb water and minerals ions into the 'leaf-like' structures, an ability not shared by the leaves of ferns or flowering plants, members of the division Tracheophyta. [4]

Question taken from CCEA's Biology Assessment Unit A2 2, Biochemistry, Genetics and Evolutionary Trends, June 2010, © CCEA 2013

2. Quality of written communication is awarded a maximum of [2] marks in this section.

   The kingdom Plantae contains the mosses (division Bryophyta), the ferns (division Tracheophyta: subdivision Pteridophyta) and the flowering plants (division Tracheophyta: subdivision Spermatophyta).

   (a) Give an account of the life cycle of flowering plants. [10]

   (b) Discuss how mosses, ferns and flowering plants are differently adapted for life on land. [6]

Question taken from CCEA's Biology Assessment Unit A2 2, Biochemistry, Genetics and Evolutionary Trends, May 2011, © CCEA 2013

3. (a) The diagram below represents the body plan of *Hydra*, a member of the phylum Cnidaria.

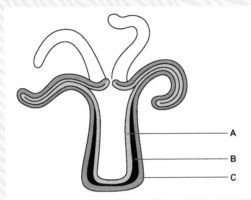

   Name the layers **A, B** and **C.** [2]

   (b) Describe **three** features found in members of the phylum Annelida, which are not found in *Hydra*. [3]

Question taken from CCEA's Biology Assessment Unit A2 2, Biochemistry, Genetics and Evolutionary Trends, June 2010, © CCEA 2013

4. The diagram below represents transverse sections through three different animal phyla, **A, B** and **C.**

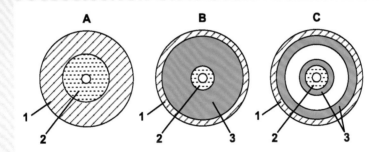

   (a) Identify the body layers **1, 2** and **3.** [3]

   (b) Identify which of the transverse sections (**A, B** or **C**) represents a member of the phylum Platyhelminthes. Give one reason for your decision. [2]

   (c) Which section (**A, B** or **C**) represents a phylum that shows radial symmetry? [1]

   (d) Which section (**A, B** or **C**) represents a phylum in which chaetae would be present? [1]

Question taken from CCEA's Biology Assessment Unit A2 2, Biochemistry, Genetics and Evolutionary Trends, May 2011, © CCEA 2013

5. (a) Ferns (pteridophytes) show alternation of generations. The gametophyte stage (prothallus) is dependent on moisture as it does not have a cuticle or stomata. A moist environment is also necessary to facilitate sexual reproduction.

(i) Explain why sexual reproduction in ferns is moisture dependent. [1]

If a female gamete (ovum) is fertilised, the dominant sporophyte stage develops. This stage has a waxy cuticle, stomata and vascular tissue and is therefore much less moisture dependent. However, due to the moisture-requiring gametophyte stage, ferns are normally restricted to damp environments.

The bracken fern *(Pteridium aquilinum)* is unusual among pteridophytes in that the sporophyte forms thick underground rhizomes (horizontal stems). Bracken is a very successful coloniser of mature sand dune systems, a habitat too dry for virtually all other ferns and even most flowering plants.

(ii) Suggest why bracken, unlike other ferns, is able to colonise the drier areas of sand dune systems. [2]

(iii) In sand dune systems, the bluebell (a traditional woodland species) frequently grows close to the bracken, rather than on more open ground.

Suggest two ways that the presence of bracken can facilitate bluebell growth in this habitat. [2]

(b) Water availability also affects distribution in the kingdom Animalia. Species of the phylum Cnidaria are common in aquatic habitats but are not found in terrestrial habitats.

Give two reasons why Cnidarians are restricted to aquatic habitats. [2]

Question taken from CCEA's Biology Assessment Unit A2 2, Biochemistry, Genetics and Evolutionary Trends, May 2012, © CCEA 2013

Chapter 16 – Statistics

It is important that students following the A2 course are able to use and interpret a range of statistical tools and tests. These include estimates of the standard deviation of the mean, confidence limits, the Student's test (*t*-test) and the chi-square test.

Statistical analysis is an important part of biology. It enables data to be analysed or compared in an **objective** way (as opposed to a subjective way) and therefore removes bias.

Biological data tends to be very variable and, due to this variation, it is not always easy to identify if differences between two sets of data indicate that real differences exist between the parameters being measured as opposed to the differences being due to random variation – the use of a statistical technique helps us do this.

Compare the information in the following graphs showing data of leaf length in oak. In Graph 1 it is very obvious that the samples A and B are different but this is less obvious in Graph 2.

Why can we be fairly sure that the two sets of data are **significantly different** in Graph 1 but less so in Graph 2?

Note: Significance is a key term in statistics. A significant difference is where the difference between data sets is due to more than random variation alone – i.e. the data sets are really different.

In Graph 1:

- the **mean** values are further apart
- there is less **variability** within each sample
- there was a larger **sample size**

Not surprisingly, many statistical tests take into account the differences in mean between samples being compared, the variability of each sample and the size of each sample.

Note: A statistical test can tell us whether two samples are significantly different but it will not tell us the reason for the difference.

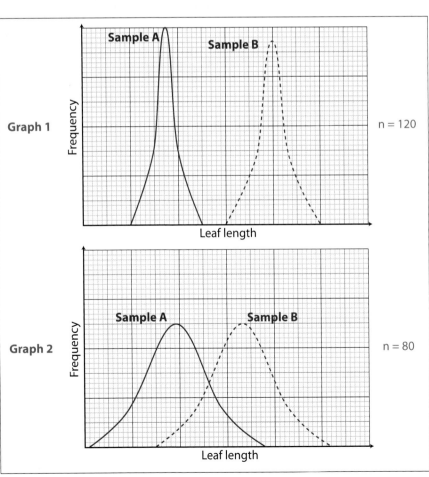

275

Note: The data in the graphs on the previous page is **normally distributed**. This means that most individuals are close to the average or mean with relatively few having extreme values for the parameter being measured.

When planning a statistical investigation it is normal to establish a **null hypothesis** (**H₀**). In the examples in the graphs earlier this could be written as:

The difference between mean leaf length in sample A and sample B is due to random variation and is not significant.

Note: When establishing a null hypothesis the starting assumption is that there is no significant difference between the two sets of data being compared.

Some key terms and formulae

Sample mean (symbol $\bar{x}$) – the average or mean value of the sample under consideration.

Note: Although the mean is the parameter most used, and most useful, as a measure of central tendency, other measures include the mode (the most common value – e.g. the tallest bar in a histogram) and the median (the value that is exactly midway between the highest value and the lowest – e.g. the sixth highest of eleven measurements of height).

Standard deviation – is a measure of the variability (spread) of the data. The standard deviation in a normally distributed sample is the value either side of the mean, between which 68% of all the values of the sample are trapped. If there is a lot of variability the standard deviation is likely to be large, whereas if most values are grouped tightly around the mean, the standard deviation will be small.

If a data set has a mean of 14 and a standard deviation of 3 this means that 68% of the sample values lie between 11 – 17.

Note 1: Standard deviation ($\hat{\sigma}$) gives an indication of the data spread in a group of values (e.g. a sample). If the standard deviation is based on a population sample, it does provide useful statistical information about the actual mean of the whole population.

Note 2: Variance ($\hat{\sigma}^2$) is another indicator of variability or spread in a group of values.

Samples and populations

It is important not to get confused between the **sample mean** (e.g. the mean length of 30 leaves if that is what is being measured) and the **population mean** (e.g. the mean length of all the leaves in that particular population of plants).

Quite often in biological investigations, we obtain a sample on the premise that it will be a reliable indicator of the entire population. The sample mean ($\bar{x}$) may or may not be close to the true population mean (μ) and it is important we get some indication of how close it is likely to be when using samples to compare populations.

The **standard deviation of the mean** (also called the **standard error**) with the symbol $\hat{\sigma}_{\bar{x}}$ can be calculated using the formula:

$$\hat{\sigma}_{\bar{x}} = \sqrt{\frac{\hat{\sigma}^2}{n}}$$

Note: $\hat{\sigma}^2$ is the best estimate of population variance and is calculated using the formula:

$$\hat{\sigma}^2 = \frac{\Sigma(x - \bar{x})}{n - 1}$$

The standard deviation of the mean gives a measure of how much, on average, the sample mean differs from the mean of the population as a whole. If the sample mean is truly representative of the population as a whole the difference between the two values (the sample and population means) should be small. If the difference is small then, for statistical purposes, the mean of the sample is **reliable**. In effect, comparing the samples is a reliable way of comparing the populations.

> **Note 1:** In a biological context, the term **reliable** means that if the data was collected again (or an experiment was repeated) the outcome would be similar.

> **Note 2:** Not surprisingly, the formula for the standard deviation of the mean takes into account both variability of data and the sample size.

95% confidence limits

The **standard deviation of the mean** gives us an indication of how close the sample mean and the population mean are likely to be. However, it is possible to use the standard deviation of the mean to give us another statistic that gives us the limits within which the true mean of the population almost certainly lies. It is not absolutely certain that the true population mean lies within these limits, but we can be 95% sure (i.e. 95 times out of 100 we will be correct).

95% confidence limits are provided by the formula: $\bar{x} \pm t(\hat{\sigma}_{\bar{x}})$

where t is determined from a table of t values at $p = 0.05$ and $n - 1$ degrees of freedom (n = sample size).

Statistical tables use probability levels, for example, between $p = 0.1$ (10% probability) and 0.001 (99.9% probability) rather than percentage probability. 95% probability is the $p = 0.05$ value. The table below summarises the different ways in which probability can be interpreted when comparing two samples.

> **Note:** Confidence limits can be worked out for any level of probability but it is biological convention that 95% confidence limits are an appropriate statistical indicator in most investigations. If we are 95% sure that two data sets are different we can regard the difference as being significant.

p value	$p = 0.1$	**0.05**	0.02	0.01	0.002	0.001
Probability that result (e.g. difference between means) is due to chance (i.e. random variation) only	10%	**5%**	2%	1%	0.2%	0.1%
Probability that result shows significant difference (e.g. difference between means is significant)	90%	**95%**	98%	99%	99.8%	99.9%

Note: The critical probability values are highlighted in blue.

95% limits can be used in tables (often as a column immediately to the right of the mean values) but are particularly useful in graphs. The graph on the right shows the mean total leaf areas of wild garlic plants throughout the growing season in more open woodland (A) compared to those in a woodland with lower light levels (B) (due to shading by rhododendron).

As can be seen from the graph, the 95% limits of the samples taken during the growing season from the two populations (A and B) do not overlap. This strongly *suggests* that the two samples are significantly different. In general, if the 95% confidence limits of two (or more samples) do not overlap we can be reasonably sure (but not certain – even at the 95% level of probability) that the samples are significantly (statistically) different.

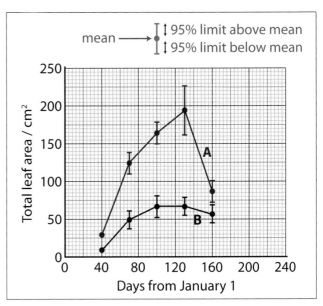

Total leaf area in wild garlic plants in different growing conditions

Note 1: As can be seen from the graph above, the 95% confidence limits are drawn both above and below the sample mean. This is because the 95% limit gives us information about how close the sample and population means are likely to be. It does not tell us whether the real population mean is likely to be higher or lower in value than the sample mean.

Note 2: 95% confidence limits are particularly valuable when comparing a number of sample means and determining which (if any) are likely to be statistically different from the others. For example, if we had been comparing a number of garlic populations with several samples taken at each time.

Worked example

The mean leaf length of a **sample** of twenty ash leaves was 60 mm. The standard deviation (error) of the mean was calculated as being 1.433.

1. As the sample size was 20, the degrees of freedom (d.f.) is 19

2. The tabulated *t* value, at $p = 0.05$ and d.f. 19 = 2.093

3. 95% confidence limits = 2.093 × 1.433 = 3

4. We can conclude, at the 95% level of probability, that the mean of the **population** falls between 57 – 63 mm.

   Note: In an exam question if you are being expected to calculate 95% limits you are likely to be given the standard deviation (error) of the mean, or an equivalent stage.

The *t*-test (Student's *t*-test)

The *t*-test is a more robust statistical procedure for comparing two sample means – it is a statistical test designed for that purpose. Sample means will invariably be different but the *t*-test allows you to determine if the difference is down to random chance or is significant (i.e. due to real differences between the two samples).

The formula for the t-test is $t = \dfrac{\bar{x}_1 - \bar{x}_2}{\sqrt{\hat{\sigma}_{\bar{x}_1}^2 + \hat{\sigma}_{\bar{x}_2}^2}}$

Note: In effect this is the difference between the sample means, divided by the square root of the sum of the squares of the standard deviation of the mean for each sample.

Once you obtain the value for the t-test it is important to determine if this value indicates that the difference between the means is significant. To do this there are a number of steps you must do.

- Work out the number of degrees of freedom. It is ($n_1 + n_2 - 2$) where n_1 is the sample size in one sample and n_2 is the sample size in the other.

- Use a table of t values (Student's t values) to check where your value for t is placed in terms of probability in the appropriate degrees of freedom row.

- Your value will almost certainly fit between two values in the appropriate row. The p values at the top of the table for the two rows, either side of the tabulated value, are the p values within which your value lies.

- Remember that $p = 0.05$ is the statistically significant cut off point in most biological experiments. A value of $p = 0.05$ means that there is a 5% chance that the difference between the means is down to random variation. More than 5% suggests that there is a reasonable chance that the variation is random – less that 5% suggests that the possibility of the differences being down to random variation are so low that it is safe to conclude that the two samples are significantly different.

- If $p > 0.05$ (falls to the left of the $p > 0.05$ column in the table) the null hypothesis is accepted; if $p < 0.05$ (falls to the right of the 0.05 column), the null hypothesis is rejected.

p value (probability value)	Significance value	Explanation
$p > 0.05$ (greater than 0.05)	No evidence of significant difference between samples	There is more than a five percent chance of the variation between the two samples being due to chance (random variation) – too high to suggest that the differences are significant
$p < 0.05$	The samples are significantly different at the 95% level of significance	There is less than a five percent chance of the variation between the two samples being due to chance (random variation) – a low enough value to suggest that the two samples are significantly different

- Although the $p < 0.05$ is normally the cut off in determining if differences are significant in biological investigations, a greater degree of significance is often required in biological or medical research before drawing conclusions that two samples (or treatments) are actually different. The table overleaf summarises the outcomes for different probability values.

p value (probability value)	Significance value	Explanation
$p > 0.05$ (greater than 0.05)	No evidence of significant difference between samples	There is more than a five percent chance of the variation between the two samples being due to random variation – too high to suggest that the differences are significant
$0.05 > p > 0.01$	The samples are significantly different at the 95% level of probability ($p = 0.05$) but not significantly different at the 99% level of probability ($p = 0.01$)	There is between a five and a one percent chance of the variation between the two samples being due to random variation – a low enough value to suggest that the two samples are **significantly different**
$0.01 > p > 0.001$	The samples are significantly different at the 99% level of probability ($p = 0.01$) but not significantly different at the 99.9% level of probability ($p = 0.001$)	There is between a one and a zero point one percent chance of the variation between the two samples being due to random variation – a low enough value to suggest that the two samples are **highly significantly different**
$p < 0.001$	The samples are significantly different at the 99.9% level of probability ($p = 0.001$)	There is less than a zero point one percent chance of the variation between the two samples being due to random variation – a low enough value to suggest that the two samples are **very highly significantly different**

Note 1: It is convention to indicate significant difference at the 95% level of probability with an asterisk*; a highly significant difference as ** and a very highly significant difference as ***.

Note 2: A *t*-test will provide information as to whether two samples are statistically different or not. It will not tell you what has caused the difference if there is one.

Worked example

The table below represents data concerning egg production per toad for two populations of toads in different rivers.

	Populations	
	A	**B**
Sample size (number of toads)	30	35
Mean (number of eggs per toad)	141	97
Standard deviation (error) of the mean	12.7	9.8

1.   Formula: $t = \dfrac{\bar{x}_1 - \bar{x}_2}{\sqrt{\hat{\sigma}_{\bar{x}_1}^2 + \hat{\sigma}_{\bar{x}_2}^2}}$

2. $t = \dfrac{141 - 97}{\sqrt{12.7^2 + 9.8^2}}$

3. $t = \dfrac{44}{16}$

4. $t = 2.75$

5. $0.01 > p > 0.002$ (at 60 d.f. – closest value to 63)

6.   The two samples are highly significantly different**.
   There is a (highly) significant difference between the mean number of eggs produced per toad in the two populations.

Note: In an exam question, it is usually enough to work out that the two samples are significantly different (or not).

The chi-square (X^2) test

In some investigations, it is not the issue of determining if the difference in samples (and populations) is significantly different but if the data fits an expected ratio. The chi-square test is an appropriate test to confirm if offspring ratios in genetic crosses fit an expected ratio.

You will be familiar with the common genetic ratios, (e.g. 3 : 1; 1 : 1 and 9 : 3 : 3 :1) but actual offspring ratios very seldom match the ratios exactly in reality. The chi-square can provide information as to whether any deviation from the expected numbers is significant (at a given - invariably 95% - level of probability).

In the chi-square it is important to work out the expected frequencies, based on the data presented and then carry out a series of calculations based on the expected and the observed data. It is normal to construct a table as shown on page 283 in the worked example.

Once the calculated X^2 value is worked out it is then necessary to refer to the appropriate statistical table (X^2), using the appropriate degrees of freedom (number of classes – 1; for example when carrying out out a test on a 9 : 3 : 3 : 1 ratio there would be 3 degrees of freedom as there are 4 categories).

As with the *t*-test, check where the calculated X^2 value fits between two tabulated values in the table columns. The two probability values at the top of the table show the probability range within which the tabulated value lies. If the calculated value lies to the right of the 0.05 level this means that there is more than a 95% chance that the observed data does not fit the expected ratio, i.e. the deviation from the expected data is too great – to confirm the expected ratio. However, if the calculated value lies to the left of the 0.05 column ($p > 0.05$) then the difference between the observed and expected values is not significant and the predicted ratio holds based on the data available.

Worked example

The photograph below shows a maize (corn) cob. Each kernel (seed-like structure), represents a single fruit, each of which contains a single seed. The photograph shows that in this particular cob the fruits (seeds) differ both in terms of colour (purple or white) and shape (smooth or wrinkled).

individual fruits (seeds)

Maize (corn) cob

Each seed is a consequence of a single fertilisation event. Consequently each seed on the cob is equivalent to a single offspring in terms of working out genetic offspring ratios.

The photograph below shows a close up photograph of the same cob with a section of the cobs highlighted.

white and smooth

white and wrinkled

purple and wrinkled

purple and smooth

Close up of maize (corn) cob

When working out offspring ratios in maize it is probably not practical to count all the kernels so a section should be sampled at random, e.g. the kernels within the yellow outline in the photograph.

The kernels within the sample identified can be (approximately) grouped as:

purple and smooth – 53
purple and wrinkled – 20
white and smooth – 19
white and wrinkled – 4
Total = 96

Based on this data it is logical to conclude that the kernels sampled represent a dihybrid ratio of **9 : 3 : 3 : 1**, the consequence of a cross between two maize plants each heterozygous for each of kernel colour and shape.

*The **null hypothesis** is that there is no significant difference between the observed and expected offspring numbers, ie the results are a good fit to a 9 : 3 : 3 : 1 ratio.*

Category	O	E	(O-E)	(O-E)²	$\frac{(O-E)^2}{E}$
purple colour smooth coat	53	54	−1	1	0.02
purple colour wrinkled coat	20	18	2	4	0.22
white colour smooth coat	19	18	1	1	0.06
white colour wrinkled coat	4	6	−2	4	0.67

$$X^2 = 0.97$$

As there are 4 categories (classes) there are **3** degree of freedom.

Using the table of X^2 values and 3 d.f. a value of 0.97 gives a probability of **$0.9 > p > 0.5$**

This means that there is more than a 5% chance (based on tabulated values somewhere between 90% and 50%) that the deviation between the expected and the observed results is due to chance (random variation). Therefore the 9 : 3 : 3 : 1 ratio stands and the null hypothesis is accepted.

The chi-square statistical test can also be used in a non-genetics setting. For example, if investigating the percentage germination in three varieties of seed the assumption can be made that percentage germination will be the same for each variety – the expected column will therefore be the mean percentage germination across the three varieties. The observed will be the data in terms of percentage germination in the three varieties.

*The **null hypothesis** could be that there is no significant difference in percentage germination among the three varieties.*

Exam questions

1. Many plant species possess natural fungicides that help protect against infection. An investigation was set up to compare the anti-fungal properties of four species: *Hyacinthoides non-scripta* (bluebell), *Ranunculus ficaria* (lesser celandine), *Arum maculatum* (cuckoo pint), and *Anemone nemorosa* (wood anemone). Petri dishes, containing malt agar, were prepared. Each dish was inoculated with the fungus *Phythium debaryanum* opposite an extract of one of the plant species as shown below.

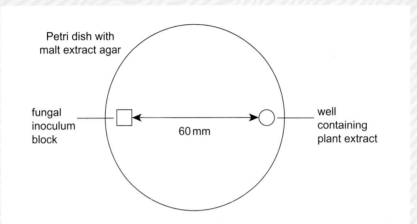

The plant extracts were prepared by grinding 5 g of fresh plant tissue in 2 cm³ of cooled boiled water. Ten replica plates were produced for each plant species and the plates were incubated at 25 °C. Following inoculation of the test plates, fungal growth was measured and recorded every 24 hours. Fungal growth was taken as the distance from the edge of the inoculum block to the colony edge, measured as the extent of growth out from the inoculum block towards the plant extract well opposite.

The bar chart below shows the mean fungal growth after 4 days for extracts of plant species and also for a control. 95% confidence limits are also shown except for *H. non-scripta*.

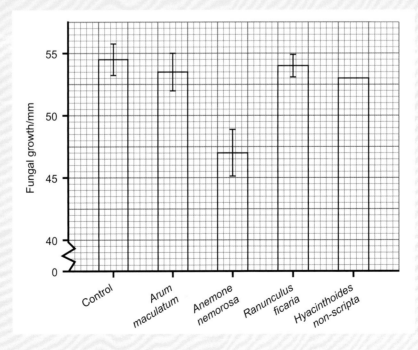

(a) Suggest a suitable control for this investigation. [1]

(b) The mean growth value for bluebell *(H. non-scripta)* after four days was 53 mm and the standard deviation (error) of the mean was 0.442.

   (i) Using the information provided and your Statistics sheets, calculate the 95% confidence limits for *H. non-scripta*.

   (ii) Copy and complete the graph provided by adding the 95% confidence limits for *H. non-scripta*. [1]

   (iii) The null hypothesis for this investigation stated that there was no significant difference between the effects of each of the plant extracts on the growth of the fungus. Based on the information provided, state your decision about the null hypothesis. Explain your answer. [2]

The plant species involved in this investigation are woodland species which grow and make use of the high light levels in spring before the tree canopy closes. During summer their leaves die and are decomposed, a process that enriches soil fertility. The anti-fungal effect of plant tissue is greatest in early spring as the delicate leaves emerge through the soil, but is significantly reduced by the summer following the closure of the tree canopy.

(c) Explain the advantage to the plants of the pattern of anti-fungal activity described above. [2]

(d) Earthworm activity is usually integral to the decay process in woodlands.

Earthworms are detritivores. They drag leaf material into their extensive network of burrows in the soil. In due course, they deposit the broken up and partially digested leaf material as worm casts throughout the soil. The presence of a large population of earthworms has proved to be very effective in promoting the processes of decomposition and nutrient (including nitrogen) recycling.

   (i) To which phylum does the earthworm belong? [1]

   (ii) Suggest how the presence of a large earthworm population, and their network of burrows, can significantly promote the processes involved in the recycling of nitrogen. [4]

Question taken from CCEA's Biology Assessment Unit A2 2, Biochemistry, Genetics and Evolutionary Trends, May 2012, © CCEA 2013

2. (a) In a survey of the relative sizes of island-dwelling mammalian species, each species was compared with mainland relatives. Four groups of mammals were surveyed. In each case the number of island-dwelling species 'smaller than' or 'the same size as' or 'larger than' related species on the mainland were recorded. The results are shown in the table below.

	Number of island-dwelling species		
	Smaller than	Same size	Larger than
Lagomorphs (rabbits and hares)	4	4	1
Rodents (mice and rats)	6	3	60
Carnivores	13	1	1
Artiodactyls (even-toed mammals such as deer)	9	2	0

State **two** conclusions which might be drawn from the results. [2]

(b) Field mice of the species *Apodemus sylvaticus* are common throughout Ireland. It was considered that the field mice of Rathlin Island are larger than the mainland field mice in Northern Ireland. The table below summaries data collected for the mass of a sample of adult field mice trapped on Rathlin Island and the mainland.

		Location of field mice	
		Rathlin	Mainland
Number of mice in the sample	(n)	17	120
Mean mass of mice	($\bar{x}$)	33.15	23.8
Standard deviation of the mean	($\hat{\sigma}_{\bar{x}}$)	2.56	1.65

A t-test can be used to compare the mean mass of the Rathlin and the mainland mice.

(i) State the null hypothesis for this test. [1]

(ii) Calculate the value of t using the data in the table above. (Show your working.) [2]

(iii) State the degrees of freedom used in reading the statistical table. [1]

(iv) State the probability value for the calculated t. [1]

(v) State your decision about the null hypothesis. [1]

(c) The mice population on Rathlin is isolated from mainland mice. In this island population large size may provide a selective advantage.

(i) Explain the evolution of large size on Rathlin Island. [2]

(ii) Explain what may eventually lead to a new mouse species on Rathlin. [2]

Question taken from CCEA's Biology Assessment Unit A2 2, Biochemistry, Genetics and Evolutionary Trends, June 2010, © CCEA 2013

3. In fruit flies of the genus *Drosophila*, the allele for normal wings, **A**, is dominant to the allele for vestigial wing, **a**. The allele for normal body colour, **B**, is dominant to the allele for ebony body, **b**.

(a) (i) Flies with vestigial wings and heterozygous for normal body colour were crossed.

State the parental genotypes and possible gametes produced by copying and completing the table below:

Parental phenotypes	vestigial wings normal body	vestigial wings normal body
Parental genotypes	_____	_____
Gametes	_____	_____

Complete a genetic cross to show the genotypes and phenotypes of the offspring. [4]

(ii) During which stage in the production of gametes does Mendel's Second Law (the Law of Independent Assortment) apply? [1]

(b) The numbers of offspring produced from another cross were recorded.

- normal body, normal wing 471
- normal body, vestigial wing 519
- ebony body, normal wing 479
- ebony body, vestigial wing 531

A total of 2000 flies were produced.

The chi squared test can be used to check if these results statistically fit an expected ratio of 1:1:1:1.

(i) Suggest a suitable null hypothesis for this test. [1]

(ii) Copy and complete the table below and calculate the X^2 value for these results. [2]

Category	Observed (O)	Expected (E)	(O – E)	(O – E)^2	$\dfrac{(O-E)^2}{E}$
Normal body normal wing	471				
Normal body vestigial wing	519				
Ebony body normal wing	479				
Ebony body vestigial wing	531				

(iii) On the basis of your calculated X^2 value, state the following.

- the degrees of freedom for the test
- the probability value
- your decision about the null hypothesis [3]

(iv) Explain the outcome of your statistical test. [1]

(c) In an isolated colony of *Drosophila* on an offshore island, it was found that 176 Drosophila had vestigial wings and 924 had normal wings.

(i) Using the Hardy–Weinberg equation, calculate the number of *Drosophila* expected to be heterozygous for normal wings. [3]

(ii) Certain conditions must be met in order to apply the Hardy–Weinberg equation. State one way in which this *Drosophila* population met these conditions. [1]

Question taken from CCEA's Biology Assessment Unit A2 2, Biochemistry, Genetics and Evolutionary Trends, May 2011, © CCEA 2013

Copyright